Cryptography:

An Introduction

Nigel Smart

Cryptography:

An Introduction

Nigel Smart

A McGraw–Hill Publication
McGraw–Hill

London - Burr Ridge IL - New York
St Louis - San Francisco - Auckland
Bogotá - Caracas - Lisbon - Madrid
Mexico - Milan - Montreal - New Delhi
Panama - Paris - San Juan - Sáo Paulo
Singapore - Sydney - Tokyo - Toronto

Cryptography: An introduction
Nigel Smart
ISBN 0077099877

 **Education**

Published by McGraw-Hill Education
Shoppenhangers Road
Maidenhead
Berkshire
SL6 2QL
Telephone: 44 (0) 1628 502 500
Fax: 44 (0) 1628 770 224
Website: www.mcgraw-hill.co.uk

British Library Cataloguing in Publication Data
A catalogue record for this book is available from the British Library

Library of Congress Cataloguing in Publication Data
The Library of Congress data for this book has been applied for from the Library of Congress

Acquisitions Editor: Conor Graham
Editorial Assistant: Paul Von Kesmark
Senior Marketing Manager: Jackie Harbor
Senior Production Manager: Max Elvey
New Media Developer: Douglas Greenwood

Typeset by Sunrise Setting Ltd
Text and Cover design by Senate Design
Printed and bound in the UK by Bath Press Ltd

ISBN 0077099877

Brief Contents

Preface

One may ask why does one need yet another book on cryptography? There are already plenty of books which either give a rapid introduction to all areas, like that of Schneier, or one which gives an encyclopedic overview, like the *Handbook of Applied Cryptography* (hereafter called *HAC*). However, neither of these books is suitable for an undergraduate course. In addition, the approach to engineering public key algorithms has changed remarkably over the last few years, with the advent of 'provable security'. No longer does a cryptographer informally argue why his new algorithm is secure, there is now a framework within which one can demonstrate the security relative to other well-studied notions.

Cryptography courses are now taught at all major universities, sometimes these are taught in the context of a Mathematics degree, sometimes in the context of a Computer Science degree and sometimes in the context of an Electrical Engineering degree. Indeed, a single course often needs to meet the requirements of all three types of students, plus maybe some from other subjects who are taking the course as an 'open unit'. The backgrounds and needs of these students are different, some will require a quick overview of the current algorithms in use, whilst others will want an introduction to the current research directions. Hence, there seems to be a need for a textbook which starts from a low level and builds confidence in students until they are able to read, for example *HAC* without any problems.

The background I assume is what one could expect of a third or fourth year under-graduate in computer science. One can assume that such students have met the basics of discrete mathematics (modular arithmetic) and a little probability before. In addition, they would have at some point done (but probably forgotten) elementary calculus. Not that one needs calculus for cryptography, but the ability to happily deal with equations and symbols is certainly helpful. Apart from that I introduce everything needed from scratch. For those students who wish to dig into the mathematics a little more, or who need some further reading, I have provided an appendix (Appendix A) which covers most of the basic algebra and notation needed to cope with modern public key cryptosystems.

It is quite common for computer science courses not to include much of complexity theory or formal methods. Many such courses are based more on software engineering and applications of computer science to areas such as graphics, vision or artificial intelligence. The main goal of such courses is in training students for the workplace rather than delving into the theoretical aspects of the subject. Hence, I have introduced what parts of theoretical computer science I need, as and when required. One chapter is therefore dedicated to the application of complexity theory in cryptography and one deals with formal approaches to protocol design. Both of these chapters can be read without having met complexity theory or formal methods before.

Much of the approach of the book in relation to public key algorithms is reductionist in nature. This is the modern approach to protocol design and this differentiates the book from other treatments. This reductionist approach is derived from techniques used in complexity theory, where one shows that one problem reduces to another. This is done by assuming an oracle for the second problem and showing how this can be used to solve the first. At many places in the book cryptographic schemes are examined from this reductionist approach and at the end I provide a quick overview of provable security.

I am not mathematically rigorous at all steps, given the target audience, but aim to give a flavour of the mathematics involved. For example I often only give proof outlines, or may not worry about the success probabilities of many of our reductions. I try to give enough of the gory details to demonstrate why a protocol has been designed in a certain way. Readers wishing a more in-depth study of the various points covered or a more mathematically rigorous coverage should consult one of the textbooks in the Further Reading sections at the end of each chapter.

On the other hand we use the terminology of groups and finite fields from the outset. This is for two reasons. Firstly, it equips students with the vocabulary to read the latest research papers, and hence enables students to carry on their studies at the research level. Secondly, students who do not progress to study cryptography at the postgraduate level will find that to understand practical issues in the 'real world', such as API descriptions and standards documents, a knowledge of this terminology is crucial. We have taken this approach with our students in Bristol, who do not have any prior exposure to this form of mathematics, and find that it works well as long as abstract terminology is introduced alongside real-world concrete examples and motivation.

I have always found that when reading protocols and systems for the first time the hardest part is to work out what is public information and which information one is trying to keep private. This is particularly true when one meets a public key encryption algorithm for the first time, or one is deciphering a substitution cipher. I have hence introduced a little colour coding into the book, generally speaking items in red are secret and should never be divulged to anyone. Items in blue are public information and are known to everyone, or are known to the party one is currently pretending to be.

For example, suppose one is trying to break a system and recover some secret message m; suppose the attacker computes some quantity b. Here the red refers to the quantity the attacker does not know and blue refers to the quantity the attacker does know. If one is then able to write down, after some algebra,

$$b = \cdots = m,$$

then it is clear something is wrong with our cryptosystem. The attacker has found out something he should not.

This colour coding will be used at all places where it adds something to the discussion. In other situations, where the context is clear or all data is meant to be secret, I do not bother with the colours.

To aid self-study each chapter is structured as follows:

- A list of items the chapter will cover, so you know what you will be told about.

- The actual chapter contents.

- A summary of what the chapter contains. This will be in the form of revision notes, if you wish to commit anything to memory it should be these facts.

- Further Reading. Each chapter contains a list of a few books or papers from which further information could be obtained. Such pointers are mainly to material which you should be able to tackle given that you have read the prior chapter. Since further information on almost any topic in cryptography can be obtained from reading *HAC* I do not include a pointer to *HAC* in any chapter. It is left, as a general recommendation to the reader, to follow up any topic in further detail by reading what *HAC* has to say.

- Exercises. There are three types of exercises.

  1. Review: These should be answered as you read them from memory. Essentially they are testing whether anything has gone in at all from your reading of the prior chapter.

  2. Programming: Since many students in more applied disciplines now require practical assignments I have included in some chapters examples of possible programming exercises. See below for the level of programming ability I assume of the student.

  3. Standard: These should take you a little time, or could be essay style questions. Their aim is to stretch you and help you to understand the material in more depth. Some of the mathematical details which are taken on trust in the main text are asked to be proved in some of these questions. Hence, many of these questions may aid instructors looking for homework assignments, or they could be used as possible exam questions.

There are no references made to other work in this book, it is a textbook and I did not want to break the flow with references to this, that and the other. Therefore, you should not assume that ANY of the results in this book are my own, in fact NONE are my own. For those who wish to obtain pointers to the literature, you should consult one of the books mentioned in the Further Reading sections, or you should consult *HAC*.

Different students at different institutions learn different programming languages. Whilst one may expect a Computer Science student to be proficient in C or Java, one cannot assume this of a Mathematics student, who may be more happy with a computer algebra system such as Maple. Some students may be more happy with functional languages such as Haskell, some with more object-oriented ones such as C++. At Bristol we try to make our students multilingual from the first year onwards by teaching a number of computer languages simultaneously. This philosophy is used in this book by using various ways (and languages) to present the algorithms.

The programming assignments are essentially language neutral and could be accomplished by any student who does not have a pathological hatred of computers. At some points in the text I use a specific language, but only where I wish to bring out a point. For example, recursive function definitions are more natural to express in a language such as Haskell. Most of the time I use plain language or a C-like pseudo-code to describe algorithms.

For those wishing to implement some of the algorithms in this book, being able to deal with arbitrary precision integers or elements of finite fields would seem to be a must. Languages such as Java, Haskell and Maple have arbitrary precision integers built-in. Those such as C or C++ require one to use special libraries to access this functionality. Many of the built in (or library) implementations of large integers are suitable for learning purposes, but one should be under no illusions that real production line cryptographic code will often be written using specialized code for efficiency reasons.

Some languages such as Java have built-in cryptographic algorithms available in the standard development environment. For example, the standard Java library classes contain facilities for computing hash functions and digital signatures, and facilities for dealing with X.509 certificates. There are also various cryptographic libraries, called Java Cryptographic Engines or JCEs, which enable various encryption algorithms.

I do not delve into the full details of the standard library classes in this book, any competent student should be able to work out the details in a few hours in any case. As an aid to the reader in Appendix B there can be found a number of examples using both the standard library classes and the API for the SUN JCE, more precisely I use the Cryptix version of the SUN JCE.

The workings of the standard library classes and the JCE API is similar to how many C or C++ libraries work, so I only present Java examples as this is the most widely used teaching language in universities at present. Such readily available cryptographic libraries give the opportunity for instructors to develop some real-world assignments or projects for students.

The book is divided into four parts. Part I gives the mathematical background needed and could be skipped at first reading and referred back to when needed. Part II discusses symmetric key encryption algorithms and the key distribution problem that results from their use. Part III discusses public key algorithms for encryption and signatures and some additional key concepts such as certificates, commitment schemes and zero-knowledge proofs. Part IV is the most advanced section and covers a number of issues at the more theoretical end of cryptography, including the modern notion of provable security. Our presentation of the public key algorithms in Part III has been designed as a gentle introduction to some of the key concepts in Part IV. Part IV should be considered a gentle, and non-rigorous, introduction to theoretical aspects of modern cryptography.

For those instructors who wish to give a rapid introduction to modern cryptography, in a 20–30 lecture course, I Chapters 3, 5, 7, 10 and 12 with enough of Chapter 1 so as to enable the students to understand the following material. For those instructors wishing to use this book to give a grounding in the mathematics required for modern public key cryptography (for example a course aimed at Math Majors) then I suggest covering Chapters 3, 7, 8, 9 and 11. Instructors teaching an audience of Computer Scientists are probably advised to skip Chapters 2, 8 and 9, since these chapters are more mathematical in nature.

If time allows then one could cover the material in most of this book. For example in our courses in Bristol we have one course focusing on encryption only, which touches on material from Chapters 3, 4, 5, 7 and 15. Then in another course we cover the issues related to key management, digital signatures and PKI by covering material in Chapters 6, 10, 12 and 13, plus other topics in general computer security not covered by this book. In this latter course one treats encryption simply as a black box operation.

A number of topics are not covered which are becoming increasingly important. The first major omission is that I do not discuss in detail either linear or differential cryptanalysis of block ciphers. I have found this to be a subject which is better suited to a project or background reading. The second major omission is that I do not mention timing analysis, differential power analysis and other forms of side channel analysis. This is becoming an increasingly important area related to the implementation of cryptographic algorithms, since most deployed cryptographic implementations reside in a hostile environment such as the smart-card in your wallet.

I would like to thank the students at Bristol who have commented on both our courses and a draft of this book. In addition the following people have helped me by providing detailed feedback on a variety of chapters and topics: Ian Blake, Florian Hess, Nick Howgrave-Graham, John Malone-Lee, Wenbo Mao, John Merriman, Phong Nguyen, Dan Page, Vincent Rijmen, Edlyn Teske and Frederik Vercauteren. I would also like to thank the people at McGraw-Hill who have been very helpful during the writing of this book, especially Conor Graham and Max Elvey.

Nigel Smart

University of Bristol

Further Reading

A.J. Menezes, P. van Oorschot and S.A. Vanstone. *The Handbook of Applied Cryptography.* CRC Press, 1997.

Additional Acknowledgements

The publishers would like to thank the following academics who assisted in the development of this book.

- Dr. H. Ashman – University of Nottingham.

- Prof. D. Aspinall – University of Edinburgh.

- Dr. M. Huth – Imperial College, University of London.

- Dr. S. Jassim – University of Buckingham.

- Dr. S. Murphy – Royal Holloway College, University of London.

- Prof. F. Murtagh – Queen's University, Belfast.

- Dr. R. Poet – University of Glasgow.

- Dr. N. Zhang – Manchester University.

Contents

List of Figures

PART
I

Mathematical Background

Before we tackle cryptography we need to cover some basic facts from mathematics. Much of the following can be found in a number of university 'Discrete Mathematics' courses aimed at Computer Science or Engineering students, hence one hopes not all of this section is new. For those who want more formal definitions of concepts, there is Appendix A at the end of the book.

This part is mainly a quick overview to allow you to start on the main book proper, hence you may want to first start on Part II and return to Part I when you meet some concept you are not familiar with.

Modular Arithmetic, Groups, Finite Fields and Probability

Chapter Goals

- To understand modular arithmetic.

- To become acquainted with groups and finite fields.

- To learn about basic techniques such as Euclid's algorithm, the Chinese Remainder Theorem and Legendre symbols.

- To recap on basic ideas from probability theory.

1.1 MODULAR ARITHMETIC

Much of this book will be spent looking at the applications of modular arithmetic, since it is fundamental to modern cryptography and public key cryptosystems in particular. Hence, in this chapter we introduce the basic concepts and techniques we shall require.

The idea of modular arithmetic is essentially very simple and is identical to the 'clock arithmetic' you learn in school. For example, converting between the 24-hour and the 12-hour clock systems is easy. One takes the value in the 24-hour clock system and reduces the hour by 12. For example 13 : 00 in the 24-hour clock system is one o'clock in the 12-hour clock system, since 13 modulo 12 is equal to one.

More formally, we fix a positive integer N which we call the *modulus*. For two integers a and b we write $a = b \pmod N$ if N divides $b - a$, and we say that a and b are *congruent* modulo N. Often we are lazy and just write $a = b$, if it is clear we are working modulo N.

We can also consider (mod N) as a postfix operator on an integer which returns the smallest positive value equal to the argument modulo N. For example

$$18 \ (\text{mod } 7) = 4,$$
$$-18 \ (\text{mod } 7) = 3.$$

The modulo operator is like the C operator %, except that in this book we usually take representatives which are positive. For example in C or Java we have,

```
(-3)%2 = -1
```

whilst we shall assume that $(-3) \pmod 2 = 1$.

For convenience we define the set:

$$\mathbb{Z}/N\mathbb{Z} = \{0, \ldots, N-1\}$$

which is the set of remainders modulo N. This is the set of values produced by the postfix operator (mod N). Note, some authors use the alternative notation of $\mathbb{Z}_N$ for the set $\mathbb{Z}/N\mathbb{Z}$, however, in this book we shall stick to $\mathbb{Z}/N\mathbb{Z}$.

The set $\mathbb{Z}/N\mathbb{Z}$ has two basic operations on it, namely addition and multiplication. These are defined in the obvious ways, for example:

$$(11 + 13) \pmod{16} = 24 \pmod{16} = 8$$

since $24 = 1 \cdot 16 + 8$ and

$$(11 \cdot 13) \pmod{16} = 143 \pmod{16} = 15$$

since $143 = 8 \cdot 16 + 15$.

1.1.1 Groups and Rings

Addition and multiplication modulo N work almost the same as arithmetic over the reals or the integers. In particular we have the following properties:

1. Addition is closed :
$$\forall a, b \in \mathbb{Z}/N\mathbb{Z} : a + b \in \mathbb{Z}/N\mathbb{Z}.$$

2. Addition is associative :
$$\forall a, b, c \in \mathbb{Z}/N\mathbb{Z} : (a + b) + c = a + (b + c).$$

3. 0 is an additive identity :
$$\forall a \in \mathbb{Z}/N\mathbb{Z} : a + 0 = 0 + a = a.$$

4. The additive inverse always exists :
$$\forall a \in \mathbb{Z}/N\mathbb{Z} : a + (N - a) = (N - a) + a = 0.$$

5. Addition is commutative :
$$\forall a, b \in \mathbb{Z}/N\mathbb{Z} : a + b = b + a.$$

6. Multiplication is closed :
$$\forall a, b \in \mathbb{Z}/N\mathbb{Z} : a \cdot b \in \mathbb{Z}/N\mathbb{Z}.$$

7. Multiplication is associative :
$$\forall a, b, c \in \mathbb{Z}/N\mathbb{Z} : (a \cdot b) \cdot c = a \cdot (b \cdot c).$$

8. 1 is a multiplicative identity :

$$\forall a \in \mathbb{Z}/N\mathbb{Z} : a \cdot 1 = 1 \cdot a = a.$$

9. Multiplication and addition satisfy the distributive law :

$$\forall a, b, c \in \mathbb{Z}/N\mathbb{Z} : (a + b) \cdot c = a \cdot c + b \cdot c.$$

10. Multiplication is commutative :

$$\forall a, b \in \mathbb{Z}/N\mathbb{Z} : a \cdot b = b \cdot a.$$

Many of the sets we will encounter have a number of these properties, so we give special names to these sets as a shorthand.

Definition 1.1 (Groups) *A group is a set with an operation which*

- *is closed,*
- *has an identity,*
- *is associative,*
- *every element has an inverse.*

A group which is commutative is often called *abelian*. Almost all groups that one meets in cryptography are abelian, since the commutative property is what makes them cryptographically interesting. Hence, any set with properties 1, 2, 3 and 4 above is called a group, whilst a set with properties 1, 2, 3, 4 and 5 is called an abelian group.

Standard examples of groups which one meets all the time at high school are:

- The integer, real or complex numbers under addition. Here the identity is 0 and the inverse of x is $-x$, since $x + (-x) = 0$.

- The non-zero rational, real or complex numbers under multiplication. Here the identity is 1 and the inverse of x is x^{-1}, since $x \cdot x^{-1} = 1$.

A group is called *multiplicative* if we tend to write its group operation in the same way as one does for multiplication, i.e.

$$f = g \cdot h \text{ and } g^5 = g \cdot g \cdot g \cdot g \cdot g.$$

We use the notation $(G, \cdot)$ in this case if there is some ambiguity as to which operation on G we are considering. A group is called *additive* if we tend to write its group operation in the same way as one does for addition, i.e.

$$f = g + h \text{ and } 5 \cdot g = g + g + g + g + g.$$

In this case we use the notation $(G, +)$ if there is some ambiguity. An abelian group is called *cyclic* if there is a special element, called the *generator*, from which every other element can be obtained by repeated application of the group operation. For example, in the integers under addition every integer can be obtained by repeated addition of 1 to itself, e.g. 7 can be expressed by

$$7 = 1 + 1 + 1 + 1 + 1 + 1 + 1.$$

In this case we say that 1 is a generator of the integers under addition.

If g is a generator of the cyclic group G we often write $G = \langle g \rangle$. If G is multiplicative then every element h of G can be written as

$$h = g^x,$$

whilst if G is additive then every element h of G can be written as

$$h = x \cdot g,$$

where x in both cases is some integer called the discrete logarithm of h to the base g.

As well as groups we also define the concept of a ring.

Definition 1.2 (Rings) *A ring is a set with two operations, usually denoted by $+$ and $\cdot$ for addition and multiplication, which satisfies properties 1 to 9 above. We can denote a ring and its two operations by the triple $(R, \cdot, +)$.*

If it also happens that multiplication is commutative we say that the ring is commutative.

This may seem complicated but it sums up the type of sets one deals with all the time, for example the infinite commutative rings of integers, real or complex numbers. In fact in cryptography things are even easier since we only need to consider finite rings, like the commutative ring of integers modulo N, $\mathbb{Z}/N\mathbb{Z}$.

1.1.2 Euler's ϕ Function

In modular arithmetic it will be important to know when, given a and b, the equation

$$a \cdot x = b \ (\mathrm{mod}\ N)$$

has a solution. For example there is exactly one solution to the equation

$$7x = 3 \ (\mathrm{mod}\ 143),$$

but there are no solutions to the equation

$$11x = 3 \ (\mathrm{mod}\ 143),$$

however there are 11 solutions to the equation

$$11x = 22 \ (\mathrm{mod}\ 143).$$

Luckily, it is very easy to test when such an equation has one, many or no solutions. We simply compute the greatest common divisor, or gcd, of a and N, i.e. $\gcd(a, N)$.

- If $\gcd(a, N) = 1$ then there is exactly one solution. We find the value c such that $a \cdot c = 1 \ (\mathrm{mod}\ N)$ and then we compute $x = b \cdot c \ (\mathrm{mod}\ N)$.

- If $g = \gcd(a, N) \neq 1$ and $\gcd(a, N)$ divides b then there are g solutions. Here we divide the whole equation by g to produce the equation

$$a' \cdot x' = b' \pmod{N'},$$

where $a' = a/g$, $b' = b/g$ and $N' = N/g$. If x' is a solution to the above equation then

$$x = x' + i \cdot N'$$

for $0 \le i < g$ is a solution to the original one.

- Otherwise there are no solutions.

The case where $\gcd(a, N) = 1$ is so important we have a special name for it, we say a and N are relatively prime or coprime.

The number of integers in $\mathbb{Z}/N\mathbb{Z}$ which are relatively prime to N is given by the Euler ϕ function, $\phi(N)$. Given the prime factorization of N it is easy to compute the value of $\phi(N)$. If N has the prime factorization

$$N = \prod_{i=1}^{n} p_i^{e_i}$$

then

$$\phi(N) = \prod_{i=1}^{n} p_i^{e_i - 1}(p_i - 1).$$

Note, the last statement it is very important for cryptography: *Given the factorization of N it is easy to compute the value of $\phi(N)$.* The most important cases for the value of $\phi(N)$ in cryptography are:

1. If p is prime then

$$\phi(p) = p - 1.$$

2. If p and q are both prime and $p \neq q$ then

$$\phi(p \cdot q) = (p - 1)(q - 1).$$

1.1.3 Multiplicative Inverse Modulo N

We have just seen that when we wish to solve equations of the form

$$ax = b \pmod{N}$$

we reduce to the question of examining when an integer a modulo N has a multiplicative inverse, i.e. whether there is a number c such that

$$ac = ca = 1 \pmod{N}.$$

Such a value of c is often written a^{-1}. Clearly a^{-1} is the solution to the equation

$$ax = 1 \pmod{N}.$$

Hence, the inverse of a only exists when a and N are coprime, i.e. $\gcd(a, N) = 1$. Of particular interest is when N is a prime p, since then for all non-zero values of $a \in \mathbb{Z}/p\mathbb{Z}$ we always obtain a unique solution to

$$ax = 1 \pmod{p}.$$

Hence, if p is a prime then every non-zero element in $\mathbb{Z}/p\mathbb{Z}$ has a multiplicative inverse. A ring like $\mathbb{Z}/p\mathbb{Z}$ with this property is called a field.

Definition 1.3 (Fields) *A field is a set with two operations $(G, \cdot, +)$ such that*

- $(G, +)$ *is an abelian group with identity denoted by 0,*

- $(G \setminus \{0\}, \cdot)$ *is an abelian group,*

- $(G, \cdot, +)$ *satisfies the distributive law.*

Hence, a field is a commutative ring for which every non-zero element has a multiplicative inverse. You have met fields before, for example consider the infinite fields of rational, real or complex numbers.

We define the set of all invertible elements in $\mathbb{Z}/N\mathbb{Z}$ by

$$(\mathbb{Z}/N\mathbb{Z})^* = \{x \in \mathbb{Z}/N\mathbb{Z} : \gcd(x, N) = 1\}$$

The $*$ in A^* for any ring A refers to the largest subset of A which forms a group under multiplication. Hence, the set $(\mathbb{Z}/N\mathbb{Z})^*$ is a group with respect to multiplication and it has size $\phi(N)$.

In the special case when N is a prime p we have

$$(\mathbb{Z}/p\mathbb{Z})^* = \{1, \ldots, p-1\}$$

since every non-zero element of $\mathbb{Z}/p\mathbb{Z}$ is coprime to p. For an arbitrary field F the set F^* is equal to the set $F \setminus \{0\}$. To ease notation, for this very important case, define

$$\mathbb{F}_p = \mathbb{Z}/p\mathbb{Z} = \{0, \ldots, p-1\}$$

and

$$\mathbb{F}_p^* = (\mathbb{Z}/p\mathbb{Z})^* = \{1, \ldots, p-1\}.$$

The set $\mathbb{F}_p$ is a finite field of characteristic p. In the next section we shall discuss a more general type of finite field, but for now recall the important point that the integers modulo N are only a field when N is a prime.

We end this section with the most important theorem in elementary group theory.

Theorem 1.4 (Lagrange's Theorem) *If $(G, \cdot)$ is a group of order (size) $n = \#G$ then for all $a \in G$ we have $a^n = 1$.*

So if $x \in (\mathbb{Z}/N\mathbb{Z})^*$ then

$$x^{\phi(N)} = 1 \pmod{N}$$

since $\#(\mathbb{Z}/N\mathbb{Z})^* = \phi(N)$. This leads us to Fermat's Little Theorem, not to be confused with Fermat's Last Theorem which is something entirely different.

Theorem 1.5 (Fermat's Little Theorem) *Suppose p is a prime and $a \in \mathbb{F}_p^*$ then*

$$a^p = a \pmod{p}.$$

Fermat's Little Theorem is a special case of Lagrange's Theorem and will form the basis of one of the primality tests considered in a later chapter.

1.2   FINITE FIELDS

The integers modulo a prime p are not the only types of finite field. In this section we shall introduce another type of finite field which is particularly important. At first reading you may wish to skip this section. We shall only be using these general forms of finite fields when discussing the Rijndael block cipher, stream ciphers based on linear feedback shift registers and when we look at elliptic curve based systems.

For this section we let p denote a prime number. Consider the set of polynomials in X whose coefficients are reduced modulo p. We denote this set $\mathbb{F}_p[X]$, which forms a ring with the natural definition of addition and multiplication.

Of particular interest is the case when $p = 2$, from which we draw all our examples in this section. For example, in $\mathbb{F}_2[X]$ we have

$$(1 + X + X^2) + (X + X^3) = 1 + X^2 + X^3,$$
$$(1 + X + X^2) \cdot (X + X^3) = X + X^2 + X^4 + X^5.$$

Just as with the integers modulo a number N, where the integers modulo N formed a ring, we can take a polynomial $f(X)$ and then the polynomials modulo $f(X)$ also form a ring. We denote this ring by

$$\mathbb{F}_p[X]/f(X)\mathbb{F}_p[X]$$

or more simply

$$\mathbb{F}_p[X]/(f(X)).$$

When $f(X) = X^4 + 1$ and $p = 2$ we have, for example,

$$(1 + X + X^2) \cdot (X + X^3) \pmod{X^4 + 1} = 1 + X^2$$

since

$$X + X^2 + X^4 + X^5 = (X + 1) \cdot (X^4 + 1) + (1 + X^2).$$

When checking the above equation you should remember we are working modulo two.

Recall, when we looked at the integers modulo N we looked at the equation

$$ax = b \pmod{N}.$$

We can consider a similar question for polynomials. Given a, b and f, all of which are polynomials in $\mathbb{F}_p[X]$, does there exist a solution α to the equation

$$a\alpha = b \pmod{f}?$$

With integers the answer depended on the greatest common divisor of a and f, and we counted three possible cases. A similar three cases can occur for polynomials, with the most important one being when a and f are coprime and so have greatest common divisor equal to one.

A polynomial is called irreducible if it has no proper factors other than itself and the constant polynomials. Hence, irreducibility of polynomials is the same as primality of numbers. Just as with the integers modulo N, when N was prime we obtained a finite field, so when $f(X)$ is irreducible the ring $\mathbb{F}_p[X]/f(X)$ also forms a finite field.

Consider the case $p = 2$ and the two different irreducible polynomials

$$f_1 = X^7 + X + 1$$

and

$$f_2 = X^7 + X^3 + 1.$$

Now, consider the two finite fields

$$F_1 = \mathbb{F}_2[X]/f_1(X) \text{ and } F_2 = \mathbb{F}_2[X]/f_2(X).$$

These both consist of the 2^7 binary polynomials of degree less than seven. Addition in these two fields is identical in that one just adds the coefficients of the polynomials modulo two. The only difference is in how multiplication is performed

$$(X^3 + 1) \cdot (X^4 + 1) \pmod{f_1(X)} = X^4 + X^3 + X,$$
$$(X^3 + 1) \cdot (X^4 + 1) \pmod{f_2(X)} = X^4.$$

A natural question arises as to whether these fields are 'really' different, or whether they just "look" different. In mathematical terms the question is whether the two fields are *isomorphic*. It turns out that they are isomorphic if there is a map

$$\phi : F_1 \longrightarrow F_2,$$

called a field isomorphism, which satisfies

$$\phi(\alpha + \beta) = \phi(\alpha) + \phi(\beta),$$
$$\phi(\alpha \cdot \beta) = \phi(\alpha) \cdot \phi(\beta).$$

Such an isomorphism exists for every two finite fields of the same order, although we will not show it here. To describe the map above you only need to show how to express a root of $f_2(X)$ in terms of a polynomial in the root of $f_1(X)$.

The above construction is in fact the only way of producing finite fields, hence all finite fields are essentially equal to polynomials modulo a prime and modulo an irreducible polynomial (for that prime). Hence, we have the following basic theorem

Theorem 1.6 *There is (up to isomorphism) just one finite field of each prime power order.*

The notation we use for these fields is either $\mathbb{F}_q$ or $GF(q)$, with $q = p^d$ where d is the degree of the irreducible polynomial used to construct the finite field. We of course have $\mathbb{F}_p = \mathbb{F}_p[X]/X$. The notation $GF(q)$ means the Galois Field of q elements. Finite fields are sometimes named after the 19th century French mathematician Galois. Galois had an interesting life, he accomplished most of his scientific work at an early age before dying in a dual.

There are a number of technical definitions associated with finite fields which we need to cover. Each finite field K contains a copy of the integers modulo p for some prime p, we call this prime the *characteristic* of the field, and often write this as char K. The subfield of integers modulo p of a finite field is called the prime subfield.

There is a map Φ called the p-th power *Frobenius map* defined for any finite field by

$$\Phi : \begin{cases} \mathbb{F}_q \longrightarrow \mathbb{F}_q \\ \alpha \longmapsto \alpha^p \end{cases}$$

where p is the characteristic of $\mathbb{F}_q$. The Frobenius map is an isomorphism of $\mathbb{F}_q$ with itself, such an isomorphism is called an automorphism. An interesting property is that the set of elements fixed by the Frobenius map is the prime field, i.e.

$$\{\alpha \in \mathbb{F}_q : \alpha^p = \alpha\} = \mathbb{F}_p.$$

Notice that this is a kind of generalization of Fermat's Little Theorem to finite fields. For any automorphism χ of a finite field the set of elements fixed by χ is a field, called the fixed field of χ. Hence the previous statement says that the fixed field of the Frobenius map is the prime field $\mathbb{F}_p$.

Not only does $\mathbb{F}_q$ contain a copy of $\mathbb{F}_p$ but $\mathbb{F}_{p^d}$ contains a copy of $\mathbb{F}_{p^e}$ for every value of e dividing d. In addition $\mathbb{F}_{p^e}$ is the fixed field of the automorphism Φ^e, i.e.

$$\{\alpha \in \mathbb{F}_{p^d} : \alpha^{p^e} = \alpha\} = \mathbb{F}_{p^e}.$$

Another interesting property is that if p is the characteristic of $\mathbb{F}_q$ then if we take any element $\alpha \in \mathbb{F}_q$ and add it to itself p times we obtain zero, e.g. in $\mathbb{F}_{49}$ we have

$$X + X + X + X + X + X + X = 7X = 0 \pmod{7}.$$

The non-zero elements of a finite field, usually denoted $\mathbb{F}_q^*$, form a cyclic finite abelian group. We call a generator of $\mathbb{F}_q^*$ a primitive element in the finite field. Such primitive elements always exist and so the multiplicative group is always cyclic. In other words there always exists an element $g \in \mathbb{F}_q$ such that every non-zero element α can be written as

$$\alpha = g^x$$

for some integer value of x.

As an example consider the field of eight elements defined by

$$\mathbb{F}_{2^3} = \mathbb{F}_2[X]/(X^3 + X + 1).$$

In this field there are seven non-zero elements namely

$$1, \alpha, \alpha + 1, \alpha^2, \alpha^2 + 1, \alpha^2 + \alpha, \alpha^2 + \alpha + 1$$

where α is a root of $X^3 + X + 1$. We see that α is a primitive element in $\mathbb{F}_{2^3}$ since

$$\alpha^1 = \alpha,$$
$$\alpha^2 = \alpha^2,$$
$$\alpha^3 = \alpha + 1,$$
$$\alpha^4 = \alpha^2 + \alpha,$$
$$\alpha^5 = \alpha^2 + \alpha + 1,$$
$$\alpha^6 = \alpha^2 + 1,$$
$$\alpha^7 = 1.$$

Notice that for a prime p this means that the integers modulo a prime also have a primitive element, since $\mathbb{Z}/p\mathbb{Z} = \mathbb{F}_p$ is a finite field.

1.3   BASIC ALGORITHMS

There are several basic numerical algorithms or techniques which everyone should know since they occur in many places in this book. The ones we shall concentrate on here are

- Euclid's gcd algorithm,

- the Chinese Remainder Theorem,

- computing Jacobi and Legendre symbols.

1.3.1   Greatest Common Divisors

In the previous sections we said that when trying to solve

$$a \cdot x = b \ (\mathrm{mod}\ N)$$

in integers, or

$$a\alpha = b \ (\mathrm{mod}\ f)$$

for polynomials modulo a prime, we needed to compute the greatest common divisor. This was particularly important in determining whether $a \in \mathbb{Z}/N\mathbb{Z}$ or $a \in \mathbb{F}_p[X]/f$ had a multiplicative inverse or not, i.e. $\gcd(a, N) = 1$ or $\gcd(a, f) = 1$. We did not explain how this greatest common divisor is computed, neither did we explain how the inverse is to be computed when we know it exists. We shall now address this omission by explaining one of the oldest algorithms known to man, namely the Euclidean algorithm.

   If we were able to factor a and N into primes, or a and f into irreducible polynomials, then computing the greatest common divisor would be particularly easy. For example if

$$a = 230\,895\,588\,646\,864 = 2^4 \cdot 157 \cdot 4513^3,$$
$$b = 33\,107\,658\,350\,407\,876 = 2^2 \cdot 157 \cdot 2269^3 \cdot 4513,$$

then it is easy, from the factorization, to compute the gcd as

$$\gcd(a, b) = 2^2 \cdot 157 \cdot 4513 = 2\,834\,164.$$

However, factoring is an expensive operation for integers, but computing greatest common divisors is easy as we shall show. Although factoring for polynomials modulo a prime is very easy, it turns out that almost all algorithms to factor polynomials require access to an algorithm to compute greatest common divisors. Hence, in both situations we need to be able to compute greatest common divisors without recourse to factoring.

1.3.1.1   Euclidean Algorithm: In the following we will consider the case of integers only, the generalization to polynomials is easy since both integers and polynomials allow Euclidean division. For integers Euclidean division is the operation of, given a and b, finding q and r with $0 \le r < |b|$ such that

$$a = q \cdot b + r.$$

For polynomials Euclidean division is given polynomials f, g finding polynomials q, r with $0 \leq \deg r < \deg g$ such that

$$f = q \cdot g + r.$$

To compute the gcd of $r_0 = a$ and $r_1 = b$ we compute $r_2, r_3, r_4, \ldots$ as follows;

$$r_2 = q_1 r_1 - r_0$$
$$r_3 = q_2 r_2 - r_1$$
$$\vdots \quad \vdots$$
$$r_m = q_{m-1} r_{m-1} - r_{m-2}$$
$$r_{m+1} = q_m r_m.$$

If d divides a and b then d divides r_2, r_3, r_4 and so on. Hence

$$\gcd(a, b) = \gcd(r_0, r_1) = \gcd(r_1, r_2) = \cdots = \gcd(r_{m-1}, r_m) = r_m.$$

As an example of this algorithm we want to show that

$$3 = \gcd(21, 12).$$

Using the Euclidean algorithm we compute $\gcd(21, 12)$ in the steps

$$
\begin{aligned}
\gcd(21, 12) &= \gcd(21 \ (\mathrm{mod}\ 12), 12) \\
&= \gcd(9, 12) \\
&= \gcd(12 \ (\mathrm{mod}\ 9), 9) \\
&= \gcd(3, 9) \\
&= \gcd(9 \ (\mathrm{mod}\ 3), 3) \\
&= \gcd(0, 3) = 3.
\end{aligned}
$$

Or, as an example with larger numbers,

$$
\begin{aligned}
\gcd(1\,426\,668\,559\,730,\ 810\,653\,094\,756) &= \gcd(810\,653\,094\,756,\ 616\,015\,464\,974), \\
&= \gcd(616\,015\,464\,974,\ 194\,637\,629\,782), \\
&= \gcd(194\,637\,629\,782,\ 32\,102\,575\,628), \\
&= \gcd(32\,102\,575\,628,\ 2\,022\,176\,014), \\
&= \gcd(2\,022\,176\,014,\ 1\,769\,935\,418), \\
&= \gcd(1\,769\,935\,418,\ 252\,240\,596), \\
&= \gcd(252\,240\,596,\ 4\,251\,246), \\
&= \gcd(4\,251\,246,\ 1\,417\,082), \\
&= \gcd(1\,417\,082,\ 0), \\
&= 1\,417\,082.
\end{aligned}
$$

This algorithm is particular easy to implement using a functional programming language such as Haskell, since it is naturally implemented in a recursive manner:

```
myGcd :: Int -> Int -> Int
myGcd a b = gcdstep (abs a) (abs b)

gcdstep :: Int -> Int -> Int
gcdstep a b
  | a == 0     = b
  | otherwise  = gcdstep (b 'mod' a) a
```

In many languages, such as Java, C or in computer algebra packages, a recursive definition of a function may not be the best way to proceed because of the overhead of function calls. Luckily we do not have to implement a gcd algorithm only in a recursive manner. For example in Java we could write:

```
static public long gcd(long a,long b)
{
    a=Math.abs(a);
    b=Math.abs(b);
    while (a != 0)
        { long temp=b%a;
            b=a;
            a=temp;
        }
    return b;
}
```

The Euclidean algorithm essentially works because the map

$$(a,b) \longmapsto (a \pmod{b}, b),$$

for $a \geq b$ is a gcd preserving mapping. The trouble is that computers find it much easier to add and multiply numbers than to take remainders or quotients. Hence, implementing a gcd algorithm with the above gcd preserving mapping will usually be very inefficient. Fortunately, there are a number of other gcd preserving mappings, for example

$$(a,b) \longmapsto \begin{cases} ((a-b)/2, b) & \text{If } a \text{ and } b \text{ are odd.} \\ (a/2, b) & \text{If } a \text{ is even and } b \text{ is odd.} \\ (a, b/2) & \text{If } a \text{ is odd and } b \text{ is even.} \end{cases}$$

Recall that computers find it easy to divide by two, since in binary this is accomplished by a cheap bit shift operation. This latter mapping gives rise to the binary Euclidean algorithm, which is the one usually implemented on a computer. Essentially, this algorithm uses the above gcd preserving mapping after first removing any power of two in the gcd. The following pseudo-code explains how this works, on input of two positive integers a and b:

```
g=1 ;
/* Remove powers of two from the gcd */
  while ((a%2==0) and (b%2==0))
    { a=a/2;
      b=b/2;
```

```
      g=2*g;
   }
/* At least one of a and b is now odd */
   while (a != 0)
     { while (a%2==0) { a=a/2; }
       while (b%2==0) { b=b/2; }
/*     Now both a and b are odd  */
       if (a>=b) then a=(a-b)/2;
       else            b=(b-a)/2;
     }
   Return g*b;
```

1.3.1.2 Extended Euclidean Algorithm:

Using the Euclidean algorithm we can determine when a has an inverse modulo m by testing whether

$$\gcd(a, m) = 1.$$

But we still do not know how to determine the inverse when it exists. To do this we use a variant of Euclid's gcd algorithm, called the extended Euclidean algorithm. Recall we had

$$r_{i-2} = q_{i-1}r_{i-1} + r_i$$

with $r_m = \gcd(r_0, r_1)$. Now we unwind the above and write each r_i, for $i \geq 2$, in terms of a and b. For example

$$r_2 = r_0 - q_1 r_1 = a - q_1 b$$
$$r_3 = r_1 - q_2 r_2 = b - q_2(a - q_1 b) = -q_2 a + (1 + q_1 q_2)b$$
$$\vdots \quad \vdots$$
$$r_{i-2} = s_{i-2}a + t_{i-2}b$$
$$r_{i-1} = s_{i-1}a + t_{i-1}b$$
$$r_i = r_{i-2} - q_{i-1}r_{i-1}$$
$$= a(s_{i-2} - q_{i-1}s_{i-1}) + b(t_{i-2} - q_{i-1}t_{i-1})$$
$$\vdots \quad \vdots$$
$$r_m = s_m a + t_m b.$$

The extended Euclidean algorithm takes as input a and b and outputs r_m, s_m and t_m such that

$$r_m = \gcd(a, b) = s_m a + t_m b.$$

Hence, we can now solve our original problem of determining the inverse of a modulo N, when such an inverse exists. We first apply the extended Euclidean algorithm to a and N so as to compute d, x, y such that

$$d = \gcd(a, N) = xa + yN.$$

We can solve the equation $ax = 1 \pmod{N}$, since we have $d = xa + yN = xa \pmod{N}$. Hence, we have a solution $x = a^{-1}$, precisely when $d = 1$.

As an example suppose we wish to compute the inverse of 7 modulo 19. We first set $r_0 = 7$ and $r_1 = 19$ and then we compute

$$r_2 = 5 = 19 - 2 \cdot 7$$
$$r_3 = 2 = 7 - 5 = 7 - (19 - 2 \cdot 7) = -19 + 3 \cdot 7$$
$$r_4 = 1 = 5 - 2 \cdot 2 = (19 - 2 \cdot 7) - 2 \cdot (-19 + 3 \cdot 7) = 3 \cdot 19 - 8 \cdot 7.$$

Hence,

$$1 = -8 \cdot 7 \ (\text{mod } 19)$$

and so

$$7^{-1} = -8 = 11 \ (\text{mod } 19).$$

1.3.2 Chinese Remainder Theorem (CRT)

The Chinese Remainder Theorem, or CRT, is also a very old piece of mathematics, which dates back at least 2000 years. We shall use the CRT in a few places, for example to improve the performance of the decryption operation of RSA and in a number of other protocols. In a nutshell the CRT states that if we have the two equations

$$x = a \ (\text{mod } N) \text{ and } x = b \ (\text{mod } M)$$

then there is a unique solution modulo $M \cdot N$ if and only if $\gcd(N, M) = 1$. In addition it gives a method to easily find the solution. For example if the two equations are given by

$$x = 4 \ (\text{mod } 7),$$
$$x = 3 \ (\text{mod } 5),$$

then we have

$$x = 18 \ (\text{mod } 35).$$

It is easy to check that this is a solution, since 18 (mod 7) = 4 and 18 (mod 5) = 3. But how did we produce this solution?

We shall first show how this can be done naively from first principles and then we shall give the general method. We have the equations

$$x = 4 \ (\text{mod } 7) \text{ and } x = 3 \ (\text{mod } 5).$$

Hence for some u we have

$$x = 4 + 7u \text{ and } x = 3 \ (\text{mod } 5).$$

Putting these latter two equations into one gives,

$$4 + 7u = 3 \ (\text{mod } 5).$$

We then rearrange the equation to find

$$2u = 7u = 3 - 4 = 4 \ (\text{mod } 5).$$

Now since $\gcd(2,5) = \gcd(7,5) = 1$ we can solve the above equation for u. First we compute $2^{-1} \pmod{5} = 3$, since $2 \cdot 3 = 6 = 1 \pmod{5}$. Then we compute the value of $u = 3 \cdot 4 \pmod{5}$. Then substituting this value of u back into our equation for x gives the solution

$$x = 4 + 7u = 4 + 7 \cdot 2 = 18.$$

The case of two equations is so important we now give a general formula. We assume $\gcd(N, M) = 1$, and assume we are given the equations

$$x = a \pmod{N} \text{ and } x = b \pmod{M}.$$

We first compute

$$T = M^{-1} \pmod{N}$$

which is possible since we have assumed $\gcd(N, M) = 1$. We then compute

$$u = (b - a)T \pmod{N}.$$

The solution modulo $M \cdot N$ is then given by

$$x = a + uM.$$

To see this always works we compute

$$x \pmod{M} = a + uM \pmod{M}$$
$$= a,$$
$$x \pmod{N} = a + uM \pmod{N}$$
$$= a + (b - a)TM \pmod{N}$$
$$= a + (b - a)M^{-1}M \pmod{N}$$
$$= a + (b - a) \pmod{N}$$
$$= b.$$

Now we turn to the general case of the CRT where we consider more than two equations at once. Let $m_1, \ldots, m_r$ be pairwise relatively prime and let $a_1, \ldots, a_r$ be given. We want to find x modulo $M = m_1 m_2 \cdots m_r$ such that

$$x = a_i \pmod{m_i} \text{ for all } i.$$

The Chinese Remainder Theorem guarantees a unique solution given by

$$x = \sum_{i=1}^{r} a_i M_i y_i \pmod{M}$$

where

$$M_i = M/m_i,$$
$$y_i = M_i^{-1} \pmod{m_i}.$$

As an example suppose we wish to find the unique x modulo

$$M = 1001 = 7 \cdot 11 \cdot 13$$

such that

$$x = 5 \ (\text{mod } 7),$$
$$x = 3 \ (\text{mod } 11),$$
$$x = 10 \ (\text{mod } 13).$$

We compute

$$M_1 = 143, \quad y_1 = 5,$$
$$M_2 = 91, \quad y_1 = 4,$$
$$M_3 = 77, \quad y_3 = 12.$$

Then, the solution is given by

$$x = \sum_{i=1}^{r} a_i M_i y_i \ (\text{mod } M)$$
$$= 715 \cdot 5 + 364 \cdot 3 + 924 \cdot 10 \ (\text{mod } 1001)$$
$$= 894.$$

1.3.3 Legendre and Jacobi Symbols

Let p denote a prime, greater than two. Consider the mapping

$$\mathbb{F}_p \longrightarrow \mathbb{F}_p$$
$$\alpha \longmapsto \alpha^2.$$

This mapping is exactly two-to-one on the non-zero elements of $\mathbb{F}_p$. So if an element x in $\mathbb{F}_p$ has a square root, then it has exactly two square roots (unless $x = 0$) and exactly half of the elements of $\mathbb{F}_p^*$ are squares. The set of squares in $\mathbb{F}_p^*$ are called the *quadratic residues* and they form a subgroup, of order $(p-1)/2$ of the multiplicative group $\mathbb{F}_p^*$. The elements of $\mathbb{F}_p^*$ which are not squares are called the *quadratic non-residues*.

To make it easy to detect squares modulo p we define the *Legendre symbol*

$$\left(\frac{a}{p} \right).$$

This is defined to be equal to 0 if p divides a, it is equal to $+1$ if a is a quadratic residue and it is equal to -1 if a is a quadratic non-residue.

It is easy to compute the Legendre symbol, for example via

$$\left(\frac{a}{p} \right) = a^{(p-1)/2} \ (\text{mod } p).$$

However, using the above formula turns out to be very inefficient. In practice one uses the *law of quadratic reciprocity*

$$\left(\frac{q}{p} \right) = \left(\frac{p}{q} \right) (-1)^{(p-1)(q-1)/2}. \tag{1.1}$$

In other words we have

$$\left(\frac{q}{p}\right) = \begin{cases} -\left(\frac{p}{q}\right) & \text{If } p = q = 3 \pmod 4, \\ \left(\frac{p}{q}\right) & \text{Otherwise} \end{cases}$$

Using this law with the following additional formulae gives rise to a recursive algorithm

$$\left(\frac{q}{p}\right) = \left(\frac{q \pmod p}{p}\right), \tag{1.2}$$

$$\left(\frac{q \cdot r}{p}\right) = \left(\frac{q}{p}\right) \cdot \left(\frac{r}{p}\right), \tag{1.3}$$

$$\left(\frac{2}{p}\right) = (-1)^{(p^2-1)/8}. \tag{1.4}$$

Assuming we can factor, we can now compute the Legendre symbol

$$\left(\frac{15}{17}\right) = \left(\frac{3}{17}\right) \cdot \left(\frac{5}{17}\right) \text{ by Equation (1.3)}$$
$$= \left(\frac{17}{3}\right) \cdot \left(\frac{17}{5}\right) \text{ by Equation (1.1)}$$
$$= \left(\frac{2}{3}\right) \cdot \left(\frac{2}{5}\right) \text{ by Equation (1.2)}$$
$$= (-1) \cdot (-1)^3 \text{ by Equation (1.4)}$$
$$= 1.$$

In a moment we shall see a more efficient algorithm which does not require us to factor integers.

Computing square roots of elements in $\mathbb{F}_p^*$, when the square root exists turns out to be an easy task. The following gives one method, called Shank's Algorithm, of computing the square root of a modulo p, when such a square root exists.

1. Choose a random n until one is found such that

$$\left(\frac{n}{p}\right) = -1.$$

2. Let e, q be integers such that q is odd and $p - 1 = 2^e q$.

3. Set $y = n^q \pmod p$, $r = e$, $x = a^{(q-1)/2} \pmod p$,

4. Set $b = ax^2 \pmod p$, $x = ax \pmod p$.

5. While $b \neq 1 \pmod p$ do:

   - Find the smallest m such that $b^{2^m} = 1 \pmod p$,
   - Set $t = y^{2^{r-m-1}} \pmod p$, $y = t^2 \pmod p$, $r = m$,

- Set $x = xt \pmod{p}$, $b = by \pmod{p}$.

6. Return x.

When $p = 3 \pmod 4$, instead of the above algorithm, we can use the following formulae

$$x = a^{(p+1)/4} \pmod{p},$$

which has the advantage of being deterministic and more efficient than the general method of Shanks. That this formula works is because

$$x^2 = a^{(p+1)/2} = a^{(p-1)/2} \cdot a = \left(\frac{a}{p}\right) \cdot a = a$$

where the last equality holds since we have assumed that a is a quadratic residue modulo p and so it has Legendre symbol equal to one.

The Legendre symbol above is only defined when its denominator is a prime, but there is a generalization to composite denominators called the *Jacobi symbol*. Suppose $n \geq 3$ is odd and

$$n = p_1^{e_1} p_2^{e_2} \cdots p_k^{e_k}$$

then the Jacobi symbol

$$\left(\frac{a}{n}\right)$$

is defined in terms of the Legendre symbol by

$$\left(\frac{a}{n}\right) = \left(\frac{a}{p_1}\right)^{e_1} \left(\frac{a}{p_2}\right)^{e_2} \cdots \left(\frac{a}{p_k}\right)^{e_k}.$$

The Jacobi symbol can be computed using a similar method to the Legendre symbol by making use of the identity, derived from the law of quadratic reciprocity,

$$\left(\frac{a}{n}\right) = \left(\frac{2}{n}\right)^{e} \left(\frac{n \pmod{a_1}}{a_1}\right) (-1)^{(a_1-1)(n-1)/4}.$$

where $a = 2^e a_1$ and a_1 is odd. We also require the identities, for n odd,

$$\left(\frac{1}{n}\right) = 1,$$

$$\left(\frac{2}{n}\right) = (-1)^{(n^2-1)/8},$$

$$\left(\frac{-1}{n}\right) = (-1)^{(n-1)/2}.$$

This now gives us a fast algorithm, which does not require factoring of integers, to determine the Jacobi symbol, and so the Legendre symbol in the case where the denominator is prime. The only factoring required is that of extracting the even part of a number:

$$\left(\frac{15}{17}\right) = (-1)^{56} \left(\frac{17}{15}\right)$$

$$= \left(\frac{2}{15}\right)$$

$$= (-1)^{28} = 1.$$

Recall the Legendre symbol $\left(\frac{a}{p}\right)$ tells us whether a is a square modulo p, for p a prime. Alas, the Jacobi symbol $\left(\frac{a}{n}\right)$ does not tell us the whole story about whether a is a square modulo n, when n is a composite. If a is a square modulo n then the Jacobi symbol will be equal to plus one, however if the Jacobi symbol is equal to plus one then it is not always true that a is a square.

Let $n \geq 3$ be odd and let the set of squares in $(\mathbb{Z}/n\mathbb{Z})^*$ be denoted

$$Q_n = \{x^2 \pmod{n} : x \in (\mathbb{Z}/n\mathbb{Z})^*\}.$$

Now let J_n denote the set of elements with Jacobi symbol equal to plus one, i.e.

$$J_n = \left\{ x \in (\mathbb{Z}/n\mathbb{Z})^* : \left(\frac{a}{N}\right) = 1 \right\}.$$

The set of pseudo-squares is the difference $J_n \setminus Q_n$.

There are two important cases for cryptography, either n is prime or n is the product of two primes:

- n is a prime p.
  - $Q_n = J_n$.
  - $\#Q_n = (n-1)/2$.
- n is the product of two primes, $n = p \cdot q$.
  - $Q_n \subset J_n$.
  - $\#Q_n = \#(J_n \setminus Q_n) = (p-1)(q-1)/4$.

The sets Q_n and J_n will be seen to be important in a number of algorithms and protocols, especially in the case where n is a product of two primes.

Finally, we look at how to compute a square root modulo a composite number $n = p \cdot q$. Suppose we wish to compute the square root of a modulo n. We assume we know p and q, and that a really is a square modulo n, which can be checked by demonstrating that

$$\left(\frac{a}{p}\right) = \left(\frac{a}{q}\right) = 1.$$

We first compute the square root of a modulo p, call this s_p. Then we compute the square root of a modulo q, call this s_q. Finally to deduce the square root modulo n, we apply the Chinese Remainder Theorem to the equations

$$x = s_p \pmod{p} \text{ and } x = s_q \pmod{q}.$$

As an example suppose we wish to compute the square root of $a = 217$ modulo $n = 221 = 13 \cdot 17$. Now the square root of a modulo 13 and 17 is given by

$$s_{13} = 3 \text{ and } s_{17} = 8.$$

Applying the Chinese Remainder Theorem we find

$$s = 42$$

and we can check that s really is a square root by computing

$$s^2 = 42^2 = 217 \;(\text{mod } n).$$

There are three other square roots, since n has two prime factors. These other square roots are obtained by applying the Chinese Remainder Theorem to the three other equations

$$
\begin{aligned}
s_{13} &= 10, & s_{17} &= 8, \\
s_{13} &= 3, & s_{17} &= 9, \\
s_{13} &= 10, & s_{17} &= 9,
\end{aligned}
$$

Hence, all four square roots of 217 modulo 221 are given by

$$42, 94, 127 \text{ and } 179.$$

1.4 PROBABILITY

At some points we will need a basic understanding of elementary probability theory. In this section we summarize the theory we require and give a few examples. Most readers should find this a revision of the type of probability encountered in high school.

A *random variable* is a variable X which takes certain values with given probabilities. If X takes on the value s with probability 0.01 we write this as

$$p(X = s) = 0.01.$$

As an example, let T be the random variable representing tosses of a fair coin, we then have the probabilities

$$p(T = \text{Heads}) = \frac{1}{2},$$
$$p(T = \text{Tails}) = \frac{1}{2}.$$

As another example let E be the random variable representing letters in English text. An analysis of a large amount of English text allows us to approximate the relevant probabilities by

$$p(E = a) = 0.082,$$

$$\vdots$$

$$p(E = e) = 0.127,$$

$$\vdots$$

$$p(E = z) = 0.001.$$

Basically if X is a discrete random variable and $p(X = x)$ is the *probability distribution* then we have the two following properties:

$$p(X = x) \geq 0,$$
$$\sum_{x} p(X = x) = 1.$$

It is common to illustrate examples from probability theory using a standard deck of cards. We shall do likewise and let V denote the random variable that a card is a particular value, let S denote the random variable that a card is a particular suit and let C denote the random variable of the colour of a card. So for example

$$p(C = \text{Red}) = \frac{1}{2},$$

$$p(V = \text{Ace of Clubs}) = \frac{1}{52},$$

$$p(S = \text{Clubs}) = \frac{1}{4}.$$

Let X and Y be two random variables, where $p(X = x)$ is the probability that X takes the value x and $p(Y = y)$ is the probability that Y takes the value y. The *joint probability* $p(X = x, Y = y)$ is defined as the probability that X takes the value x and Y takes the value y. So if we let $X = C$ and $Y = S$ then we have

$$p(C = \text{Red}, S = \text{Club}) = 0, \qquad p(C = \text{Red}, S = \text{Diamonds}) = \frac{1}{4},$$

$$p(C = \text{Red}, S = \text{Hearts}) = \frac{1}{4}, \qquad p(C = \text{Red}, S = \text{Spades}) = 0,$$

$$p(C = \text{Black}, S = \text{Club}) = \frac{1}{4}, \qquad p(C = \text{Black}, S = \text{Diamonds}) = 0,$$

$$p(C = \text{Black}, S = \text{Hearts}) = 0, \qquad p(C = \text{Black}, S = \text{Spades}) = \frac{1}{4}.$$

Two random variables X and Y are said to be *independent* if, for all values of x and y,

$$p(X = x, Y = y) = p(X = x) \cdot p(Y = y).$$

Hence, the random variables C and S are not independent. As an example of independent random variables consider the two random variables, T_1 the value of the first toss of an unbiased coin and T_2 the value of a second toss of the coin. Since, assuming standard physical laws, the toss of the first coin does not affect the outcome of the toss of the second coin, we say that T_1 and T_2 are independent. This is confirmed by the joint probability distribution

$$p(T_1 = H, T_2 = H) = \frac{1}{4}, \quad p(T_1 = H, T_2 = T) = \frac{1}{4},$$

$$p(T_1 = T, T_2 = H) = \frac{1}{4}, \quad p(T_1 = T, T_2 = T) = \frac{1}{4}.$$

1.4.1 Bayes' Theorem

The *conditional probability* $p(X = x | Y = y)$ of two random variables X and Y is defined as the probability that X takes the value x given that Y takes the value y.

Returning to our random variables based on a pack of cards we have

$$p(S = \text{Spades} | C = \text{Red}) = 0$$

and

$$p(V = \text{Ace of Spades} | C = \text{Black}) = \frac{1}{26}.$$

The first follows since if we know a card is red, then the probability that it is a spade is zero, since a red card cannot be a spade. The second follows since if we know a card is black then we have restricted the set of cards in half, one of which is the ace of spades.

The following is one of the most crucial statements in probability theory

Theorem 1.7 (Bayes' Theorem) *If $p(Y = y) > 0$ then*

$$p(X = x | Y = y) = \frac{p(X = x) \cdot p(Y = y | X = x)}{p(Y = y)}$$
$$= \frac{p(X = x, Y = y)}{p(Y = y)}.$$

We can apply Bayes' Theorem to our examples above as follows

$$p(S = \text{Spades} | C = \text{Red}) = \frac{p(S = \text{Spades}, C = \text{Red})}{p(C = \text{Red})}$$
$$= 0 \cdot \left(\frac{1}{4}\right)^{-1} = 0.$$

$$p(V = \text{Ace of Spades} | C = \text{Black}) = \frac{p(V = \text{Ace of Spades}, C = \text{Black})}{p(C = \text{Black})}$$
$$= \frac{1}{52} \cdot \left(\frac{1}{2}\right)^{-1}$$
$$= \frac{2}{52} = \frac{1}{26}.$$

If X and Y are independent then we have

$$p(X = x | Y = y) = p(X = x),$$

i.e. the value which X takes does not depend on the value that Y takes.

1.4.2 Birthday Paradox

Another useful result from elementary probability theory that we require is the *birthday paradox*. Suppose a bag has m balls in it, all of different colours. We draw one ball at a time from the bag and write down its colour, we then replace the ball in the bag and draw again.

If we define

$$m^{(n)} = m \cdot (m - 1) \cdot (m - 2) \cdots (m - n + 1)$$

then the probability, after n balls have been taken out of the bag, that we have obtained at least one matching colour (or coincidence) is

$$1 - \frac{m^{(n)}}{m^n}.$$

As m becomes larger the expected number of balls we have to draw before we obtain the first coincidence is

$$\sqrt{\frac{\pi m}{2}}.$$

To see why this is called the birthday paradox consider the probability of two people in a room sharing the same birthday. Most people initially think that this probability should be quite low, since they are thinking of the probability that someone in the room shares the same birthday as them. One can now easily compute that the probability of at least two people in a room of 23 people having the same birthday is

$$1 - \frac{365^{(23)}}{365^{23}} \approx 0.507.$$

In fact this probability increases quite quickly since in a room of 30 people we obtain a probability of approximately 0.706, and in a room of 100 people we obtain a probability of over 0.999 999 6.

Chapter Summary

- A group is a set with an operation which has an identity, is associative and every element has an inverse. Modular arithmetic, both addition and multiplication, provides examples of groups. However, for multiplication we need to be careful which set of numbers we take when defining a group with respect to modular multiplication.

- A ring is a set with two operations which behaves like the set of integers under addition and multiplication. Modular arithmetic is an example of a ring.

- A field is a ring in which all non-zero elements have a multiplicative inverse. Integers modulo a prime are examples of fields.

- Multiplicative inverses for modular arithmetic can be found using the extended Euclidean algorithm.

- Sets of simultaneous linear modular equations can be solved using the Chinese Remainder Theorem.

- Square elements modulo a prime can be detected using the Legendre symbol, square roots can be efficiently computed using Shanks' Algorithm.

- Square elements and square roots modulo a composite can be determined efficiently as long as one knows the factorization of the modulus.

- Bayes' theorem allows us to compute conditional probabilities.

- The birthday paradox allows us to estimate how quickly collisions occur when one repeatedly samples from a finite space.

Further Reading

Bach and Shallit is the best introductory book I know which deals with Euclid's algorithm and finite fields. It contains a lot of historical information, plus excellent pointers to the relevant research literature. Whilst aimed in some respects at Computer Scientists, Bach and Shallit's book may be a little too mathematical for some. For a more traditional introduction to the basic discrete mathematics we shall need, at the level of a first year course in Computer Science, see the books by Biggs or Rosen.

E. Bach and J. Shallit. *Algorithmic Number Theory. Volume 1: Efficient Algorithms*. MIT Press, 1996.

N.L. Biggs. *Discrete Mathematics*. Oxford University Press, 1989.

K.H. Rosen. *Discrete Mathematics and its Applications*. McGraw-Hill, 1999.

Review Exercises

1.1.1   What are the axioms of a group, ring and field?

1.1.2   Why are the non-zero integers not a group under multiplication?

1.1.3   Why do we say non-zero real numbers or non-zero rational numbers when we look at the reals as a group under multiplication?

1.1.4   Why are the integers not a field?

1.1.5   Why is $\mathbb{F}_p[X]/(f(X))$ always a ring?

1.1.6   What is the value of the Euler ϕ function evaluated at $N = p$ and $N = p \cdot q$, where p and q are prime numbers.

1.1.7   Define the Legendre symbol and explain how this is used to test for squares modulo a prime p.

1.1.8   If an integer a modulo a composite number N has Jacobi symbol 1 with respect to N, is it a square modulo N?

1.1.9   If there are 60 different coloured balls in a bag, how many do I have to take out on average (with replacement) before I obtain a repeated colour.

Programming Exercises

1.2.1   Implement in your favourite language the standard and binary Euclidean algorithm for the gcd. Compare their running times as you increase the size of their arguments.

1.2.2   Work out how to implement the extended Euclidean algorithm. First use the standard gcd preserving mapping and then use a binary variant.

1.2.3   Implement an algorithm to compute Legendre symbols which uses the law of quadratic reciprocity.

Standard Exercises

1.3.1   Show that the Euclidean and extended Euclidean algorithm can be adapted to work with polynomials.

1.3.2   Write down an analogue of the binary extended Euclidean algorithm for binary polynomials. Hence, compute the inverse of $x^7 + x + 1$ in the finite field

$$\mathbb{F}_{2^8} = \mathbb{F}_2[x]/(x^8 + x^4 + x^3 + x + 1).$$

1.3.3   The Fibonacci numbers are defined by

$$F_0 = 0, \; F_1 = 1, \; F_n = F_{n-1} + F_{n-2}.$$

Show that if the quotients q_i appearing in the Euclidean algorithm are all equal to one then a and b are consecutive Fibonacci numbers.

1.3.4   Show that if n is odd and has k distinct prime factors then the number of solutions of $x^2 = 1 \pmod{n}$ is equal to 2^k.

1.3.5   Show that g is a generator of $\mathbb{F}_p^*$ if and only if $g^{p-1} = 1 \pmod{p}$ and $g^q \neq 1 \pmod{p}$ for all prime divisors q of $p - 1$.

1.3.6   Given a composite integer N and the integers a, b, $a^{1/3}b^{1/5} \pmod{N}$, compute $a^{1/3} \pmod{N}$ and $b^{1/5} \pmod{N}$.

1.3.7   Determine a primitive element for each of the finite fields $\mathbb{F}_{2^n}$, for $1 \leq n \leq 8$.

1.3.8   By hand, or only using a basic calculator, compute the Jacobi symbols

$$\left(\frac{311}{653}\right) \text{ and } \left(\frac{666}{777}\right).$$

Elliptic Curves

Chapter Goals

- To describe what an elliptic curve is.

- To explain the basic mathematics behind elliptic curve cryptography.

- To show how projective coordinates can be used to improve computational efficiency.

- To show how point compression can be used to improve communications efficiency.

2.1 INTRODUCTION

This chapter is devoted to introducing elliptic curves. Some of the more modern public key systems make use of elliptic curves since they can offer improved efficiency and bandwidth. Since much of this book can be read by understanding that an elliptic curve provides another finite abelian group in which one can pose a discrete logarithm problem, you may decide to skip this chapter on an initial reading.

Let K be any field. The projective plane $\mathbb{P}^2(K)$ over K is defined as the set of triples

$$(X, Y, Z)$$

where $X, Y, Z \in K$ are not all simultaneously zero. On these triples is defined an equivalence relation

$$(X, Y, Z) \equiv (X', Y', Z')$$

if there exists a $\lambda \in K$ such that

$$X = \lambda X', \ Y = \lambda Y' \text{ and } Z = \lambda Z'.$$

So, for example, if $K = \mathbb{F}_7$, the finite field of seven elements, then the two points

$$(4, 1, 1) \text{ and } (5, 3, 3)$$

are equivalent. Such a triple is called a projective point.

An *elliptic curve* over K will be defined as the set of solutions in the projective plane $\mathbb{P}^2(K)$ of a homogeneous Weierstrass equation of the form

$$E : Y^2 Z + a_1 XYZ + a_3 YZ^2 = X^3 + a_2 X^2 Z + a_4 XZ^2 + a_6 Z^3,$$

with $a_1, a_2, a_3, a_4, a_6 \in K$. This equation is also referred to as the long Weierstrass form. Such a curve should be non-singular in the sense that, if the equation is written in the form $F(X, Y, Z) = 0$, then the partial derivatives of the curve equation

$$\partial F/\partial X, \ \partial F/\partial Y \text{ and } \partial F/\partial Z$$

should not vanish simultaneously at any point on the curve.

The set of K-rational points on E, i.e. the solutions in $\mathbb{P}^2(K)$ to the above equation, is denoted by $E(K)$. Notice, that the curve has exactly one rational point with coordinate Z equal to zero, namely $(0, 1, 0)$. This is the point at infinity, which will be denoted by $\mathcal{O}$.

For convenience, we will most often use the affine version of the Weierstrass equation, given by

$$E : Y^2 + a_1 XY + a_3 Y = X^3 + a_2 X^2 + a_4 X + a_6, \tag{2.1}$$

where $a_i \in K$.

The K-rational points in the affine case are the solutions to E in K^2, plus the point at infinity $\mathcal{O}$. Although most protocols for elliptic curve based cryptography make use of the affine form of a curve, it is often computationally important to be able to switch to projective coordinates. Luckily this switch is easy:

- The point at infinity always maps to the point at infinity in either direction.

- To map a projective point (X, Y, Z) which is not at infinity, so $Z \neq 0$, to an affine point we simply compute $(X/Z, Y/Z)$.

- To map an affine point (X, Y), which is not at infinity, to a projective point we take a random non-zero $Z \in K$ and compute $(X \cdot Z, Y \cdot Z, Z)$.

As we shall see later it is often more convenient to use a slightly modified form of projective point where the projective point (X, Y, Z) represents the affine point $(X/Z^2, Y/Z^3)$.

Given an elliptic curve defined by Equation (2.1), it is useful to define the following constants for use in later formulae:

$$b_2 = a_1^2 + 4a_2,$$
$$b_4 = a_1 a_3 + 2a_4,$$
$$b_6 = a_3^2 + 4a_6,$$
$$b_8 = a_1^2 a_6 + 4a_2 a_6 - a_1 a_3 a_4 + a_2 a_3^2 - a_4^2,$$
$$c_4 = b_2^2 - 24b_4,$$
$$c_6 = -b_2^3 + 36b_2 b_4 - 216b_6.$$

The discriminant of the curve is defined as

$$\Delta = -b_2^2 b_8 - 8b_4^3 - 27b_6^2 + 9b_2 b_4 b_6.$$

When char $K \neq 2, 3$ the discriminant can also be expressed as

$$\Delta = (c_4^3 - c_6^2)/1728.$$

Notice that $1728 = 2^6 3^3$ so, if the characteristic is not equal to 2 or 3, dividing by this latter quantity makes sense. A curve is then non-singular if and only if $\Delta \neq 0$; from now on we shall assume that $\Delta \neq 0$ in all our discussions.

When $\Delta \neq 0$, the j-invariant of the curve is defined as

$$j(E) = c_4^3/\Delta.$$

As an example, which we shall use throughout this chapter, we consider the elliptic curve

$$E : Y^2 = X^3 + X + 3$$

defined over the field $\mathbb{F}_7$. Computing the various quantities above we find that we have

$$\Delta = 3 \text{ and } j(E) = 5.$$

The j-invariant is closely related to the notion of elliptic curve isomorphism. Two elliptic curves defined by Weierstrass equations E (with variables X, Y) and E' (with variables X', Y') are isomorphic over K if and only if there exist constants $r, s, t \in K$ and $u \in K^*$, such that the change of variables

$$X = u^2 X' + r, \quad Y = u^3 Y' + su^2 X' + t$$

transforms E into E'. Such an isomorphism defines a bijection between the set of rational points in E and the set of rational points in E'. Notice that isomorphism is defined relative to the field K.

As an example consider again the elliptic curve

$$E : Y^2 = X^3 + X + 3$$

over the field $\mathbb{F}_7$. Now make the change of variables defined by $[u, r, s, t] = [2, 3, 4, 5]$, i.e.

$$X = 4X' + 3 \text{ and } Y = Y' + 2X' + 5.$$

We then obtain the isomorphic curve

$$E' : Y'^2 + 4X'Y' + 3Y' = X'^3 + X' + 1,$$

and we have

$$j(E) = j(E') = 5.$$

Curve isomorphism is an equivalence relation. The following lemma establishes the fact that, over the algebraic closure $\overline{K}$, the j-invariant characterizes the equivalence classes in this relation.

Lemma 2.1 *Two elliptic curves that are isomorphic over K have the same j-invariant. Conversely, two curves with the same j-invariant are isomorphic over $\overline{K}$.*

But curves with the same *j*-invariant may not necessarily be isomorphic over the ground field. For example, consider the elliptic curve, also over $\mathbb{F}_7$,

$$E'' : Y''^2 = X''^3 + 4X'' + 4.$$

This has *j*-invariant equal to 5 so it is isomorphic to E, but it is not isomorphic over $\mathbb{F}_7$ since the change of variable required is given by

$$X = 3X'' \text{ and } Y = \sqrt{6}Y''.$$

However, $\sqrt{6} \notin \mathbb{F}_7$. Hence, we say both E and E'' are defined over $\mathbb{F}_7$, but they are isomorphic over $\mathbb{F}_{7^2} = \mathbb{F}_7[\sqrt{6}]$.

2.2 THE GROUP LAW

Assume, for the moment, that char $K \neq 2, 3$, and consider the change of variables given by

$$X = X' - \frac{b_2}{12},$$
$$Y = Y' - \frac{a_1}{2}\left(X' - \frac{b_2}{12}\right) - \frac{a_3}{2}.$$

This change of variables transforms the long Weierstrass form given in Equation (2.1) to the equation of an isomorphic curve given in short Weierstrass form,

$$E : Y^2 = X^3 + aX + b,$$

for some $a, b \in K$. One can then define a group law on an elliptic curve using the chord-tangent process.

The chord process is defined as follows, see Fig. 2.1 for a diagrammatic description. Let P and Q be two distinct points on E. The straight line joining P and Q must intersect the curve at one further point, say R, since we are intersecting a line with a cubic curve. The point R will also be defined over the same field of definition as the curve and the two points P and Q. If we then reflect R in the x-axis we obtain another point over the same field which we shall call $P + Q$.

The tangent process is given diagrammatically in Fig. 2.2 or as follows. Let P denote a point on the curve E. We take the tangent to the curve at P. Such a line must intersect E in at most one other point, say R, as the elliptic curve E is defined by a cubic equation. Again we reflect R in the x-axis to obtain a point which we call $[2]P = P + P$. If the tangent to the point is vertical, it 'intersects' the curve at the point at infinity and $P + P = \mathcal{O}$, and P is said to be a point of order 2.

One can show that the chord-tangent process turns E into an abelian group with the point at infinity $\mathcal{O}$ being the zero. The above definition can be easily extended to the long Weierstrass form (and so to characteristic two and three). One simply changes the definition by replacing reflection in the x-axis by reflection in the line

$$Y = a_1 X + a_3.$$

Fig. 2.1 Adding two points on an elliptic curve

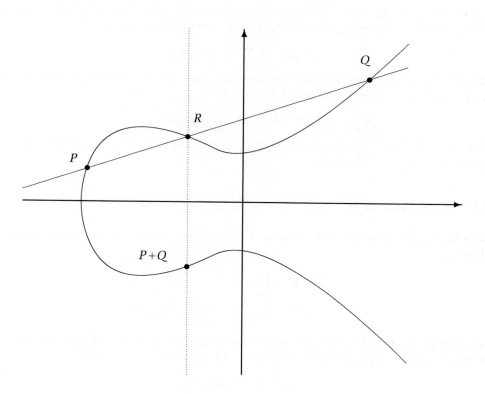

In addition a little calculus will result in explicit algebraic formulae for the chord-tangent process. This is necessary since drawing diagrams as above is not really allowed in a field of finite characteristic. The algebraic formulae are summarized in the following lemma.

Lemma 2.2 *Let E denote an elliptic curve given by*

$$E : Y^2 + a_1 XY + a_3 Y = X^3 + a_2 X^2 + a_4 X + a_6$$

and let $P_1 = (x_1, y_1)$ and $P_2 = (x_2, y_2)$ denote points on the curve. Then

$$-P_1 = (x_1, -y_1 - a_1 x_1 - a_3).$$

Set

$$\lambda = \frac{y_2 - y_1}{x_2 - x_1},$$
$$\mu = \frac{y_1 x_2 - y_2 x_1}{x_2 - x_1}$$

Fig. 2.2 Doubling a point on an elliptic curve

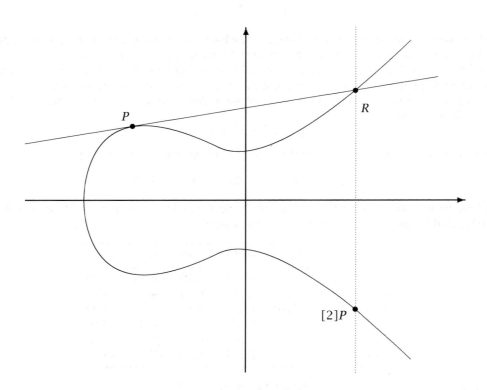

when $x_1 \neq x_2$, and set

$$\lambda = \frac{3x_1^2 + 2a_2x_1 + a_4 - a_1y_1}{2y_1 + a_1x_1 + a_3},$$

$$\mu = \frac{-x_1^3 + a_4x_1 + 2a_6 - a_3y_1}{2y_1 + a_1x_1 + a_3}$$

when $x_1 = x_2$ and $P_2 \neq -P_1$. If

$$P_3 = (x_3, y_3) = P_1 + P_2 \neq \mathcal{O}$$

then x_3 and y_3 are given by the formulae

$$x_3 = \lambda^2 + a_1\lambda - a_2 - x_1 - x_2,$$
$$y_3 = -(\lambda + a_1)x_3 - \mu - a_3.$$

The elliptic curve isomorphisms described earlier then become group isomorphisms as they respect the group structure.

For a positive integer m we let $[m]$ denote the multiplication-by-m map from the curve to itself. This map takes a point P to

$$P + P + \cdots + P,$$

where we have m summands. This map is the basis of elliptic curve cryptography, since whilst it is easy to compute, it is believed to be hard to invert, i.e. given $P = (x, y)$ and $[m]P = (x', y')$ it is hard to compute m. Of course this statement of hardness assumes a well-chosen elliptic curve etc., something we will return to later in the book.

We end this section with an example of the elliptic curve group law. Again we take our elliptic curve

$$E : Y^2 = X^3 + X + 3$$

over the field $\mathbb{F}_7$. It turns out there are six points on this curve given by

$$\mathcal{O}, \; (4, 1), \; (6, 6), \; (5, 0), \; (6, 1) \text{ and } (4, 6).$$

These form a group with the group law being given by the following table, which is computed using the addition formulae given above.

+	$\mathcal{O}$	$(4,1)$	$(6,6)$	$(5,0)$	$(6,1)$	$(4,6)$
$\mathcal{O}$	$\mathcal{O}$	$(4,1)$	$(6,6)$	$(5,0)$	$(6,1)$	$(4,6)$
$(4,1)$	$(4,1)$	$(6,6)$	$(5,0)$	$(6,1)$	$(4,6)$	$\mathcal{O}$
$(6,6)$	$(6,6)$	$(5,0)$	$(6,1)$	$(4,6)$	$\mathcal{O}$	$(4,1)$
$(5,0)$	$(5,0)$	$(6,1)$	$(4,6)$	$\mathcal{O}$	$(4,1)$	$(6,6)$
$(6,1)$	$(6,1)$	$(4,6)$	$\mathcal{O}$	$(4,1)$	$(6,6)$	$(5,0)$
$(4,6)$	$(4,6)$	$\mathcal{O}$	$(4,1)$	$(6,6)$	$(5,0)$	$(6,1)$

As an example of the multiplication-by-m map, if we let

$$P = (4, 1)$$

then we have

$$[2]P = (6, 6),$$
$$[3]P = (5, 0),$$
$$[4]P = (6, 1),$$
$$[5]P = (4, 6),$$
$$[6]P = \mathcal{O}.$$

So we see in this example that $E(\mathbb{F}_7)$ is a finite cyclic abelian group of order six generated by the point P. For all elliptic curves over finite fields the group is always finite and it is also highly likely to be cyclic (or 'nearly' cyclic).

2.3   ELLIPTIC CURVES OVER FINITE FIELDS

Over a finite field $\mathbb{F}_q$, the number of rational points on a curve is finite, and its size will be denoted by $\#E(\mathbb{F}_q)$. The expected number of points on the curve is around $q + 1$ and

if we set
$$\#E(\mathbb{F}_q) = q + 1 - t$$
then the value t is called the *trace of Frobenius* at q.

A first approximation to the order of $E(\mathbb{F}_q)$ is given by the following well-known theorem of Hasse.

Theorem 2.3 (H. Hasse, 1933) *The trace of Frobenius satisfies*
$$|t| \le 2\sqrt{q}.$$

Consider our example of
$$E : Y^2 = X^3 + X + 3$$
then recall this has six points over the field $\mathbb{F}_7$, and so the associated trace of Frobenius is equal to 2, which is less than $2\sqrt{q} = 2\sqrt{7} = 5.29$.

The qth-power Frobenius map, on an elliptic curve E defined over $\mathbb{F}_q$, is given by
$$\varphi : \begin{cases} E(\overline{\mathbb{F}}_q) \longrightarrow E(\overline{\mathbb{F}}_q) \\ (x, y) \longmapsto (x^q, y^q) \\ \mathcal{O} \longmapsto \mathcal{O}. \end{cases}$$

The map φ sends points on E to points on E, no matter what the field of definition of the point is. In addition the map φ respects the group law in that
$$\varphi(P + Q) = \varphi(P) + \varphi(Q).$$

In other words the map φ is a group endomorphism of E over $\overline{\mathbb{F}}_q$, referred to as the Frobenius endomorphism.

The trace of Frobenius t and the Frobenius endomorphism φ are linked by the equation
$$\varphi^2 - [t]\varphi + [q] = [0].$$
Hence, for any point $P = (x, y)$ on the curve, we have
$$(x^{q^2}, y^{q^2}) - [t](x^q, y^q) + [q](x, y) = \mathcal{O},$$
where addition and subtraction denote curve operations.

There are two particular classes of curves which, under certain conditions, will prove to be cryptographically weak:

- The curve $E(\mathbb{F}_q)$ is said to be anomalous if its trace of Frobenius is one, giving $\#E(\mathbb{F}_q) = q$. These curves are weak when $q = p$, the field characteristic.

- The curve $E(\mathbb{F}_q)$ is said to be supersingular if the characteristic p divides the trace of Frobenius, t. Such curves are usually considered weak cryptographically and are usually avoided. If $q = p$ then this means that $E(\mathbb{F}_p)$ has $p + 1$ points since we must have $t = 0$. For other finite fields the possible values of t corresponding to supersingular elliptic curves are given by, where $q = p^f$,

    - f odd: $t = 0$, $t^2 = 2q$ and $t^2 = 3q$.
    - f even : $t^2 = 4q$, $t^2 = q$ if $p = 1 \pmod 3$ and $t = 0$ if $p \ne 1 \pmod 4$.

We will also need to choose a curve such that the group order $\#E(\mathbb{F}_q)$ is divisible by a large prime number. This means we need to be able to compute the group order $\#E(\mathbb{F}_q)$, so as to check both this and the above two conditions.

For any elliptic curve and any finite field the group order $\#E(\mathbb{F}_q)$ can be computed in polynomial time. But this is a usually done via a complicated algorithm that we cannot go into in this book. Hence, you should just remember that computing the group order is easy. We shall see in a later chapter, when considering algorithms to solve discrete logarithm problems, that knowing the group order is important in understanding how secure a group is.

One of the advantages of elliptic curves is that there is a very large number of possible groups. One can choose both the finite field and the coefficients of the curve. In addition finding elliptic curves with the correct cryptographic properties to make them secure is relatively easy.

As was apparent from the earlier discussion, the cases char $K = 2, 3$ often require separate treatment. Practical implementations of elliptic curve cryptosystems are usually based on either $\mathbb{F}_{2^n}$, i.e. characteristic two, or $\mathbb{F}_p$ for large primes p. Therefore, in the remainder of this chapter we will focus on fields of characteristic two and $p > 3$, and will omit the separate treatment of the case char $K = 3$. Most arguments, though, carry easily to characteristic three, with modifications that are well documented in the literature.

2.3.1   Curves over Fields of Characteristic $p > 3$

Assume that our finite field is given by $K = \mathbb{F}_q$, where $q = p^n$ for a prime $p > 3$ and an integer $n \geq 1$. As mentioned, the curve equation in this case can be simplified to the short Weierstrass form

$$E : Y^2 = X^3 + aX + b.$$

The discriminant of the curve then reduces to $\Delta = -16(4a^3 + 27b^2)$, and its j-invariant to $j(E) = -1728(4a)^3/\Delta$. The formulae for the group law in Lemma 2.2 also simplify to

$$-P_1 = (x_1, -y_1),$$

and if

$$P_3 = (x_3, y_3) = P_1 + P_2 \neq \mathcal{O},$$

then x_3 and y_3 are given by the formulae

$$x_3 = \lambda^2 - x_1 - x_2,$$
$$y_3 = (x_1 - x_3)\lambda - y_1,$$

where if $x_1 \neq x_2$ we set

$$\lambda = \frac{y_2 - y_1}{x_2 - x_1},$$

and if $x_1 = x_2$, $y_1 \neq 0$ we set

$$\lambda = \frac{3x_1^2 + a}{2y_1}.$$

2.3.2 Curves over Fields of Characteristic Two

We now specialize to the case of finite fields where $q = 2^n$ with $n \geq 1$. In this case, the expression for the j-invariant reduces to $j(E) = a_1^{12}/\Delta$. In characteristic two, the condition $j(E) = 0$, i.e. $a_1 = 0$, is equivalent to the curve being supersingular. As mentioned earlier, this very special type of curve is avoided in cryptography. We assume, therefore, that $j(E) \neq 0$.

Under these assumptions, a representative for each isomorphism class of elliptic curves over $\mathbb{F}_q$ is given by

$$E : Y^2 + XY = X^3 + a_2 X^2 + a_6, \qquad (2.2)$$

where $a_6 \in \mathbb{F}_q^*$ and $a_2 \in \{0, \gamma\}$ with γ a fixed element in $\mathbb{F}_q$ such that $\mathrm{Tr}_{q|2}(\gamma) = 1$, where $\mathrm{Tr}_{q|2}$ is the absolute trace

$$\mathrm{Tr}_{2^n|2}(\alpha) = \sum_{i=0}^{n-1} \alpha^{2^i}.$$

The formulae for the group law in Lemma 2.2 then simplify to

$$-P_1 = (x_1, y_1 + x_1),$$

and if

$$P_3 = (x_3, y_3) = P_1 + P_2 \neq \mathcal{O},$$

then x_3 and y_3 are given by the formulae

$$x_3 = \lambda^2 + \lambda + a_2 + x_1 + x_2,$$
$$y_3 = (\lambda + 1)x_3 + \mu$$
$$= (x_1 + x_3)\lambda + x_3 + y_1,$$

where if $x_1 \neq x_2$ we set

$$\lambda = \frac{y_2 + y_1}{x_2 + x_1},$$
$$\mu = \frac{y_1 x_2 + y_2 x_1}{x_2 + x_1}$$

and if $x_1 = x_2 \neq 0$ we set

$$\lambda = \frac{x_1^2 + y_1}{x_1},$$
$$\mu = x_1^2.$$

2.4 PROJECTIVE COORDINATES

One of the problems with the above formulae for the group laws given in both large and even characteristic is that at some stage they involve a division operation. Division in finite fields is considered as an expensive operation, since it usually involves some variant of the extended Euclidean algorithm, which although of approximately the same complexity as multiplication can usually not be implemented as efficiently.

To avoid these division operations one can use projective coordinates. Here one writes the elliptic curve using three variables (X, Y, Z) instead of just (X, Y). Instead of using the projective representation given at the start of this chapter we instead use one where the curve is written as

$$E : Y^2 + a_1 XYZ + a_2 YZ^4 = X^3 + a_2 X^2 Z^2 + a_4 XZ^4 + a_6 Z^6.$$

The point at infinity is still denoted by $(0, 1, 0)$, but now the map from projective to affine coordinates is given by

$$(X, Y, Z) \longmapsto (X/Z^2, Y/Z^3).$$

This choice of projective coordinates is made to provide a more efficient arithmetic operation.

2.4.1   Large Prime Characteristic

The formulae for point addition when our elliptic curve is written as

$$Y^2 = X^3 + aXZ^2 + bZ^6$$

are now given by the law

$$(X_3, Y_3, Z_3) = (X_1, Y_1, Z_1) + (X_2, Y_2, Z_2)$$

where (X_3, Y_3, Z_3) are derived from the formulae

$$
\begin{aligned}
\lambda_1 &= X_1 Z_2^2, & \lambda_2 &= X_2 Z_1^2, \\
\lambda_3 &= \lambda_1 - \lambda_2, & \lambda_4 &= Y_1 Z_2^3, \\
\lambda_5 &= Y_2 Z_1^3, & \lambda_6 &= \lambda_4 - \lambda_5, \\
\lambda_7 &= \lambda_1 + \lambda_2, & \lambda_8 &= \lambda_4 + \lambda_5, \\
Z_3 &= Z_1 Z_2 \lambda_3, & X_3 &= \lambda_6^2 - \lambda_7 \lambda_3^2, \\
\lambda_9 &= \lambda_7 \lambda_3^2 - 2X_3, & Y_3 &= (\lambda_9 \lambda_6 - \lambda_8 \lambda_3^3)/2.
\end{aligned}
$$

Notice the avoidance of any division operation, bar division by 2 which can be easily accomplished by multiplication of the precomputed value of $2^{-1} \pmod{p}$.

Doubling a point,

$$(X_3, Y_3, Z_3) = [2](X_1, Y_1, Z_1),$$

can be accomplished using the formulae

$$
\begin{aligned}
\lambda_1 &= 3X_1^2 + aZ_1^4, & Z_3 &= 2Y_1 Z_1, \\
\lambda_2 &= 4X_1 Y_1^2, & X_3 &= \lambda_1^2 - 2\lambda_2, \\
\lambda_3 &= 8Y_1^4, & Y_3 &= \lambda_1(\lambda_2 - X_3) - \lambda_3.
\end{aligned}
$$

2.4.2 Even Characteristic

In even characteristic we write our elliptic curve in the form

$$Y^2 + XYZ = X^3 + a_2 X^2 Z^4 + a_6 Z^6.$$

Point addition,

$$(X_3, Y_3, Z_3) = (X_1, Y_1, Z_1) + (X_2, Y_2, Z_2)$$

is now accomplished using the recipe

$$\lambda_1 = X_1 Z_2^2, \qquad\qquad \lambda_2 = X_2 Z_1^2,$$
$$\lambda_3 = \lambda_1 + \lambda_2, \qquad\qquad \lambda_4 = Y_1 Z_2^3,$$
$$\lambda_5 = Y_2 Z_1^3, \qquad\qquad \lambda_6 = \lambda_4 + \lambda_5,$$
$$\lambda_7 = Z_1 \lambda_3, \qquad\qquad \lambda_8 = \lambda_6 X_2 + \lambda_7 Y_2,$$
$$Z_3 = \lambda_7 Z_2, \qquad\qquad \lambda_9 = \lambda_6 + Z_3,$$
$$X_3 = a_2 Z_3^2 + \lambda_6 \lambda_9 + \lambda_3^3, \quad Y_3 = \lambda_9 X_3 + \lambda_8 \lambda_7^2.$$

Doubling is then performed using

$$Z_3 = X_1 Z_1^2, \qquad\qquad X_3 = (X_1 + d_6 Z_1^2)^4,$$
$$\lambda = Z_3 + X_1^2 + Y_1 Z_1, \quad Y_3 = X_1^4 Z_3 + \lambda X_3.$$

Notice how in both even and odd characteristic we have avoided a division operation.

2.5 POINT COMPRESSION

In many cryptographic protocols we need to store or transmit an elliptic curve point. Using affine coordinates this can be accomplished using two field elements, i.e. by transmitting x and then y. However, one can do better using a technique called point compression.

Point compression works by the observation that for every x-coordinate on the curve there are at most two corresponding y-coordinates. Hence, we can represent a point by storing the x-coordinate along with a bit b to say which value of the y-coordinate we should take. All that remains to decide is how to compute the bit b and how to reconstruct the y-coordinate given the x-coordinate and the bit b.

2.5.1 Large Prime Characteristic

For elliptic curves over fields of large prime characteristic we notice that if $\alpha \in \mathbb{F}_p^*$ then the two square roots $\pm\beta$ of α have different parities, when represented as integers in the range $[1, \ldots, p-1]$. This is because

$$-\beta = p - \beta.$$

Hence, as the bit b we choose the parity of the y-coordinate.

Then, given (x, b), we can reconstruct y by computing

$$\beta = \sqrt{x^3 + ax + b} \pmod{p}.$$

If the parity of β is equal to b we set $y = \beta$, otherwise we set $y = p - \beta$. If $\beta = 0$ then no matter which value of b we have we set $y = 0$.

2.5.2   Even Characteristic

In even characteristic we need to be slightly more clever. Suppose we are given a point $P = (x, y)$ on the elliptic curve

$$Y^2 + XY = X^3 + a_2 X + a_6.$$

If $y = 0$ then we set $b = 0$, otherwise we compute

$$z = y/x$$

and let b denote the least significant bit of z. To recover y given (x, b), for $x \neq 0$, we set

$$\alpha = x + a_2 + \frac{a_6}{x^2}$$

and let β denote a solution of

$$z^2 + z = \alpha.$$

Then if the least significant bit of β is equal to b we set $y = x\beta$, otherwise we set $y = x(\beta + 1)$. To see why this works notice that if (x, y) is a solution of

$$Y^2 + XY = X^3 + a_2 X^2 + a_6$$

then $(x, y/x)$ and $(x, 1 + y/x)$ are the two solutions of

$$Z^2 + Z = X + a_2 + \frac{a_6}{X^2}.$$

As an example consider the curve

$$E : Y^2 = X^3 + X + 3$$

over the field $\mathbb{F}_7$. Then the points $(4, 1)$ and $(4, 6)$ which in bits we need to represent as

$$(0b100, 0b001) \text{ and } (0b100, 0b110),$$

i.e. requiring six bits for each point, can be represented as

$$(0b100, 0b1) \text{ and } (0b100, 0b0),$$

where we only use four bits for each point.

In larger, cryptographically interesting, examples the advantage becomes more pronounced. For example consider the same curve over the field

$$p = 1\,125\,899\,906\,842\,679 = 2^{50} + 55.$$

then the point

$$(1\,125\,899\,906\,842\,675, 245\,132\,605\,757\,739)$$

can be represented by the integers

$$(1\,125\,899\,906\,842\,675, 1).$$

So instead of requiring 102 bits we only require 52 bits.

Chapter Summary

- Elliptic curves over finite fields are another example of a finite abelian group. There are a lot of such groups since we are free to choose both the curve and the field.

- For cryptography we need to be able to compute the number of elements in the group. Although this is done using a complicated algorithm, it can be done in polynomial time.

- One should usually avoid supersingular and anomalous curves in cryptographic applications.

- Efficient algorithms for the group law can be produced by using projective coordinates. These algorithms avoid the need for costly division operations in the underlying finite field.

- To save bandwidth and space it is possible to efficiently compress elliptic curve points (x, y) down to x and a single bit b. The uncompression can also be performed efficiently.

Further Reading

For those who wish to learn more about elliptic curves in general try the textbook by Silverman (which is really aimed at mathematics graduate students). For those who are simply interested in the cryptographic applications of elliptic curves and the associated algorithms and techniques see the book by Blake, Seroussi and Smart.

I.F. Blake, G. Seroussi and N.P. Smart. *Elliptic Curves in Cryptography.* Cambridge University Press, 1999.

J.H. Silverman. *The Arithmetic of Elliptic Curves.* Springer-Verlag, 1985.

Review Exercises

2.1.1   When is an elliptic curve singular?

2.1.2   If two elliptic curves have the same j-invariant what does it mean?

2.1.3   Describe the chord-tangent process and how it relates to the elliptic curve group law.

2.1.4   What is the trace of Frobenius, and what inequality does it satisfy?

2.1.5   When is an elliptic curve anomalous?

2.1.6   Why does one use projective coordinate systems?

2.1.7   By roughly what percentage does point compression reduce the amount of bandwidth needed to transmit an elliptic curve point?

Programming Exercises

2.2.1   Implement a software library to perform elliptic curve addition and doubling over the integers modulo p.

2.2.2   Extend your library to include projective coordinate representations and to deal with compression and decompression of points.

Standard Exercises

2.3.1   From the geometric definition of the group law derive the formulae in Lemma 2.2.

2.3.2   Let E denote the elliptic curve

$$Y^2 = X^3 + aX + b$$

over a field of characteristic greater than three. Describe the possible points of order three on the curve.

2.3.3   Show that the curves

$$E : Y^2 = X^3 + aX + b,$$
$$E' : Y^2 = X^3 + ad^2X + bd^3,$$

defined over the field K, are isomorphic over the algebraic closure of K. When are they isomorphic over K?

II

Symmetric Encryption

Encryption of most data is accomplished using fast block and stream ciphers. These are examples of symmetric encryption algorithms. In addition all historical, i.e. pre-1960, ciphers are symmetric in nature and share some design principles with modern ciphers.

The main drawback with symmetric ciphers is that they give rise to a problem of how to distribute the secret keys between users. In the following chapters we explain the theory and practice of modern symmetric ciphers, but first we consider historical ciphers.

Historical Ciphers

Chapter Goals

- To explain a number of historical ciphers, such as the Caesar cipher, substitution cipher and the Enigma machine.

- To show how these historical ciphers can be broken because they do not hide the underlying statistics of the plaintext.

- To introduce the concepts of substitution and permutation as basic cipher components.

- To introduce a number of attack techniques, such as chosen plaintext attacks.

3.1 INTRODUCTION

An encryption algorithm, or cipher, is a means of transforming plaintext into ciphertext under the control of a secret key. This process is called encryption or encipherment. We write

$$c = e_k(m),$$

where

- m is the plaintext,

- e is the cipher function,

- k is the secret key,

- c is the ciphertext.

The reverse process is called decryption or decipherment, and we write

$$m = d_k(c).$$

Note, that the encryption and decryption algorithms e, d are public, the secrecy of m given c depends totally on the secrecy of k.

The above process requires that each party needs access to the secret key. This needs to be known to both sides, but needs to be kept secret. Encryption algorithms which have this property are called *symmetric cryptosystems* or secret key cryptosystems. There is a form of cryptography which uses two different types of key, one is publicly available and used for encryption whilst the other is private and used for decryption. These latter types of cryptosystems are called *asymmetric cryptosystems* or *public key cryptosystems*, to which we shall return in a later chapter.

Usually in cryptography the communicating parties are denoted by *A* and *B*. However, often one uses the more user-friendly names of Alice and Bob. But you should not assume that the parties are necessarily human, we could be describing a communication being carried out between two autonomous machines. The eavesdropper, bad girl, adversary or attacker is usually given the name Eve.

In this chapter we shall present some historical ciphers which were used in the pre-computer age to encrypt data. We shall show that these ciphers are easy to break as soon as one understands the statistics of the underlying language, in our case English. In Chapter 4 we shall study this relationship between how easy the cipher is to break and the statistical distribution of the underlying plaintext.

Table 3.1   English letter frequencies

Letter	Percentage	Letter	Percentage
A	8.2	N	6.7
B	1.5	O	7.5
C	2.8	P	1.9
D	4.2	Q	0.1
E	12.7	R	6.0
F	2.2	S	6.3
G	2.0	T	9.0
H	6.1	U	2.8
I	7.0	V	1.0
J	0.1	W	2.4
K	0.8	X	2.0
L	4.0	Y	0.1
M	2.4	Z	0.1

The distribution of English letter frequencies is described in Table 3.1, or graphically in Fig. 3.1. As one can see the most common letters are E and T. It often helps to know second order statistics about the underlying language, such as which are the most common sequences of two or three letters, called bigrams and trigrams. The most common bigrams in English are given by Table 3.2, with the associated approximate percentages. The most common trigrams are, in decreasing order,

THE, ING, AND, HER, ERE, ENT, THA, NTH, WAS, ETH, FOR.

Armed with this information about English we are now able to examine and break a number of historical ciphers.

Fig. 3.1 English letter frequencies

Table 3.2 English bigram frequencies

Bigram	Percentage	Bigram	Percentage
TH	3.15	HE	2.51
AN	1.72	IN	1.69
ER	1.54	RE	1.48
ES	1.45	ON	1.45
EA	1.31	TI	1.28
AT	1.24	ST	1.21
EN	1.20	ND	1.18

3.2 SHIFT CIPHER

We first present one of the earliest ciphers, called the shift cipher. Encryption is performed by replacing each letter by the letter a certain number of places on in the alphabet. So for example if the key was three, then the plaintext A would be replaced by the ciphertext D, the letter B would be replaced by E and so on. The plaintext word HELLO would be encrypted as the ciphertext KHOOR. When this cipher is used with the key three, it is often called the Caesar cipher, although in many books the name Caesar cipher is sometimes given to the shift cipher with any key. Strictly this is not correct since we only have evidence that Julius Caesar used the cipher with the key three.

There is a more mathematical explanation of the shift cipher which will be instructive for future discussions. First we need to identify each letter of the alphabet with a number. It is usual to identify the letter A with the number 0, the letter B with number 1, the letter C with the number 2 and so on until we identify the letter Z with the number 25. After we convert our plaintext message into a sequence of numbers, the ciphertext in the shift cipher is obtained by adding to each number the secret key k modulo 26, where the key is a number in the range 0 to 25. In this way we can interpret the shift cipher as a *stream cipher*, with key stream given by the repeating sequence

$$k, k, k, k, k, k, \ldots$$

This key stream is not very random, which results in it being easy to break the shift cipher. A naive way of breaking the shift cipher is to simply try each of the possible keys in turn, until the correct one is found. There are only 26 possible keys so the time for this exhaustive key search is very small, particularly if it is easy to recognize the underlying plaintext when it is decrypted.

We shall show how to break the shift cipher by using the statistics of the underlying language. Whilst this is not strictly necessary for breaking this cipher, later we shall see a cipher that is made up of a number of shift ciphers applied in turn and then the following statistical technique will be useful. Using a statistical technique on the shift cipher is also instructive as to how statistics of the underlying plaintext can arise in the resulting ciphertext.

Take the following example ciphertext, which since it is public knowledge we represent in blue.

GB OR, BE ABG GB OR: GUNG VF GUR DHRFGVBA:
JURGURE 'GVF ABOYRE VA GUR ZVAQ GB FHSSRE
GUR FYVATF NAQ NEEBJF BS BHGENTRBHF SBEGHAR,
BE GB GNXR NEZF NTNVAFG N FRN BS GEBHOYRF,
NAQ OL BCCBFVAT RAQ GURZ? GB QVR: GB FYRRC;
AB ZBER; NAQ OL N FYRRC GB FNL JR RAQ
GUR URNEG-NPUR NAQ GUR GUBHFNAQ ANGHENY FUBPXF
GUNG SYRFU VF URVE GB, 'GVF N PBAFHZZNGVBA
QRIBHGYL GB OR JVFU'Q. GB QVR, GB FYRRC;
GB FYRRC: CREPUNAPR GB QERNZ: NL, GURER'F GUR EHO;
SBE VA GUNG FYRRC BS QRNGU JUNG QERNZF ZNL PBZR
JURA JR UNIR FUHSSYRQ BSS GUVF ZBEGNY PBVY,
ZHFG TVIR HF CNHFR: GURER'F GUR ERFCRPG
GUNG ZNXRF PNYNZVGL BS FB YBAT YVSR;

One technique of breaking the previous sample ciphertext is to notice that the ciphertext still retains details about the word lengths of the underlying plaintext. For example the ciphertext letter N appears as a single letter word. Since the only single letter words in English are A and I we can conclude that the key is either 13, since N is thirteen letters on from A in the alphabet, or the key is equal to 5, since N is five letters on from I in the alphabet. Hence, the moral here is to always remove word breaks from the underlying plaintext before encrypting using the shift cipher. But even if we ignore this information about the words we can still break this cipher using frequency analysis.

We compute the frequencies of the letters in the ciphertext and compare them with the frequencies obtained from English which we saw in Fig. 3.1. We present the two bar graphs one above each other in Fig. 3.2 so you can see that one graph looks almost like a shift of the other graph. The statistics obtained from the sample ciphertext are given in blue, whilst the statistics obtained from the underlying plaintext language are given in red. Note, we do not compute the red statistics from the actual plaintext since we do not know this yet, we only make use of the knowledge of the underlying language.

By comparing the two bar graphs in Fig. 3.2 we can see by how much we think the blue graph has been shifted compared with the red graph. By examining where we think the plaintext letter E may have been shifted, one can hazard a guess that it is shifted by one of

$$2, 9, 13 \text{ or } 23.$$

Fig. 3.2 Comparison of plaintext and ciphertext frequencies for the shift cipher example

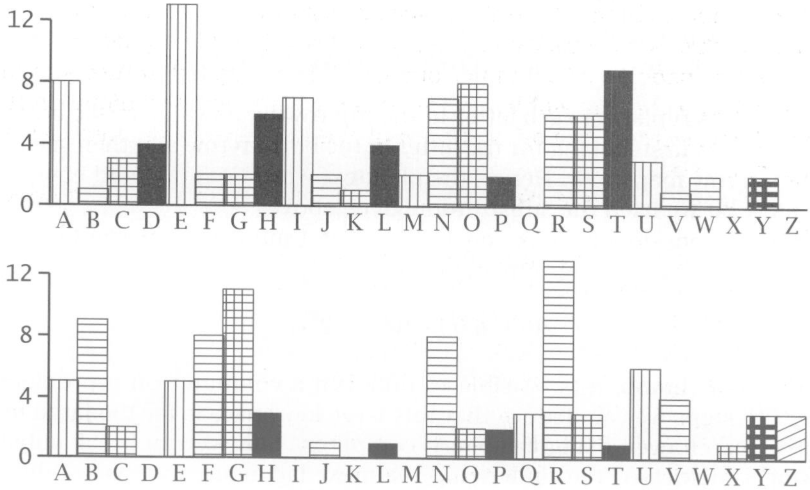

Then by trying to deduce by how much the plaintext letter A has been shifted we can guess that it has been shifted by one of

$$1, 6, 13 \text{ or } 17.$$

The only shift value which is consistent appears to be the value 13, and we conclude that this is the most likely key value. We can now decrypt the ciphertext, using this key. This reveals, that the underlying plaintext is:

To be, or not to be: that is the question:
Whether 'tis nobler in the mind to suffer
The slings and arrows of outrageous fortune,
Or to take arms against a sea of troubles,
And by opposing end them? To die: to sleep;
No more; and by a sleep to say we end
The heart-ache and the thousand natural shocks
That flesh is heir to, 'tis a consummation
Devoutly to be wish'd. To die, to sleep;
To sleep: perchance to dream: ay, there's the rub;
For in that sleep of death what dreams may come
When we have shuffled off this mortal coil,
Must give us pause: there's the respect
That makes calamity of so long life;

The above text is obviously taken from *Hamlet* by William Shakespeare.

3.3 SUBSTITUTION CIPHER

The main problem with the shift cipher is that the number of keys is too small, we only have 26 possible keys. To increase the number of keys a *substitution cipher* was invented. To write down a key for the substitution cipher we first write down the alphabet, and then a permutation of the alphabet directly below it. This mapping gives the substitution we make between the plaintext and the ciphertext

Plaintext alphabet   ABCDEFGHIJKLMNOPQRSTUVWXYZ
Ciphertext alphabet   GOYDSIPELUAVCRJWXZNHBQFTMK

Encryption involves replacing each letter in the top row by its value in the bottom row. Decryption involves first looking for the letter in the bottom row and then seeing which letter in the top row maps to it. Hence, the plaintext word HELLO would encrypt to the ciphertext ESVVJ if we used the substitution given above.

The number of possible keys is equal to the total number of permutations on 26 letters, namely the size of the group S_{26}, which is

$$26! \approx 4.03 \cdot 10^{26} \approx 2^{88}.$$

Since, as a rule of thumb, it is feasible to only run a computer on a problem which takes under 2^{80} steps we can deduce that this large key space is far too large to enable a brute force search even using a modern computer. Still we can break substitution ciphers using statistics of the underlying plaintext language, just as we did for the shift cipher.

Whilst the shift cipher can be considered as a stream cipher since the ciphertext is obtained from the plaintext by combining it with a keystream, the substitution cipher operates much more like a modern block cipher, with a block length of one English letter. A ciphertext block is obtained from a plaintext block by applying some (admittedly simple) key dependent algorithm.

Substitution ciphers are the types of ciphers commonly encountered in puzzle books, they have an interesting history and have occurred in literature. See for example the Sherlock Holmes story *The Adventure of the Dancing Men* by Arthur Conan–Doyle. The plot of this story rests on a substitution cipher where the ciphertext characters are taken from an alphabet of 'stick men' in various positions. The method of breaking the cipher as described by Holmes to Watson in this story is precisely the method we shall adopt below.

We give a detailed example, which we make slightly easier by keeping in the ciphertext details about the underlying word spacing used in the plaintext. This is only for ease of exposition, the techniques we describe can still be used if we ignore these word spacings, although more care and thought is required.

Consider the ciphertext

XSO MJIWXVL JODIVA STW VAO VY OZJVCO'W LTJDOWX
KVAKOAXJTXIVAW VY SIDS XOKSAVLVDQ IAGZWXJQ.
KVUCZXOJW, KVUUZAIKTXIVAW TAG UIKJVOLOKXJVAIKW
TJO HOLL JOCJOWOAXOG, TLVADWIGO GIDIXTL UOGIT,
KVUCZXOJ DTUOW TAG OLOKXJVAIK KVUUOJKO. TW HOLL TW
SVWXIAD UTAQ JOWOTJKS TAG CJVGZKX GONOLVCUOAX
KOAXJOW VY UTPVJ DLVMTL KVUCTAIOW, XSO JODIVA
STW T JTCIGLQ DJVHIAD AZUMOJ VY IAAVNTXINO AOH
KVUCTAIOW. XSO KVUCZXOJ WKIOAKO GOCTJXUOAX STW
KLVWO JOLTXIVAWSICW HIXS UTAQ VY XSOWO

VJDTAIWTXIVAW NIT KVLLTMVJTXINO CJVPOKXW, WXTYY
WOKVAGUOAXW TAG NIWIXIAD IAGZWXJITL WXTYY. IX STW
JOKOAXLQ IAXJVGZKOG WONOJTL UOKSTAIWUW YVJ
GONOLVCIAD TAG WZCCVJXIAD OAXJOCJOAOZJITL WXZGOAXW
TAG WXTYY, TAG TIUW XV CLTQ T WIDAIYIKTAX JVLO IA
XSO GONOLVCUOAX VY SIDS-XOKSAVLVDQ IAGZWXJQ
IA XSO JODIVA.

XSO GOCTJXUOAX STW T LTJDO CJVDJTUUO VY JOWOTJKS
WZCCVJXOG MQ IAGZWXJQ, XSO OZJVCOTA ZAIVA, TAG
ZE DVNOJAUOAX JOWOTJKS OWXTMLIWSUOAXW TAG
CZMLIK KVJCVJTXIVAW. T EOQ OLOUOAX VY XSIW IW
XSO WXJVAD LIAEW XSTX XSO GOCTJXUOAX STW HIXS
XSO KVUCZXOJ, KVUUZAIKTXIVAW, UIKJVOLOKXJVAIKW
TAG UOGIT IAGZWXJIOW IA XSO MJIWXVL JODIVA .
XSO TKTGOUIK JOWOTJKS CJVDJTUUO IW VJDTAIWOG
IAXV WONOA DJVZCW, LTADZTDOW TAG TJKSIXOKXZJO,
GIDIXTL UOGIT, UVMILO TAG HOTJTMLO KVUCZXIAD,
UTKSIAO LOTJAIAD, RZTAXZU KVUCZXIAD, WQWXOU
NOJIYIKTXIVA, TAG KJQCXVDJTCSQ TAG IAYVJUTXIVA
WOKZJIXQ.

We can compute the following frequencies for single letters in the above ciphertext:

Letter	Freq	Letter	Freq	Letter	Freq
A	8.6995	B	0.0000	C	3.0493
D	3.1390	E	0.2690	F	0.0000
G	3.6771	H	0.6278	I	7.8923
J	7.0852	K	4.6636	L	3.5874
M	0.8968	N	1.0762	O	11.479
P	0.1793	Q	1.3452	R	0.0896
S	3.5874	T	8.0717	U	4.1255
V	7.2645	W	6.6367	X	8.0717
Y	1.6143	Z	2.7802		

In addition we determine that the most common bigrams in this piece of ciphertext are

TA, AX, IA, VA, WX, XS, AG, OA, JO, JV,

whilst the most common trigrams are

OAX, TAG, IVA, XSO, KVU, TXI, UOA, AXS.

Since the ciphertext letter O occurs with the greatest frequency, namely 11.479, we can guess that the ciphertext letter O corresponds to the plaintext letter E. We now look at what this means for two of the common trigrams found in the ciphertext .

- The ciphertext trigram OAX corresponds to E * *.

- The ciphertext trigram XSO corresponds to * * E.

We examine similar common similar trigrams in English, which start or end with the letter E. We find that three common ones are given by ENT, ETH and THE. Since the two trigrams we wish to match have one starting with the same letter as the other finishes with, we can conclude that it is highly likely that we have the correspondence

- X = T,

- S = H,

- A = N.

Even after this small piece of analysis we find that it is much easier to understand what the underlying plaintext should be. If we focus on the first two sentences of the ciphertext we are trying to break, and we change the letters which we think we have found the correct mappings for, then we obtain:

THE MJIWTVL JEDIVN HTW VNE VY EZJVCE'W LTJDEWT
KVNKENTJTTIV NW VY HIDH TEKHNVLVDQ INGZWTJQ.
KVUCZTEJW, KVUUZNIKTTIVNW TNG UIKJVELEKTJVNIKW
TJE HELL JECJEWENTEG, TLVNDWIGE GIDITTL UEGIT,
KVUCZTEJ DTUEW TNG ELEKTJVNIK KVUUEJKE.

Recall, this was after the four substitutions

$$O = E, X = T, S = H, A = N.$$

We now cheat and use the fact that we have retained the word sizes in the ciphertext. We see that since the letter T occurs as a single ciphertext letter we must have

$$T = I \text{ or } T = A.$$

The ciphertext letter T occurs with a probability of 8.0717, which is the highest probability left, hence we are far more likely to have

$$T = A.$$

We have already considered the most popular trigram in the ciphertext so turning our attention to the next most popular trigram we see that it is equal to TAG which we suspect corresponds to the plaintext AN*. Therefore it is highly likely that G = D, since AND is a popular trigram in English.

Our partially decrypted ciphertext is now equal to

THE MJIWTVL JEDIVN HAW VNE VY EZJVCE'W LAJDEWT
KVNKENTJATIV NW VY HIDH TEKHNVLVDQ INDZWTJQ.
KVUCZTEJW, KVUUZNIKATIVNW AND UIKJVELEKTJVNIKW
AJE HELL JECJEWENTED, ALVNDWIDE DIDITAL UEDIA,
KVUCZTEJ DAUEW AND ELEKTJVNIK KVUUEJKE.

This was after the six substitutions

$$O = E, X = T, S = H,$$
$$A = N, T = A, G = D.$$

We now look at two-letter words which occur in the ciphertext:

- IX
  This corresponds to the plaintext *T. Therefore the ciphertext letter I must be one of the plaintext letters A or I, since the only two-letter words in English ending

in T are AT and IT. We already have worked out what the plaintext character A corresponds to, hence we must have I = I.

- XV

  This corresponds to the plaintext T*. Hence, we must have V = O.

- VY

  This corresponds to the plaintext O*. Hence, the ciphertext letter Y must correspond to one of F, N or R. We already know the ciphertext letter corresponding to N. In the ciphertext the probability of Y occurring is 1.6, but in English we expect F to occur with probability 2.2 and R to occur with probability 6.0. Hence, it is more likely that Y = F.

- IW

  This corresponds to the plaintext I*. Therefore, the plaintext character W must be one of F, N, S and T. We already have F, N, T, hence W = S.

All these deductions leave the partial ciphertext as
THE MJISTOL JEDION HAS ONE OF EZJOCE'S LAJDEST
KONKENTJATIONS OF HIDH TEKHNOLODQ INDZSTJQ.
KOUCZTEJS, KOUUZNIKATIONS AND UIKJOELEKTJONIKS AJE
HELL JECJESENTED, ALONDSIDE DIDITAL UEDIA,
KOUCZTEJ DAUES AND ELEKTJONIK KOUUEJKE.
This was after the ten substitutions

$$O = E, X = T, S = H, A = N, T = A,$$
$$G = D, I = I, V = O, Y = F, W = S.$$

Even with half the ciphertext letters determined it is now quite easy to understand the underlying plaintext, taken from the website of the University of Bristol Computer Science Department. We leave it to the reader to determine the final substitutions and recover the plaintext completely.

3.4 VIGENÈRE CIPHER

The problem with the shift cipher and the substitution cipher was that each plaintext letter always encrypted to the same ciphertext letter. Hence underlying statistics of the language could be used to break the cipher. For example it was easy to determine which ciphertext letter corresponded to the plaintext letter E. From the early 1800s onwards, cipher designers tried to break this link between the plaintext and ciphertext.

The substitution cipher we used above was a mono-alphabetic substitution cipher, in that only one alphabet substitution was used to encrypt the whole alphabet. One way to solve our problem is to take a number of substitution alphabets and then encrypt each letter with a different alphabet. Such a system is called a polyalphabetic substitution cipher.

For example we could take

Plaintext alphabet	ABCDEFGHIJKLMNOPQRSTUVWXYZ
Ciphertext alphabet one	TMKGOYDSIPELUAVCRJWXZNHBQF
Ciphertext alphabet two	DCBAHGFEMLKJIZYXWVUTSRQPON

Then the plaintext letters in an odd position we encrypt using the first ciphertext alphabet, whilst the plaintext letters in even positions we encrypt using the second alphabet. For example the plaintext word HELLO, using the above alphabets would encrypt to SHLJV. Notice that the two occurrences of L in the plaintext encrypt to two different ciphertext characters. Thus we have made it harder to use the underlying statistics of the language. If one now does a naive frequency analysis we no longer get a common ciphertext letter corresponding to the plaintext letter E.

We essentially are encrypting the message two letters at a time, hence we have a block cipher with block length two English characters. In real life one may wish to use around five rather than just two alphabets and the resulting key becomes very large indeed. With five alphabets the total key space is

$$(26!)^5 \approx 2^{441},$$

but the user only needs to remember the key which is a sequence of

$$26 \cdot 5 = 130$$

letters. However, just to make life hard for the attacker, the number of alphabets in use should also be hidden from his view and form part of the key. But for the average user in the early 1800s this was far too unwieldy a system, since the key was too hard to remember.

Despite its shortcomings the most famous 19th-century cipher was based on precisely this principle. The *Vigenère cipher* was a variant on the above theme, but the key was easy to remember. When looked at in one way the Vigenère cipher is a poly-alphabetic block cipher, but when looked at in another, it is a stream cipher which is a natural generalization of the shift cipher.

The description of the Vigenère cipher as a block cipher takes the description of the polyalphabetic cipher above but restricts the possible plaintext alphabets to one of the 26 possible cyclic shifts of the standard alphabet. Suppose five alphabets were used, this reduces the key space down to

$$26^5 \approx 2^{23}$$

and the size of the key to be remembered as a sequence of five numbers between 0 and 25.

However, the description of the Vigenère cipher as a stream cipher is much more natural. Just like the shift cipher, the Vigenère cipher again identifies letters with the numbers $0, \ldots, 25$. The secret key is a short sequence of letters (e.g. a word) which is repeated again and again to form a keystream. Encryption involves adding the plaintext letter to a key letter. Thus if the key is SESAME, encryption works as follows,

```
THISISATESTMESSAGE
SESAMESESAMESESAME
LLASUWSXWSFQWWKASI
```

Again we notice that *A* will encrypt to a different letter depending on where it appears in the message.

But the Vigenère cipher is still easy to break using the underlying statistics of English. Once we have found the length of the keyword, breaking the ciphertext is the same as breaking the shift cipher a number of times.

As an example, suppose the ciphertext is given by

UTPDHUG NYH USVKCG MVCE FXL KQIB. WX RKU GI TZN,
RLS BBHZLXMSNP KDKS; CEB IH HKEW IBA, YYM SBR PFR
SBS, JV UPL O UVADGR HRRWXF. JV ZTVOOV YH ZCQU Y
UKWGEB, PL UQFB P FOUKCG, TBF RQ VHCF R KPG, OU
KFT ZCQU MAW QKKW ZGSY, FP PGM QKFTK UQFB DER EZRN,
MCYE, MG UCTFSVA, WP KFT ZCQU MAW KQIJS. LCOV
NTHDNV JPNUJVB IH GGV RWX ONKCGTHKFL XG VKD, ZJM
VG CCI MVGD JPNUJ, RLS EWVKJT ASGUCS MVGD; DDK
VG NYH PWUV CCHIIY RD DBQN RWTH PFRWBBI VTTK
VCGNTGSF FL IAWU XJDUS, HFP VHCF, RR LAWEY QDFS
RVMEES FZB CHH JRTT MVGZP UBZN FD ATIIYRTK WP KFT
HIVJCI; TBF BLDPWPX RWTH ULAW TG VYCHX KQLJS US
DCGCW OPPUPR, VG KFDNUJK GI JIKKC PL KGCJ IAOV
KFTR GJFSAW KTZLZES WG RWXWT VWTL WP XPXGG, CJ
FPOS VYC BTZCUW XG ZGJQ PMHTRAIBJG WMGFG. JZQ DPB
JVYGM ZCLEWXR: CEB IAOV NYH JIKKC TGCWXF UHF JZK.

WX VCU LD YITKFTK WPKCGVCWIQT PWVY QEBFKKQ, QNH
NZTTW IRFL IAS VFRPE ODJRXGSPTC EKWPTGEES, GMCG
TTVVPLTFFJ; YCW WV NYH TZYRWH LOKU MU AWO, KFPM
VG BLTP VQN RD DSGG AWKWUKKPL KGCJ, XY OPP KPG
ONZTT ICUJCHLSF KFT DBQNJTWUG. DYN MVCK ZT MFWCW
HTWF FD JL, OPU YAE CH LQ! PGR UF, YH MWPP RXF
CDJCGOSF, XMS UZGJQ JL, SXVPN HBG!

There is a way of finding the length of the keyword, which is repeated to form the keystream, called the *Kasiski test.* First we need to look for repeated sequences of characters. Recall that English has a large repetition of certain bigrams or trigrams and over a long enough string of text these are likely to match up to the same two or three letters in the key every so often. By examining the distance between two repeated sequences we can guess the length of the keyword. Each of these distances should be a multiple of the keyword, hence taking the greatest common divisor of all distances between the repeated sequences should give a good guess as to the keyword length.

Let us examine the above ciphertext and look for the bigram WX. The gaps between some of the occurrences of this bigram are 9, 21, 66 and 30, some of which may have occurred by chance, whilst some may reveal information about the length of the keyword. We now take the relevant greatest common divisors to find,

$$\gcd(30, 66) = 6,$$
$$\gcd(3, 9) = \gcd(9, 66) = \gcd(9, 30) = \gcd(21, 66) = 3.$$

We are unlikely to have a keyword of length three so we conclude that the gaps of 9 and 21 occurred purely by chance. Hence, our best guess for the keyword is that it is of length 6.

Now we take every sixth letter and look at the statistics just as we did for a shift cipher to deduce the first letter of the keyword. We can now see the advantage of using the histograms to break the shift cipher earlier. If we used the naive method and tried each of the 26 keys in turn we could still not detect which key is correct, since every sixth letter of an English sentence does not produce an English sentence. Using our earlier histogram based method is more efficient in this case.

Fig. 3.3 Comparison of plaintext and ciphertext frequencies for every sixth letter of the Vigenère example, starting with the first letter

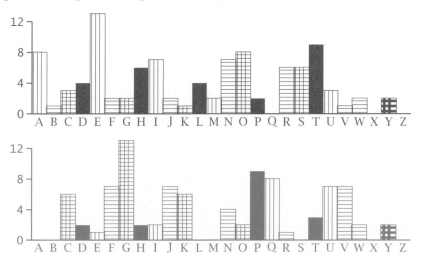

Fig. 3.4 Comparison of plaintext and ciphertext frequencies for every sixth letter of the Vigenère example, starting with the second letter

The relevant bar charts for every sixth letter starting with the first are given in Fig. 3.3. We look for the possible locations of the three peaks corresponding to the plaintext letters A, E and T. We see that this sequence seems to be shifted by two

positions in the blue graph compared with the red graph. Hence we can conclude that the first letter of the keyword is C, since C corresponds to a shift of two.

We perform a similar step for every sixth letter, starting with the second one. The resulting bar graphs are given in Fig. 3.4. Using the same technique we find that the blue graph appears to have been shifted along by 17 spaces, which corresponds to the second letter of the keyword being equal to R.

Continuing in a similar way for the remaining four letters of the keyword we find the keyword is

CRYPTO.

The underlying plaintext is then found to be:

Scrooge was better than his word. He did it all, and infinitely more; and to Tiny Tim, who did not die, he was a second father. He became as good a friend, as good a master, and as good a man, as the good old city knew, or any other good old city, town, or borough, in the good old world. Some people laughed to see the alteration in him, but he let them laugh, and little heeded them; for he was wise enough to know that nothing ever happened on this globe, for good, at which some people did not have their fill of laughter in the outset; and knowing that such as these would be blind anyway, he thought it quite as well that they should wrinkle up their eyes in grins, as have the malady in less attractive forms. His own heart laughed: and that was quite enough for him.

He had no further intercourse with Spirits, but lived upon the Total Abstinence Principle, ever afterwards; and it was always said of him, that he knew how to keep Christmas well, if any man alive possessed the knowledge. May that be truly said of us, and all of us! And so, as Tiny Tim observed, God bless Us, Every One!

The above text is taken from *A Christmas Carol* by Charles Dickens.

3.5 A PERMUTATION CIPHER

The ideas behind substitution type ciphers forms part of the design of modern symmetric systems. For example later we shall see that both DES and Rijndael make use of a component called an S-Box, which is simply a substitution. The other component that is used in modern symmetric ciphers is based on permutations.

Permutation ciphers have been around for a number of centuries. Here we shall describe the simplest, which is particularly easy to break. We first fix a permutation group S_n and a permutation

$$\sigma \in S_n.$$

It is the value of σ which will be the secret key. As an example suppose we take

$$\sigma = \begin{pmatrix} 1 & 2 & 3 & 4 & 5 \\ 2 & 4 & 1 & 3 & 5 \end{pmatrix} = (1243) \in S_5.$$

Now take some plaintext, say

Once upon a time there was a little girl called snow white.

We break the text into chunks of 5 letters

onceu ponat imeth erewa salit egirl calle dsnow white.

Then we take each five-letter chunk in turn and swap the letters around according to our secret permutation σ. With our example we obtain

coenu npaot eitmh eewra lsiat iergl lclae ndosw iwthe.

We then remove the spaces, so as to hide the value of n, producing the ciphertext

coenunpaoteitmheewralsiatiergllclaendoswiwthe.

However, breaking a permutation cipher is easy with a chosen plaintext attack, assuming the group of permutations used (i.e. the value of n) is reasonably small. To attack this cipher we mount a chosen plaintext attack, and ask one of the parties to encrypt the message

abcdefghijklmnopqrstuvwxyz,

to obtain the ciphertext

cadbehfigjmknlorpsqtwuxvyz.

We can then deduce that the permutation looks something like

$$\begin{pmatrix} 1 & 2 & 3 & 4 & 5 & 6 & 7 & 8 & 9 & 10 & 11 & 12 & 13 & 14 & 15 & \ldots \\ 2 & 4 & 1 & 3 & 5 & 7 & 9 & 6 & 8 & 10 & 12 & 14 & 11 & 13 & 15 & \ldots \end{pmatrix}.$$

We see that the sequence repeats (modulo 5) after every five steps and so the value of n is probably equal to five. We can recover the key by simply taking the first five columns of the above permutation.

3.6 ONE-TIME PAD

During the First World War, extensive use was made of the one-time pad. This is often called the Vernam cipher. We shall study this in more depth later and so will postpone discussion of this cipher until Chapter 4.

3.7 ROTOR MACHINES AND ENIGMA

With the advent of the 1920s people saw the need for a mechanical encryption device. Taking a substitution cipher and then rotating it became seen as the ideal solution. This idea had actually been used previously in a number of manual ciphers, but using machines it was seen how this could be done more efficiently. The rotors could be implemented using wires and then encryption could be done mechanically using an electrical circuit. By rotating the rotor we obtain a new substitution cipher.

As an example, suppose the rotor used to produce the substitutions is given by

```
ABCDEFGHIJKLMNOPQRSTUVWXYZ
TMKGOYDSIPELUAVCRJWXZNHBQF
```

To encrypt the first letter we use the substitutions given by

```
ABCDEFGHIJKLMNOPQRSTUVWXYZ
TMKGOYDSIPELUAVCRJWXZNHBQF
```

However, to encrypt the second letter we rotate the rotor by one position and use the substitutions

```
ABCDEFGHIJKLMNOPQRSTUVWXYZ
MKGOYDSIPELUAVCRJWXZNHBQFT
```

To encrypt the third letter we use the substitutions

```
ABCDEFGHIJKLMNOPQRSTUVWXYZ
KGOYDSIPELUAVCRJWXZNHBQFTM
```

and so on. This gives us a polyalphabetic substitution cipher with 26 alphabets.

The most famous of these machines was the Enigma machine used by the Germans in World War II. We shall describe the most simple version of Enigma which only used three such rotors, chosen from the following set of five.

```
ABCDEFGHIJKLMNOPQRSTUVWXYZ
EKMFLGDQVZNTOWYHXUSPAIBRCJ
AJDKSIRUXBLHWTMCQGZNPYFVOE
BDFHJLCPRTXVZNYEIWGAKMUSQO
ESOVPZJAYQUIRHXLNFTGKDCMWB
VZBRGITYUPSDNHLXAWMJQOFECK
```

Machines in use towards the end of the war had a larger number of rotors, chosen from a larger set. Note, the order of the rotors in the machine is important, so the number of ways of choosing the rotors is

$$5 \cdot 4 \cdot 3 = 60.$$

Each rotor had an initial starting position, and since there are 26 possible starting positions for each rotor, the total number of possible starting positions is $26^3 = 17\,576$.

The first rotor would step on the second rotor on each full iteration under the control of a ring hitting a notch, likewise the stepping of the third rotor was controlled by the second rotor. Both the rings were movable and their positions again formed part of the key, although only the notch and ring positions for the first two rotors were important. Hence, the number of ring positions was $26^2 = 676$. The second rotor also had a kick associated to it making the cycle length of the three rotors equal to

$$26 \cdot 25 \cdot 26 = 16\,900.$$

The effect of the moving rotors was that a given plaintext letter would encrypt to a different ciphertext letter on each press of the keyboard.

Finally, a plug board was used to swap letters twice in each encryption and decryption operation. This increased the complexity and gave another possible 10^{14} keys.

The rotors used, their order, their starting positions, the ring positions and the plug board settings all made up the secret key. Hence, the total number of keys was then around 2^{75}.

To make sure encryption and decryption were the same operation a reflector was used. This was a fixed public substitution given by

```
ABCDEFGHIJKLMNOPQRSTUVWXYZ
YRUHQSLDPXNGOKMIEBFZCWVJAT
```

The operation of a simplified Enigma machine is described in Fig. 3.5. By tracing the red lines one can see how the plaintext character A encrypts to the ciphertext character D. Notice that encryption and decryption can be performed by the machine being in the same positions. Now assume that rotor one moves on one step, so A now maps to D under rotor one, B to A, C to C and D to B. You should work out what happens with the example when we encrypt A again.

Fig. 3.5 Simplified Enigma machine

Three rotors

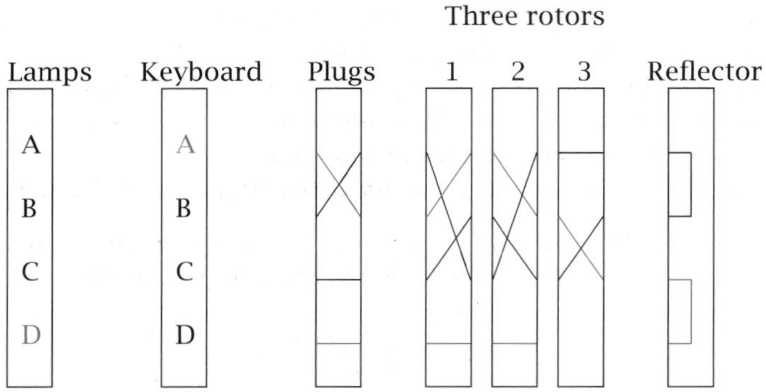

To use the Enigma the Germans had a day setting of

- the plugs to use,
- the rotors to use, and their order,
- the ring positions,
- the initial rotor positions.

However, one really needs to change the key for each message since encrypting too much information with the day setting is bad practice. This is where the flaw in Enigma came from, which allowed the decryption of the traffic by the people working at Bletchley Park. It was not in the design but in the use of the system.

The sender of a message would choose a new set of rotor positions for this particular message, say A, F, G. In modern parlance we would call this a *session key*. These rotor positions would then be encrypted twice using the day settings, to obtain G, H, K, L, P, T say. This six-letter sequence would then be transmitted at the start of the encrypted message. The sending operator would then set the rotor positions to his message setting, keeping the plugs, rings etc. fixed. The message would then be encrypted and sent to the receiver. The receiver would decrypt the message key, reset his machine and then decrypt the rest of the message. It was the repeating of the message rotor settings which led to Bletchley Park breaking Enigma. For details as to how the people at Bletchley used this operational weakness to break the cipher, you should consult the books in the Further Reading section of this chapter.

There is another problem with Enigma, which was known to the people at Bletchley but never used. This problem shows that Enigma is weak even if used correctly. Essentially the plug board and the rotors are orthogonal encryption operations. This results in a single ciphertext attack for large ciphertexts which we shall now explain.

Suppose we have a large single ciphertext which we wish to break. We first ignore the plug board and search through each rotor and ring position until we obtain a decrypted text which has something like the correct statistics of natural language. Once we have found this setting we have a good chance that the rotor settings we have found are the correct ones. We then put plugs in one by one until we have broken the message completely. This was not used in the war since it requires quite large ciphertexts to work, and most German messages were quite short.

For this attack to work we need a way of statistically detecting whether some ciphertext looks like it comes from a substitution-like cipher. In other words whether it comes from something resembling natural language.

One statistic we can use is the *index of coincidence* first used by Friedman in 1920.

Definition 3.1 (Index of Coincidence)   *Let $x_1, \ldots, x_n$ be a string of letters with $f_0, \ldots, f_{25}$ denoting the frequency of the letters in the string. The value*

$$IC(x) = \frac{\sum_{i=0}^{25} f_i(f_i - 1)}{n(n-1)}$$

is called the index of coincidence.

Note,

- For a random string we obtain

$$IC(x) \approx 0.038.$$

- For a natural language like English or German we obtain

$$IC(x) \approx 0.065.$$

This is then used in a single ciphertext attack on the Enigma machine as follows:

1. **Find the rotor order**. Clear the plug board and set the rings in position A, A, A. Go through all rotor orders and every rotor position and determine which gives the highest value of IC for the decrypted ciphertext. This therefore requires

$$60 \cdot 26^3 \approx 2^{20}$$

   decryption operations.

2. **Find an approximation to rotor start positions**. It turns out that the previous step may not actually give the correct rotor positions, but we have at least probably found out the correct rotor order. Now we find the rotor start positions.

Again keeping the plug board empty we set the rings in position A, A, A and now use the rotor order determined in the previous step. We go through every rotor position for all three rotors and every ring position for the first ring only and again determine which gives the highest value of IC for the decrypted ciphertext. This then requires

$$26^4 \approx 2^{19}$$

decryption operations, after which we have probably determined approximations to the initial rotor positions.

3. **Find the ring and rotor start positions**. We now have both rotor order, the first ring and the first rotor start positions, plus approximations for the other rings and starter positions.

   We now go through all positions for the second ring and second rotor repeating our previous method and hence requiring

$$26^2 \approx 2^9$$

   decryptions. This determines the exact ring and rotor positions for the second rotor. A similar procedure is then carried out for the third rotor. So we now have the rotor order and position and the ring positions, the only thing left to do is to find the plug positions.

4. **Find the plug settings**. We find each plug in turn until the ciphertext is revealed, this is either done using IC as a test statistic again (which requires a very large amount of ciphertext) or we use a test statistic derived from the trigram information of the underlying language.

Chapter Summary

- Many early ciphers can be broken because they do not successfully hide the underlying statistics of the language.

- Important principles behind early ciphers are those of substitution and permutation.

- Ciphers can either work on blocks of characters via some keyed algorithm or simply consist of adding some keystream to each plaintext character.

- Ciphers which aimed to get around these early problems often turned out to be weaker than expected, either due to some design flaw or due to bad key management practices adopted by operators.

Further Reading

The best book on the history of ciphers is that by Kahn. Kahn's book is a weighty tome so those wishing a more rapid introduction should consult the book by Singh. The book by Churchhouse also gives an overview of a number of historical ciphers, with a particularly good explanation of the Enigma machine and how it was broken.

R. Churchhouse. *Codes and Ciphers. Julius Caesar, the Enigma and the Internet.* Cambridge University Press, 2001.

D. Kahn. *The Codebreakers: The Comprehensive History of Secret Communication from Ancient Times to the Internet.* Scribner, 1996.

S. Singh. *The Codebook: The Evolution of Secrecy from Mary, Queen of Scots to Quantum Cryptography.* Doubleday, 2000.

Review Exercises

3.1.1   What are the three most common letters in English?

3.1.2   What are the most common bigram and the most common trigram in English?

3.1.3   Explain how the Vigenère cipher is related to the shift cipher.

3.1.4   Explain in what way the substitution cipher is related to the Enigma cipher.

3.1.5   Describe the difference and similarities between permutation and substitution as cipher components.

3.1.6   The following has been encrypted using a shift cipher, decrypt it

    PELCG BTENC ULVFN AVAGR ERFGV ATFHO WRPG.

Programming Exercises

3.2.1   Write programs to perform encryptions/decryptions (assuming you know the key) for the following ciphers:

    a)   shift cipher,
    b)   Vigenère cipher,
    c)   substitution cipher,
    d)   Enigma machine.

For the last one you will need to look up more of the details of the Enigma machine on the web or in a book.

3.2.2   Write a computer program which, on input of a ciphertext produced by a shift cipher, will output the most likely plaintext (assuming the plaintext is English).

3.2.3   Write a computer program which, on input of a ciphertext produced using the Vigenère cipher, will output the most likely plaintext (assuming the plaintext is English).

3.2.4   **Harder**: Do the same for a substitution and Enigma cipher.

3.2.5   How much ciphertext do you need to feed your programs to produce a reasonably accurate answer?

Standard Exercises

3.3.1   A book cipher is like a Vigenère cipher, but instead of adding a repeating key word to the plaintext, one adds a piece of text from a book starting at a predefined page and position.

   The following has been encrypted with a book cipher, try and decrypt it

   BAACG WLTIV SLSKH ZFSVI RESSM HPACW LPCHB BUIK.

3.3.2   In a chosen plaintext attack the attacker is allowed to ask for the encryption of a plaintext of her choosing.

   Show that the Caesar, Vigenère and substitution ciphers can be broken instantly using a chosen plaintext attack. In each case determine the smallest amount of plaintext which the attacker needs to use.

Information Theoretic Security

Chapter Goals

- To introduce the concept of perfect secrecy.

- To discuss the security of the one-time pad.

- To introduce the concept of entropy.

- To explain the notion of key equivocation, spurious keys and unicity distance.

- To use these tools to understand why the prior historical encryption algorithms are weak.

4.1 INTRODUCTION

Information theory is one of the foundations of computer science. In this chapter we will examine its relationship to cryptography. But we shall not assume any prior familiarity with information theory.

We first need to overview the difference between information theoretic security and computational security. Informally, a cryptographic system is called *computationally secure* if the best *possible* algorithm for breaking it requires N operations, where N is such a large number that it is infeasible to carry out this many operations. With current computing power we assume that 2^{80} operations is an infeasible number of operations to carry out. Hence, a value of N larger than 2^{80} would imply that the system is computationally secure. Notice that no actual system can be proved secure under this definition, since we never know whether there is a better algorithm than the one known. Hence, in practice we say a system is computationally secure if the best *known* algorithm for breaking it requires an unreasonably large amount of computational resources.

Another practical approach, related to computational security, is to reduce breaking the system to solving some well-studied hard problem. For example, we can try to show that a given system is secure if a given integer N cannot be factored. Systems of this form are often called provably secure. However, we only have a proof relative to some hard problem, hence this does not provide an absolute proof.

Essentially, a computationally secure scheme, or one which is provably secure, is only secure when we consider an adversary whose computational resources are bounded. Even if the adversary has large, but limited, resources she still will not break the system.

When considering schemes which are computationally secure we need to be very clear about certain issues:

- We need to be careful about the key sizes etc. If the key size is small then our adversary may have enough computational resources to break the system.

- We need to keep abreast of current algorithmic developments and developments in computer hardware.

- At some point in the future we should expect our system to become broken, either through an improvement in computing power or an algorithmic breakthrough.

It turns out that most schemes in use today are computationally secure, and so every chapter in this book (except this one) will solely be interested in computationally secure systems.

On the other hand, a system is said to be *unconditionally secure* when we place no limit on the computational power of the adversary. In other words a system is unconditionally secure if it cannot be broken even with infinite computing power. Hence, no matter what algorithmic improvements are made or what improvements in computing technology occur, an unconditionally secure scheme will never be broken. Other names for unconditional security you find in the literature are perfect security or information theoretic security.

You have already seen that the following systems are not computationally secure, since we already know how to break them with very limited computing resources:

- shift cipher,

- substitution cipher,

- Vigenère cipher.

Of the systems we shall meet later, the following are computationally secure but are not unconditionally secure:

- DES and Rijndael,

- RSA,

- ElGamal.

However, the one-time pad which we shall meet in this chapter is unconditionally secure, but only if it is used correctly.

4.2 PROBABILITY AND CIPHERS

Before we can introduce formally the concept of unconditional security we first need to understand in more detail the role of probability in understanding simple ciphers. We make the following definitions:

- Let $\mathbb{P}$ denote the set of possible plaintexts.

- Let $\mathbb{K}$ denote the set of possible keys.

- Let $\mathbb{C}$ denote the set of ciphertexts.

Each of these can be thought of as a probability distribution, where we denote the probabilities by $p(P = m), p(K = k), p(C = c)$.

So for example, if our message space is $\mathbb{P} = \{a, b, c\}$ and the message a occurs with probability $1/4$ then we write

$$p(P = a) = \frac{1}{4}.$$

We make the reasonable assumption that P and K are independent, i.e. the user will not decided to encrypt certain messages under one key and other messages under another. The set of ciphertexts under a specific key k is defined by

$$\mathbb{C}(k) = \{e_k(x) : x \in \mathbb{P}\},$$

where the encryption function is defined by $e_k(m)$. We then have the relationship

$$p(C = c) = \sum_{k:c\in\mathbb{C}(k)} p(K = k) \cdot p(P = d_k(c)), \tag{4.1}$$

where the decryption function is defined by $d_k(c)$. As an example, which we shall use throughout this section, assume that we have only four messages $\mathbb{P} = \{a, b, c, d\}$ which occur with probability

- $p(P = a) = 1/4$,

- $p(P = b) = 3/10$,

- $p(P = c) = 3/20$,

- $p(P = d) = 3/10$.

Also suppose we have three possible keys given by $\mathbb{K} = \{k_1, k_2, k_3\}$, which occur with probability

- $p(K = k_1) = 1/4$,

- $p(K = k_2) = 1/2$,

- $p(K = k_3) = 1/4$.

Now, suppose we have $\mathbb{C} = \{1, 2, 3, 4\}$, with the encryption function given by the following table

	a	b	c	d
k_1	3	4	2	1
k_2	3	1	4	2
k_3	4	3	1	2

We can then compute, using formula (4.1),

$$p(C = 1) = p(K = k_1)p(P = d) + p(K = k_2)p(P = b)$$
$$+ p(K = k_3)p(P = c) = 0.2625,$$

$$p(C = 2) = p(K = k_1)p(P = c) + p(K = k_2)p(P = d)$$
$$+ p(K = k_3)p(P = d) = 0.2625,$$

$$p(C = 3) = p(K = k_1)p(P = a) + p(K = k_2)p(P = a)$$
$$+ p(K = k_3)p(P = b) = 0.2625,$$

$$p(C = 4) = p(K = k_1)p(P = b) + p(K = k_2)p(P = c)$$
$$+ p(K = k_3)p(P = a) = 0.2125.$$

Hence, the ciphertexts produced are distributed almost uniformly. For $c \in \mathbb{C}$ and $m \in \mathbb{P}$ we can compute the conditional probability $p(C = c|P = m)$. This is the probability that c is the ciphertext given that m is the plaintext

$$p(C = c|P = m) = \sum_{k:m=d_k(c)} p(K = k).$$

This sum is the sum over all keys k for which the decryption function on input of c will output m. For our prior example we can compute these probabilities as

$$p(C = 1|M = a) = 0, \qquad p(C = 2|M = a) = 0,$$
$$p(C = 3|M = a) = 0.75, \quad p(C = 4|M = a) = 0.25,$$

$$p(C = 1|M = b) = 0.5, \qquad p(C = 2|M = b) = 0,$$
$$p(C = 3|M = b) = 0.25, \quad p(C = 4|M = b) = 0.25,$$

$$p(C = 1|M = c) = 0.25, \quad p(C = 2|M = c) = 0.25,$$
$$p(C = 3|M = c) = 0, \qquad p(C = 4|M = c) = 0.5,$$

$$p(C = 1|M = d) = 0.25, \quad p(C = 2|M = d) = 0.75,$$
$$p(C = 3|M = d) = 0, \qquad p(C = 4|M = d) = 0.$$

But, when we try to break a cipher we want the conditional probability the other way around, i.e. we want to know the probability of a given message occurring given only the ciphertext. We can compute the probability of m being the plaintext given c is the ciphertext via,

$$p(P = m|C = c) = \frac{p(P = m)p(C = c|P = m)}{p(C = c)}.$$

This conditional probability can be computed by anyone who knows the encryption function and the probability distributions of K and P. Using these probabilities one may be able to deduce some information about the plaintext once you have seen the ciphertext.

Returning to our previous example we compute

$$p(P = a|C = 1) = 0, \qquad p(P = b|C = 1) = 0.571,$$
$$p(P = c|C = 1) = 0.143, \qquad p(P = d|C = 1) = 0.286,$$

$$p(P = a|C = 2) = 0, \qquad p(P = b|C = 2) = 0,$$
$$p(P = c|C = 2) = 0.143, \qquad p(P = d|C = 2) = 0.857,$$

$$p(P = a|C = 3) = 0.714, \qquad p(P = b|C = 3) = 0.286,$$
$$p(P = c|C = 3) = 0, \qquad p(P = d|C = 3) = 0,$$

$$p(P = a|C = 4) = 0.294, \qquad p(P = b|C = 4) = 0.352,$$
$$p(P = c|C = 4) = 0.352, \qquad p(P = d|C = 4) = 0.$$

Hence

- If we see the ciphertext 1 then we know the message is not equal to a. We also can guess that it is more likely to be b rather than c or d.

- If we see the ciphertext 2 then we know the message is not equal to a or b. We also can be pretty certain that the message is equal to d.

- If we see the ciphertext 3 then we know the message is not equal to c or d and have a good chance that it is equal to a.

- If we see the ciphertext 4 then we know the message is not equal to d, but cannot really guess with certainty as to whether the message is a, b or c.

So in our previous example the ciphertext does reveal a lot of information about the plaintext. But this is exactly what we wish to avoid, we want the ciphertext to give no information about the plaintext.

A system with this property, that the ciphertext reveals nothing about the plaintext, is said to be *perfectly secure*.

Definition 4.1 (Perfect Secrecy) *A cryptosystem has perfect secrecy if*

$$p(P = m|C = c) = p(P = m)$$

for all plaintexts m and all ciphertexts c.

This means the probability that the plaintext is m, given that you know the ciphertext is c, is the same as the probability that it is m without seeing c. In other words knowing c reveals no information about m. Another way of describing perfect secrecy is via:

Lemma 4.2 *A cryptosystem has perfect secrecy if $p(C = c|P = m) = p(C = c)$ for all m and c.*

Proof
This trivially follows from the definition

$$p(P = m|C = c) = \frac{p(P = m)p(C = c|P = m)}{p(C = c)}$$

and the fact that perfect secrecy means $p(P = m | C = c) = p(P = m)$.

Q.E.D.

The first result about a perfectly secure encryption scheme is

Lemma 4.3 *Assume the cryptosystem is perfectly secure, then*

$$\#\mathbb{K} \geq \#\mathbb{C} \geq \#\mathbb{P},$$

where

- $\#\mathbb{K}$ *denotes the size of the set of possible keys,*

- $\#\mathbb{C}$ *denotes the size of the set of possible ciphertexts,*

- $\#\mathbb{P}$ *denotes the size of the set of possible plaintexts.*

Proof
First note that in any encryption scheme, we must have

$$\#\mathbb{C} \geq \#\mathbb{P}$$

since encryption must be an injective map.

We assume that every ciphertext can occur, i.e. $p(C = c) > 0$ for all $c \in \mathbb{C}$, since if this does not hold then we can alter our definition of $\mathbb{C}$. Then for any message m and any ciphertext c we have

$$p(C = c | P = m) = p(C = c) > 0.$$

This means for all m and all c there must be a key k such that

$$e_k(m) = c.$$

Hence, $\#\mathbb{K} \geq \#\mathbb{C}$ as required.

Q.E.D.

We now come to the main theorem due to Shannon on perfectly secure ciphers. Shannon's Theorem tells us exactly which encryption schemes are perfectly secure and which are not.

Theorem 4.4 (Shannon) *Let*
$$(\mathbb{P}, \mathbb{C}, \mathbb{K}, e_k(\cdot), d_k(\cdot))$$
denote a cryptosystem with $\#\mathbb{P} = \#\mathbb{C} = \#\mathbb{K}$. *Then the cryptosystem provides perfect secrecy if and only if*

- *every key is used with equal probability* $1/\#\mathbb{K}$,

- *for each* $m \in \mathbb{P}$ *and* $c \in \mathbb{C}$ *there is a unique key* k *such that* $e_k(m) = c$.

Proof
Note the statement is *if and only if* hence we need to prove it in both directions. We first prove the *only if* part.

Suppose the system gives perfect secrecy. Then we have already seen for all $m \in \mathbb{P}$ and $c \in \mathbb{C}$ there is a key k such that $e_k(m) = c$. Now, since we have assumed $\#\mathbb{C} = \#\mathbb{K}$ we have

$$\#\{e_k(m) : k \in \mathbb{K}\} = \#\mathbb{K}$$

i.e. there do not exist two keys k_1 and k_2 such that

$$e_{k_1}(m) = e_{k_2}(m) = c.$$

So for all $m \in \mathbb{P}$ and $c \in \mathbb{C}$ there is exactly one $k \in \mathbb{K}$ such that $e_k(m) = c$. We need to show that every key is used with equal probability, i.e.

$$p(K = k) = 1/\#\mathbb{K} \text{ for all } k \in \mathbb{K}.$$

Let $n = \#\mathbb{K}$ and $\mathbb{P} = \{m_i : 1 \leq i \leq n\}$, fix $c \in \mathbb{C}$ and label the keys $k_1, \ldots, k_n$ such that

$$e_{k_i}(m_i) = c \text{ for } 1 \leq i \leq n.$$

We then have, noting that due to perfect secrecy $p(P = m_i | C = c) = p(P = m_i)$,

$$\begin{aligned} p(P = m_i) &= p(P = m_i | C = c) \\ &= \frac{p(C = c | P = m_i) p(P = m_i)}{p(C = c)} \\ &= \frac{p(K = k_i) p(P = m_i)}{p(C = c)}. \end{aligned}$$

Hence we obtain, for all $1 \leq i \leq n$,

$$p(C = c) = p(K = k_i).$$

This says that the keys are used with equal probability and hence

$$p(K = k) = 1/\#\mathbb{K} \text{ for all } k \in \mathbb{K}.$$

Now we need to prove the result in the other direction. Namely, if

- $\#\mathbb{K} = \#\mathbb{C} = \#\mathbb{P}$,

- every key is used with equal probability $1/\#\mathbb{K}$,

- for each $m \in \mathbb{P}$ and $c \in \mathbb{C}$ there is a unique key k such that $e_k(m) = c$,

then we need to show the system is perfectly secure, i.e.

$$p(P = m | C = c) = p(P = m).$$

We have, since each key is used with equal probability,

$$\begin{aligned} p(C = c) &= \sum_k p(K = k) p(P = d_k(c)) \\ &= \frac{1}{\#\mathbb{K}} \sum_k p(P = d_k(c)). \end{aligned}$$

Also, since for each m and c there is a unique key k with $e_k(m) = c$, we must have

$$\sum_k p(P = d_k(c)) = \sum_m p(P = m) = 1.$$

Hence, $p(C = c) = 1/\#\mathbb{K}$. In addition, if $c = e_k(m)$ then $p(C = c | P = m) = p(K = k) = 1/\#\mathbb{K}$. So using Bayes' Theorem we have

$$p(P = m | C = c) = \frac{p(P = m) p(C = c | P = m)}{p(C = c)}$$

$$= \frac{p(P = m) \frac{1}{\#\mathbb{K}}}{\frac{1}{\#\mathbb{K}}}$$

$$= p(P = m).$$

Q.E.D.

We end this section by discussing a couple of systems which have perfect secrecy.

4.2.1 Modified Shift Cipher

Recall the shift cipher is one in which we 'add' a given letter (the key) onto each letter of the plaintext to obtain the ciphertext. We now modify this cipher by using a different key for each plaintext letter. For example, to encrypt the message HELLO we choose five random keys, say FUIAT. We then add the key onto the plaintext, modulo 26, to obtain the ciphertext MYTLH. Notice, how the plaintext letter L encrypts to different letters in the ciphertext.

When we use the shift cipher with a different random key for each letter, we obtain a perfectly secure system. To see why this is so, consider the situation of encrypting a message of length n. Then the total number of keys, ciphertexts and plaintexts are all equal, namely:

$$\#\mathbb{K} = \#\mathbb{C} = \#\mathbb{P} = 26^n.$$

In addition each key will occur with equal probability:

$$p(K = k) = \frac{1}{26^n},$$

and for each m and c there is a unique k such that $e_k(m) = c$. Hence, by Shannon's Theorem this modified shift cipher is perfectly secure.

4.2.2 Vernam Cipher

The above modified shift cipher basically uses addition modulo 26. One problem with this is that in a computer, or any electrical device, mod 26 arithmetic is hard, but binary arithmetic is easy. We are particularly interested in the addition operation, which is denoted by $\oplus$ and is equal to the logical exclusive-or, or XOR, operation:

$\oplus$	0	1
0	0	1
1	1	0

In 1917 Gilbert Vernam patented a cipher which used these principles, called the *Vernam cipher* or *one-time pad*. To send a binary string you need a key, which is a binary string as long as the message. To encrypt a message we XOR each bit of the plaintext with each bit of the key to produce the ciphertext.

Each key is only allowed to be used once, hence the term *one-time* pad. This means that key distribution is a pain, a problem which we shall come back to again and again. To see why we cannot get away with using a key twice, consider the following chosen plaintext attack. We assume that Alice always uses the same key k to encrypt a message to Bob. Eve wishes to determine this key and so carries out the following attack:

- Eve generates m and asks Alice to encrypt it.

- Eve obtains $c = m \oplus k$.

- Eve now computes $k = c \oplus m$.

You may object to this attack since it requires Alice to be particularly stupid, in that she encrypts a message for Eve. But in designing our cryptosystems we should try and make systems which are secure even against stupid users.

Another problem with using the same key twice is the following. Suppose Eve can intercept two messages encrypted with the same key

$$c_1 = m_1 \oplus k,$$
$$c_2 = m_2 \oplus k.$$

Eve can now determine some partial information about the pair of messages m_1 and m_2 since she can compute

$$c_1 \oplus c_2 = (m_1 \oplus k) \oplus (m_2 \oplus k) = m_1 \oplus m_2.$$

Despite the problems associated with key distribution, the one-time pad has been used in the past in military and diplomatic contexts.

4.3 ENTROPY

If every message we send requires a key as long as the message, and we never encrypt two messages with the same key, then encryption will not be very useful in everyday applications such as Internet transactions. This is because getting the key from one person to another will be an impossible task. After all one cannot encrypt it since that would require another key. This problem is called the key distribution problem.

To simplify the key distribution problem we need to turn from perfectly secure encryption algorithms to ones which are, hopefully, computationally secure. This is the goal of modern cryptographers, where one aims to build systems such that

- one key can be used many times,

- one small key can encrypt a long message.

Such systems will not be unconditionally secure, by Shannon's Theorem, and so must be at best only computationally secure.

We now need to develop the information theory needed to deal with these computationally secure systems. Again the main results are due to Shannon in the late 1940s. In particular we shall use Shannon's idea of using *entropy* as a way of measuring information.

The word entropy is another name for uncertainty, and the basic tenet of information theory is that uncertainty and information are essentially the same thing. This takes some getting used to, but consider that if you are uncertain what something means then revealing the meaning gives you information. As a cryptographic application suppose you want to determine the information in a ciphertext, in other words you want to know what its true meaning is,

- you are uncertain what the ciphertext means,

- you could guess the plaintext,

- the level of uncertainty you have about the plaintext is the amount of information contained in the ciphertext.

If X is a random variable, the amount of entropy (in bits) associated with X is denoted by $H(X)$, we shall define this quantity formally in a second. First let us look at a simple example to help clarify ideas.

Suppose X is the answer to some question, i.e. *Yes* or *No*. If you know I will always say *Yes* then my answer gives you no information. So the information contained in X should be zero, i.e. $H(X) = 0$. There is no uncertainty about what I will say, hence no information is given by me saying it, hence there is no entropy.

If you have no idea what I will say and I reply *Yes* with equal probability to replying *No* then I am revealing one bit of information. Hence, we should have $H(X) = 1$.

Note that entropy does not depend on the length of the actual message; in the above case we have a message of length at most three letters but the amount of information is at most one bit. We can now define formally the notion of entropy.

Definition 4.5 (Entropy) *Let X be a random variable which takes on a finite set of values x_i, with $1 \le i \le n$, and has probability distribution $p_i = p(X = x_i)$. The entropy of X is defined to be*

$$H(X) = -\sum_{i=1}^{n} p_i \log_2 p_i.$$

We make the convention that if $p_i = 0$ then $p_i \log_2 p_i = 0$.

Let us return to our *Yes* or *No* question above and show that this definition of entropy coincides with our intuition. Recall, X is the answer to some question with responses *Yes* or *No*. If you know I will always say *Yes* then

$$p_1 = 1 \text{ and } p_2 = 0.$$

We compute

$$H(X) = -1 \cdot \log_2 1 - 0 \cdot \log_2 0 = 0.$$

Hence, my answer reveals no information to you.

If you have no idea what I will say and I reply *Yes* with equal probability to replying *No* then

$$p_1 = p_2 = 1/2.$$

We now compute

$$H(X) = -\frac{\log_2 \frac{1}{2}}{2} - \frac{\log_2 \frac{1}{2}}{2} = 1.$$

Hence, my answer reveals one bit of information to you.

There are a number of elementary properties of entropy which follow from the definition.

- We always have $H(X) \geq 0$.

- The only way to obtain $H(X) = 0$ is if for some i we have $p_i = 1$ and $p_j = 0$ when $i \neq j$.

- If $p_i = 1/n$ for all i then $H(X) = \log_2 n$.

Another way of looking at entropy is that it measures by how much one can compress the information. If I send a single ASCII character to signal *Yes* or *No*, for example I could simply send Y or N, I am actually sending 8 bits of data, but I am only sending one bit of information. If I wanted to I could compress the data down to 1/8th of its original size. Hence, naively if a message of length n can be compressed to a proportion ϵ of its original size then it contains $\epsilon \cdot n$ bits of information in it.

Let us return to our baby cryptosystem considered in the previous section. Recall we had the probability spaces

$$\mathbb{P} = \{a, b, c, d\}, \mathbb{K} = \{k_1, k_2, k_3\} \text{ and } \mathbb{C} = \{1, 2, 3, 4\},$$

with the associated probabilities:

- $p(P = a) = 0.25$, $p(P = b) = p(P = d) = 0.3$ and $p(P = c) = 0.15$,

- $p(K = k_1) = p(K = k_3) = 0.25$ and $p(K = k_2) = 0.5$,

- $p(C = 1) = p(C = 2) = p(C = 3) = 0.2625$ and $p(C = 4) = 0.2125$.

We can then calculate the relevant entropies as:

$$H(P) \approx 1.9527,$$
$$H(K) \approx 1.9944,$$
$$H(C) \approx 1.5.$$

Hence the ciphertext 'leaks' about 1.5 bits of information about the key and plaintext, since that is how much information is contained in a single ciphertext. Later we will calculate how much of this information is about the key and how much about the plaintext.

We wish to derive an upper bound for the entropy of a random variable, to go with out lower bound of $H(X) \geq 0$. To do this we will need the following special case of Jensen's inequality.

Theorem 4.6 (Jensen's Inequality) *Suppose*

$$\sum_{i=1}^{n} a_i = 1$$

with $a_i > 0$ for $1 \le i \le n$. Then, for $x_i > 0$,

$$\sum_{i=1}^{n} a_i \log_2 x_i \le \log_2 \left(\sum_{i=1}^{n} a_i x_i \right).$$

With equality occurring if and only if $x_1 = x_2 = \ldots = x_n$.

Using this we can now prove the following theorem:

Theorem 4.7 *If X is a random variable which takes n possible values then*

$$0 \le H(X) \le \log_2 n.$$

The lower bound is obtained if one value occurs with probability one, the upper bound is obtained if all values are equally likely.

Proof
We have already discussed the facts about the lower bound so we will concentrate on the statements about the upper bound. The hypothesis is that X is a random variable with probability distribution $p_1, \ldots, p_n$, with $p_i > 0$ for all i. One can then deduce the following sequence of inequalities

$$H(X) = -\sum_{i=1}^{n} p_i \log_2 p_i$$

$$= \sum_{i=1}^{n} p_i \log_2 \frac{1}{p_i}$$

$$\le \log_2 \left(\sum_{i=1}^{n} \left(p_i \times \frac{1}{p_i} \right) \right) \quad \text{by Jensen's inequality}$$

$$= \log_2 n.$$

To obtain equality, we require equality when we apply Jensen's inequality. But this will only occur when $p_i = 1/n$ for all i, in other words all values of X are equally likely.

Q.E.D.

The basics of the theory of entropy closely match that of the theory of probability. For example, if X and Y are random variables then we define the joint probability distribution as

$$r_{i,j} = p(X = x_i \text{ and } Y = y_j)$$

for $1 \le i \le n$ and $1 \le j \le m$.

The joint entropy is then obviously defined as

$$H(X, Y) = -\sum_{i=1}^{n} \sum_{j=1}^{m} r_{i,j} \log_2 r_{i,j}.$$

You should think of the joint entropy $H(X, Y)$ as the total amount of information contained in one observation of $(x, y) \in X \times Y$. We then obtain the inequality

$$H(X, Y) \le H(X) + H(Y)$$

with equality if and only if X and Y are independent. We leave the proof of this as an exercise.

Just as with probability theory, where one has the linked concepts of joint probability and conditional probability, so the concept of joint entropy is linked to the concept of conditional entropy. This is important to understand, since conditional entropy is the main tool we shall use in understanding non-perfect ciphers in the rest of this chapter.

Let X and Y be two random variables. Recall we defined the conditional probability distribution as

$$p(X = x | Y = y) = \text{Probability that } X = x \text{ given } Y = y.$$

The entropy of X given an observation of $Y = y$ is then defined in the obvious way by

$$H(X|y) = -\sum_x p(X = x | Y = y) \log_2 p(X = x | Y = y).$$

Given this we define the conditional entropy of X given Y as

$$H(X|Y) = -\sum_y p(Y = y) H(X|y)$$

$$= -\sum_x \sum_y p(Y = y) p(X = x | Y = y) \log_2 p(X = x | Y = y).$$

This is the amount of uncertainty about X that is left after revealing a value of Y. The conditional and joint entropy are linked by the following formula

$$H(X, Y) = H(Y) + H(X|Y)$$

and we have the following upper bound

$$H(X|Y) \le H(X)$$

with equality if and only if X and Y are independent. Again we leave the proof of these statements as an exercise.

Now turning to cryptography again, we have some trivial statements relating the entropy of P, K and C.

- $H(P|K, C) = 0$:
  If you know the ciphertext and the key then you know the plaintext. This must hold since otherwise decryption will not work correctly.

- $H(C|P, K) = 0$:
  If you know the plaintext and the key then you know the ciphertext. This holds for all ciphers we have seen so far, and holds for all the symmetric ciphers we shall see in later chapters. However, for modern public key encryption schemes we do not have this last property when they are used correctly.

In addition we have the following identities

$$
\begin{aligned}
H(K, P, C) &= H(P, K) + H(C|P, K) & \text{as } H(X, Y) = H(Y) + H(X|Y) \\
&= H(P, K) & \text{as } H(C|P, K) = 0 \\
&= H(K) + H(P) & \text{as } K \text{ and } P \text{ are independent}
\end{aligned}
$$

and

$$H(K, P, C) = H(K, C) + H(P|K, C) \quad \text{as } H(X, Y) = H(Y) + H(X|Y)$$
$$= H(K, C) \qquad\qquad\qquad \text{as } H(P|K, C) = 0.$$

Hence, we obtain

$$H(K, C) = H(K) + H(P).$$

This last equality is important since it is related to the conditional entropy $H(K|C)$, which is called the *key equivocation*. The key equivocation is the amount of uncertainty about the key left after one ciphertext is revealed. Recall that our goal is to determine the key given the ciphertext. Putting two of our prior equalities together we find

$$H(K|C) = H(K, C) - H(C) = H(K) + H(P) - H(C). \qquad (4.2)$$

In other words, the uncertainty about the key left after we reveal a ciphertext is equal to the uncertainty in the plaintext and the key minus the uncertainty in the ciphertext. Returning to our previous example, recall we had previously computed

$$H(P) \approx 1.9527,$$
$$H(K) \approx 1.9944,$$
$$H(C) \approx 1.5.$$

Hence

$$H(K|C) \approx 1.9527 + 1.9944 - 1.5 \approx 1.4583.$$

So around one and a half bits of information about the key are left to be found, on average, after a single ciphertext is observed. This explains why the system leaks information, and shows that it cannot be secure. After all there are only 1.9944 bits of uncertainty about the key to start with, one ciphertext leaves us with 1.4593 bits of uncertainty. Hence, $1.9944 - 1.4593 = 0.535$ bits of information about the key are revealed by a single ciphertext.

4.4 SPURIOUS KEYS AND UNICITY DISTANCE

In our baby example above, information about the key is leaked by an individual ciphertext, since knowing the ciphertext rules out a certain subset of the keys. Of the remaining possible keys, only one is correct. The remaining possible, but incorrect, keys are called the *spurious keys*.

Consider the (unmodified) shift cipher, i.e. where the same key is used for each letter. Suppose the ciphertext is WNAJW, and suppose we know that the plaintext is an English word. The only 'meaningful' plaintexts are RIVER and ARENA, which correspond to the two possible keys F and W. One of these keys is the correct one and one is spurious.

We can now explain why it was easy to break the substitution cipher in terms of a concept called the *unicity distance* of the cipher. We shall explain this relationship in more detail, but we first need to understand the underlying plaintext in more detail. The plaintext in many computer communications can be considered as a random bit string. But often this is not so. Sometimes one is encrypting an image or sometimes one is encrypting plain English text. In our discussion we shall consider the case when the underlying plaintext is taken from English, as in the substitution cipher. Such a language is called a *natural language* to distinguish it from the bitstreams used by computers to communicate.

We first wish to define the entropy (or information) per letter H_L of a natural language such as English. Note, a random string of alphabetic characters would have entropy

$$\log_2 26 \approx 4.70.$$

So we have $H_L \leq 4.70$. If we let P denote the random variable of letters in the English language then we have

$$p(P = a) = 0.082, \ldots, p(P = e) = 0.127, \ldots, p(P = z) = 0.001.$$

We can then compute

$$H_L \leq H(P) \approx 4.14.$$

Hence, instead of 4.7 bits of information per letter, if we only examine the letter frequencies we conclude that English conveys around 4.14 bits of information per letter.

But this is a gross overestimate, since letters are not independent. For example Q is always followed by U and the bigram TH is likely to be very common. One would suspect that a better statistic for the amount of entropy per letter could be obtained by looking at the distribution of bigrams. Hence, we let P^2 denote the random variable of bigrams. If we let $p(P = i, P' = j)$ denote the random variable which is assigned the probability that the bigram 'ij' appears, then we define

$$H(P^2) = -\sum_{i,j} p(P = i, P' = j) \log p(P = i, P' = j).$$

A number of people have computed values of $H(P^2)$ and it is commonly accepted to be given by

$$H(P^2) \approx 7.12.$$

We want the entropy per letter so we compute

$$H_L \leq H(P^2)/2 \approx 3.56.$$

But again this is an overestimate, since we have not taken into account that the most common trigram is *THE*. Hence, we can also look at P^3 and compute $H(P^3)/3$. This will also be an overestimate and so on...

This leads us to the following definition.

Definition 4.8 *The entropy of the natural language L is defined to be*

$$H_L = \lim_{n \to \infty} \frac{H(P^n)}{n}.$$

The exact value of H_L is hard to compute exactly but we can approximate it. In fact one has, by experiment, that for English

$$1.0 \leq H_L \leq 1.5.$$

So each letter in English

- requires 5 bits of data to represent it,

- only gives at most 1.5 bits of information.

This shows that English contains a high degree of redundancy. One can see this from the following, which you can still hopefully read (just) even though I have deleted two out of every four letters,

On** up** a t**e t**re **s a **rl **al**d S**w W**te.

The *redundancy* of a language is defined by

$$R_L = 1 - \frac{H_L}{\log_2 \#\mathbb{P}}.$$

If we take $H_L \approx 1.25$ then the redundancy of English is

$$R_L \approx 1 - \frac{1.25}{\log_2 26} = 0.75.$$

So this means that we should be able to compress an English text file of around 10 MB down to 2.5 MB.

We now return to a general cipher and suppose $c \in \mathbb{C}^n$, i.e. c is a ciphertext consisting of n characters. We define $\mathbb{K}(c)$ to be the set of keys which produce a 'meaningful' decryption of c. Then, clearly $\#\mathbb{K}(c) - 1$ is the number of spurious keys given c. The average number of spurious keys is defined to be $\overline{s}_n$, where

$$
\begin{aligned}
\overline{s}_n &= \sum_{c \in \mathbb{C}^n} p(C = c)\,(\#\mathbb{K}(c) - 1) \\
&= \sum_{c \in \mathbb{C}^n} p(C = c)\#\mathbb{K}(c) - \sum_{c \in \mathbb{C}^n} p(C = c) \\
&= \left(\sum_{c \in \mathbb{C}^n} p(C = c)\#\mathbb{K}(c) \right) - 1.
\end{aligned}
$$

Now if n is sufficiently large and $\#\mathbb{P} = \#\mathbb{C}$ we obtain

$$
\begin{aligned}
\log_2(\overline{s}_n + 1) &= \log_2 \sum_{c \in \mathbb{C}^n} p(C = c)\#\mathbb{K}(c) \\
&\geq \sum_{c \in \mathbb{C}^n} p(C = c) \log_2 \#\mathbb{K}(c) && \text{Jensen's inequality} \\
&\geq \sum_{c \in \mathbb{C}^n} p(C = c) H(K|c) \\
&= H(K|C^n) && \text{By definition} \\
&= H(K) + H(P^n) - H(C^n) && \text{Equation (4.2)} \\
&\approx H(K) + n H_L - H(C^n) && \text{If } n \text{ is very large} \\
&= H(K) - H(C^n) \\
&\qquad + n(1 - R_L) \log_2 \#\mathbb{P} && \text{By definition of } R_L \\
&\geq H(K) - n \log_2 \#\mathbb{C} \\
&\qquad + n(1 - R_L) \log_2 \#\mathbb{P} && \text{As } H(C^n) \leq n \log_2 \#\mathbb{C} \\
&= H(K) - n R_L \log_2 \#\mathbb{P} && \text{As } \#\mathbb{P} = \#\mathbb{C}.
\end{aligned}
$$

So, if n is sufficiently large and $\#\mathbb{P} = \#\mathbb{C}$ then

$$\bar{s}_n \geq \frac{\#\mathbb{K}}{\#\mathbb{P}^{n R_L}} - 1.$$

As an attacker we would like the number of spurious keys to become zero, and it is clear that as we take longer and longer ciphertexts then the number of spurious keys must go down.

The unicity distance n_0 of a cipher is the value of n for which the expected number of spurious keys becomes zero. In other words this is the average amount of ciphertext needed before an attacker can determine the key, assuming the attacker has infinite computing power. For a perfect cipher we have $n_0 = \infty$, but for other ciphers the value of n_0 can be alarmingly small. We can obtain an estimate of n_0 by setting $\bar{s}_n = 0$ in

$$\bar{s}_n \geq \frac{\#\mathbb{K}}{\#\mathbb{P}^{n R_L}} - 1$$

to obtain

$$n_0 \approx \frac{\log_2 \#\mathbb{K}}{R_L \log_2 \#\mathbb{P}}.$$

In the substitution cipher we have

$$\#\mathbb{P} = 26,$$

$$\#\mathbb{K} = 26! \approx 4 \cdot 10^{26}$$

and using our value of $R_L = 0.75$ for English we can approximate the unicity distance as

$$n_0 \approx \frac{88.4}{0.75 \times 4.7} \approx 25.$$

So we require on average only 25 ciphertext characters before we can break the substitution cipher, again assuming infinite computing power. In any case after 25 characters we expect a unique valid decryption.

Now assume we have a modern cipher which encrypts bit strings using keys of bit length l, we have

$$\#\mathbb{P} = 2,$$

$$\#\mathbb{K} = 2^l.$$

Again we assume $R_L = 0.75$, which is an underestimate since we now need to encode English into a computer communications media such as ASCII. Then the unicity distance is

$$n_0 \approx \frac{l}{0.75} = \frac{4l}{3}.$$

Now assume instead of transmitting the plain ASCII we compress it first. If we assume a perfect compression algorithm then the plaintext will have no redundancy and so $R_L \approx 0$. In which case the unicity distance is

$$n_0 \approx \frac{l}{0} = \infty.$$

So you may ask if modern ciphers encrypt plaintexts with no redundancy? The answer is no, even if one compresses the data, a modern cipher often adds some redundancy to the plaintext before encryption. The reason is that we have only considered passive attacks, i.e. an attacker has been only allowed to examine ciphertexts and from these ciphertexts the attacker's goal is to determine the key. There are other types of attack called active attacks, in these an attacker is allowed to generate plaintexts or ciphertexts of her choosing and ask the key holder to encrypt or decrypt them, the two variants being called a chosen plaintext attack and a chosen ciphertext attack respectively.

In public key systems that we shall see later, chosen plaintexts attacks cannot be stopped since anyone is allowed to encrypt anything. We would however, like to stop chosen ciphertext attacks. The current wisdom for public key algorithms is to make the cipher add some redundancy to the plaintext before it is encrypted. In that way it is hard for an attacker to produce a ciphertext which has a valid decryption. The philosophy is that it is then hard for an attacker to mount a chosen ciphertext attack, since it will be hard for an attacker to choose a valid ciphertext for a decryption query. We shall discuss this more in later chapters.

Chapter Summary

- A cryptographic system for which knowing the ciphertext reveals no more information than if you did not know the ciphertext is called a perfectly secure system.

- Perfectly secure systems exist, but they require keys as long as the message and a different key to be used with each new encryption. Hence, perfectly secure systems are not very practical.

- Information and uncertainty are essentially the same thing. An attacker really wants, given the ciphertext, to determine some information about the plaintext. The amount of uncertainty in a random variable is measured by its entropy.

- The equation $H(K|C) = H(K) + H(P) - H(C)$ allows us to estimate how much uncertainty remains about the key after one observes a single ciphertext.

- The natural redundancy of English means that a naive cipher does not need to produce a lot of ciphertext before the underlying plaintext can be discovered.

Further Reading

Our discussion of Shannon's theory has closely followed the treatment in the book by Stinson. Another possible source of information is the book by Welsh. A general introduction to information theory, including its application to coding theory is in the book by van der Lubbe.

J.C.A. van der Lubbe. *Information Theory*. Cambridge University Press, 1997.

D. Stinson. *Cryptography: Theory and Practice*. CRC Press, 1995.

D. Welsh. *Codes and Cryptography*. Oxford University Press, 1988.

Review Exercises

4.1.1   What is wrong with the encryption function, from the set of plaintexts
$\{a, b, c, d\}$ to the ciphertexts $\{w, x, y, z\}$ using the keys $\{k_1, k_2, k_3, k_4\}$
described by the following table?

	a	b	c	d
k_1	w	x	y	z
k_2	z	y	z	x
k_3	x	z	w	y
k_4	y	w	x	z

4.1.2   Is an attacker more interested in $p(C = c|P = m)$ or $p(P = m|C = c)$,
where m is a plaintext message and c is a ciphertext message? Explain
your answer.

4.1.3   What property must a cipher have for it to be called information
theoretically secure?

4.1.4   What is the formal definition of entropy for a random variable X with
probability distribution $p_i = p(X = x_i)$?

4.1.5   If a random variable X takes at most t values, what are the maximum
and minimum values possible for $H(X)$?

4.1.6   Which of the following holds for all ciphers and why, or why not?

a) $H(P|K, C) = 0$.
b) $H(K, P) = H(K) + H(P)$.

4.1.7   Define the terms spurious keys and unicity distance.

4.1.8   Given two ciphers C_1 and C_2 with unicity distances n_1 and n_2, with
$n_1 > n_2$, which cipher would you prefer to use?

Programming Exercises

4.2.1   Write a program to compute the value of $H(P^n)$ for various values of
n for a piece of input text. Use your program to estimate the entropy
H_L and redundancy R_L of English text.

Standard Exercises

The first four questions are about the following baby encryption function:

Suppose an encryption function is given by the following table, where the function
is from the set of plaintexts $\{a, b, c, d\}$ to the ciphertexts $\{w, x, y, z\}$ using the keys
$\{k_1, k_2, k_3, k_4\}$:

	a	b	c	d
k_1	w	x	y	z
k_2	x	z	w	y
k_3	z	w	x	y
k_4	y	w	z	x

Assume that all plaintexts and all keys are equiprobable.

4.3.1   Compute the probabilities $p(C = w)$, $p(C = x)$, $p(C = y)$ and $p(C = z)$.

4.3.2   Compute the conditional probabilities $p(P = m | C = c)$ for all plaintexts m and all ciphertexts c.

4.3.3   Argue from the above conditional probabilities whether the above encryption function is good or not.

4.3.4   Compute the entropies $H(K), H(P), H(C)$ and $H(K|C)$. Does this support your prior reasoning?

4.3.5   **Essay:** Discuss the historical ciphers from Chapter 3 in the context of the techniques you have learned in this chapter. Compute an approximation to the unicity distance for the Caesar, Vigenère and Substitution ciphers and directly relate this to the ease of breaking the underlying cipher.

4.3.6   Prove Jensen's inequality.

4.3.7   Prove that the inequality

$$H(X, Y) \leq H(X) + H(Y)$$

holds for any random variables X and Y. In addition show that we obtain equality if and only if X and Y are independent.

4.3.8   Show that for two random variables X and Y,

$$H(X, Y) = H(Y) + H(X|Y).$$

4.3.9   Prove the following upper bound

$$H(X|Y) \leq H(X).$$

Show that equality holds if and only if X and Y are independent.

4.3.10   Show that a cipher which is perfectly secure for one probability distribution of the underlying plaintext will be secure for all possible probability distributions.

4.3.11   Show that for a system which has perfect secrecy and $\#\mathbb{P} = \#\mathbb{K} = \#\mathbb{C}$, every ciphertext is equally probable.

4.3.12   Let X and Y denote the values obtained by rolling two individual dice. Let $Z = X + Y$ denote the sum of the two values obtained. Show that

$$H(Z) < H(X, Y).$$

4.3.13   All vowels and spaces have been removed from the following sentence,

whtwldylkfrlnchtdy.

Recover the original sentence.

Symmetric Ciphers

Chapter Goals

- To understand the basic principles of modern symmetric ciphers.
- To understand the workings of the DES algorithm.
- To understand the workings of the Rijndael algorithm.
- To learn about the various standard modes of operation of block ciphers.
- To sketch the area of stream ciphers and linear feedback shift registers (LFSRs).

5.1 INTRODUCTION

A symmetric cipher works using the following two transformations

$$c = e_k(m),$$
$$m = d_k(c)$$

where

- m is the plaintext,
- e is the encryption function,
- d is the decryption function,
- k is the secret key,
- c is the ciphertext.

It should be noted that it is desirable that both the encryption and decryption functions are public knowledge and that the secrecy of the message, given the ciphertext, depends totally on the secrecy of the secret key, k. Although this a well-established principle has been known since the mid-1800s, called Kerchhoff's principle, many companies still ignore it. There are many instances of companies deploying secret proprietary encryption schemes which turn out to be insecure as soon as someone leaks the details of the algorithms. The best schemes will be the ones which have been studied by a lot of people for a very long time and which have been found to remain secure. A scheme which is a commercial secret cannot be studied by anyone outside the company.

The above setup is called a symmetric key system since both parties need access to the secret key. Sometimes symmetric key cryptography is implemented using two keys, one for encryption and one for decryption. However, if this is the case we assume that given the encryption key it is easy to compute the decryption key (and vice versa).

Later we shall meet public key cryptography where only one key is kept secret, called the private key, the other key, called the public key is allowed to be published in the clear. In this situation it is assumed to be computationally infeasible for someone to compute the private key given the public key.

Returning to symmetric cryptography, a moment's thought reveals that the number of possible keys must be very large. This is because in designing a cipher we assume the worst case scenario and give the attacker the benefit of

- full knowledge of the encryption/decryption algorithm,

- a number of plaintext/ciphertext pairs associated to the target key k.

If the number of possible keys is small then an attacker can break the system using an exhaustive search. The attacker encrypts one of the given plaintexts under all possible keys and determines which key produces the given ciphertext. Hence, the key space needs to be large enough to avoid such an attack. It is commonly assumed that a computation taking 2^{80} steps will be infeasible for a number of years to come, hence the key space size should be at least 80 bits to avoid exhaustive search.

The cipher designer must play two roles, that of someone trying to break as well as create a cipher. These days, although there is a lot of theory behind the design of many ciphers, we still rely on symmetric ciphers which are just believed to be strong, rather than ones for which we know a reason why they are strong. All this means is that the best attempts of the most experienced cryptanalysts cannot break them. This should be compared with public key ciphers, where there is now a theory which allows us to reason about how strong a given cipher is (given some explicit computational assumption).

5.1.1 A Simple Model

Fig. 5.1 describes a simple model for enciphering bits, which although simple is quite suited to practical implementations. The idea of this model is to apply a reversible operation to the plaintext to produce the ciphertext, namely combining the plaintext with a 'random stream'. The recipient can recreate the original plaintext by applying the inverse operation, in this case by combining the ciphertext with the same random stream.

This is particularly efficient since we can use the simplest operation available on a computer, namely exclusive-or $\oplus$. We saw in Chapter 4 that if the key is different for every message and the key is as long as the message, then such a system can be shown to be perfectly secure, namely we have the one-time pad. However, the one-time pad is not practical in many situations.

Fig. 5.1 Simple model for enciphering bits

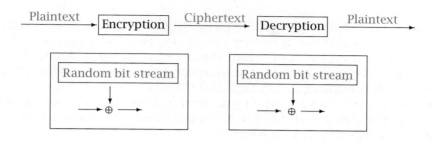

- We would like to use a short key to encrypt a long message.

- We would like to reuse keys.

Modern symmetric ciphers allow both of these properties, but this is at the expense of losing our perfect secrecy property. The reason for doing this is because using a one-time pad produces horrendous key distribution problems. We shall see that even using reusable short keys also produces bad (but not as bad) key distribution problems.

There are a number of ways to attack a bulk cipher, some of which we outline below. We divide our discussion into passive and active attacks; a passive attack is generally easier to mount than an active attack.

- **Passive Attacks:** Here the adversary is only allowed to listen to encrypted messages. Then he attempts to break the cryptosystem by either recovering the key or determining some secret that the communicating parties did not want leaked. One common form of passive attack is that of traffic analysis, a technique borrowed from the army in World War I, where a sudden increase in radio traffic at a certain point on the Western Front would signal an imminent offensive.

- **Active Attacks:** Here the adversary is allowed to insert, delete or replay messages between the two communicating parties. A general requirement is that an undetected insertion attack should require the breaking of the cipher, whilst the cipher needs to allow detection and recovery from deletion or replay attacks.

Bulk symmetric ciphers essentially come in two variants: stream ciphers, which operate on one data item (bit/letter) at a time, and block ciphers, which operate on data in blocks of items (e.g. 64 bits) at a time.

5.1.2 Stream Ciphers

Fig. 5.2 gives a simple explanation of a stream cipher. Notice how this is very similar to our previous simple model. However, the random bit stream is now produced from a short secret key using a public algorithm, called the keystream generator.

Thus we have $c_i = m_i \oplus k_i$ where

Fig. 5.2 Stream ciphers

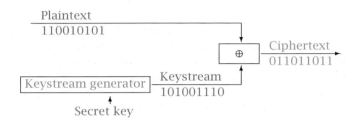

- $m_0, m_1, \ldots$ are the plaintext bits,

- $k_0, k_1, \ldots$ are the keystream bits,

- $c_0, c_1, \ldots$ are the ciphertext bits.

This means

$$m_i = c_i \oplus k_i$$

i.e. decryption is the same operation as encryption.

Stream ciphers such as that described above are simple and fast to implement. They allow very fast encryption of large amounts of data, so they are suited to real-time audio and video signals. In addition there is no error propagation, if a single bit of ciphertext gets mangled during transit (due to an attacker or a poor radio signal) then only one bit of the decrypted plaintext will be affected.

However, the same key used twice gives the same keystream, which can reveal relationships between messages. For example suppose m_1 and m_2 were encrypted under the same key k, then an adversary could work out the exclusive-or of the two plaintexts without knowing what the plaintexts were

$$c_1 \oplus c_2 = (m_1 \oplus k) \oplus (m_2 \oplus k) = m_1 \oplus m_2.$$

Hence, there is a need to change keys frequently either on a per message or on a per session basis. This results in difficult key management and distribution techniques, which we shall see later how to solve using public key cryptography. Usually public key cryptography is used to determine session or message keys, and then the actual data is rapidly encrypted using either a stream or block cipher.

The keystream generator above needs to produce a keystream with a number of properties for the stream cipher to be considered secure. As a bare minimum the keystream should

- Have a long period. Since the keystream k_i is produced via a deterministic process from the key there will exist a number N such that

$$k_i = k_{i+N}$$

for all values of i. This number N is called the period of the sequence, and should be large for the keystream generator to be considered secure.

- Have pseudo-random properties. The generator should produce a sequence which appears to be random, in other words it should pass a number of statistical random number tests.

- Have large linear complexity. See later in this chapter for what this means.

However, these conditions are not sufficient. Generally determining more of the sequence from a part should be computationally infeasible. Ideally, even if one knows the first one billion bits of the keystream sequence, the probability of guessing the next bit correctly should be no better than one half.

In Section 5.6 we shall discuss how stream ciphers are created using a combination of simple circuits called Linear Feedback Shift Registers.

5.1.3 Block Ciphers

Fig. 5.3 describes how a block cipher works. Block ciphers operate on blocks of plain-

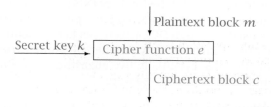

Fig. 5.3 Operation of a block cipher

text one at a time to produce blocks of ciphertext. The main difference between a block cipher and a stream cipher is that block ciphers are stateless, whilst stream ciphers maintain an internal state which is needed to determine which part of the keystream should be generated next. We write

$$c = e_k(m),$$
$$m = d_k(c)$$

where

- m is the plaintext block,

- k is the secret key,

- e is the encryption function,

- d is the decryption function,

- c is the ciphertext block.

The block sizes taken are usually reasonably large, 64 bits in DES and 128 bits or more in modern block ciphers. Often the output of the ciphertext produced by encrypting the first block is used to help encrypt the second block in what is called a *mode of operation*. These modes are used to avoid certain attacks based on deletion or insertion by giving each ciphertext block a context within the overall message. Each mode of operation offers different protection against error propagation due to transmission errors in the ciphertext. In addition, depending on the mode of operation (and the application) message/session keys may be needed. For example, many modes require a per message initial value to be input into the encryption and decryption operations. Later in this chapter we shall discuss modes of operation of block ciphers in more detail.

There are many block ciphers in use today, some which you may find used in your web browser are RC5, RC6, DES or 3DES. The most famous of these is DES, or the Data Encryption Standard. This was first published in the mid-1970s as a US Federal standard and soon become the de-facto international standard for banking applications.

The DES algorithm has stood up remarkably well to the test of time, but in the early 1990s it became clear that a new standard was required. This was because both the block length (64 bits) and the key length (56 bits) of basic DES were too small for future applications. It is now possible to recover a 56-bit DES key using either a network of computers or specialized hardware. In response to this problem the US National Institute for Standards and Technology (NIST) initiated a competition to find a new block cipher, to be called the Advanced Encryption Standard or AES.

Unlike the process used to design DES, which was kept essentially secret, the design of the AES was performed in public. A number of groups from around the world submitted designs for the AES. Eventually five algorithms, known as the AES finalists, were chosen to be studied in depth. These were

- MARS from a group at IBM,

- RC6 from a group at RSA Security,

- Twofish from a group based at Counterpane, UC Berkeley and elsewhere,

- Serpent from a group of three academics based in Israel, Norway and the UK,

- Rijndael from a couple of Belgian cryptographers.

Finally in the fall of 2000, NIST announced that the overall AES winner had been chosen to be Rijndael.

DES and all the AES finalists are examples of *iterated* block ciphers. The block ciphers obtain their security by repeated use of a simple *round function*. The round function takes an n-bit block and returns an n-bit block, where n is the block size of the overall cipher. The number of rounds r can either be a variable or fixed. As a general rule increasing the number of rounds will increase the level of security of the block cipher.

Each use of the round function employs a round key

$$k_i \text{ for } 1 \le i \le r$$

derived from the main secret key k, using an algorithm called a *key schedule*. To allow decryption, for every round key the function implementing the round must be invertible, and for decryption the round keys are used in the opposite order that they were used for encryption. That the whole round is invertible does not imply that the functions used to implement the round need to be invertible. This may seem strange at first reading but will become clearer when we discuss the DES cipher later. In DES the functions needed to implement the round function are not invertible, but the whole round is invertible. For Rijndael not only is the whole round function invertible but every function used to create the round function is also invertible.

There are a number of general purpose techniques which can be used to break a block cipher, for example: exhaustive search, using pre-computed tables of intermediate values or divide and conquer. Some (badly designed) block ciphers can be susceptible to chosen plaintext attacks, where encrypting a specially chosen plaintext can reveal properties of the underlying secret key. In cryptanalysis one needs a combination of mathematical and puzzle-solving skills, plus luck. There are a few more advanced techniques which can be employed, some of which apply in general to any cipher (and not just a block cipher).

- **Differential Cryptanalysis:** In differential cryptanalysis one looks at ciphertext pairs, where the plaintext has a particular difference. The exclusive-or of such pairs is called a differential and certain differentials have certain probabilities associated to them, depending on what the key is. By analysing the probabilities of the differentials computed in a chosen plaintext attack one can hope to reveal the underlying structure of the key.

- **Linear Cryptanalysis:** Even though a good block cipher should contain non-linear components the idea behind linear cryptanalysis is to approximate the behaviour of the non-linear components with linear functions. Again the goal is to use a probabilistic analysis to determine information about the key.

Surprisingly these two methods are quite successful against some ciphers. But they do not appear that successful against DES or Rijndael, two of the most important block ciphers in use today.

Since DES and Rijndael are likely to be the most important block ciphers in use for the next few years we shall study them in some detail. This is also important since they both show general design principles in their use of substitutions and permutations. Recall that the historical ciphers made use of such operations, so we see that not much has changed. Now, however, the substitutions and permutations used are far more intricate. On their own they do not produce security, but when used over a number of rounds one can obtain enough security for our applications.

We end this section by discussing which is best, a block cipher or a stream cipher? Alas there is no correct answer to this question. Both have their uses and different properties. Here are just a few general points.

- Block ciphers are more general, and we shall see that one can easily turn a block cipher into a stream cipher.

- Stream ciphers generally have a more mathematical structure. This either makes them easier to break or easier to study to convince oneself that they are secure.

- Stream ciphers are generally not suitable for software, since they usually encrypt one bit at a time. However, stream ciphers are highly efficient in hardware.

- Block ciphers are suitable for both hardware and software, but are not as fast in hardware as stream ciphers.

- Hardware is always faster than software, but this performance improvement comes at the cost of less flexibility.

5.2 FEISTEL CIPHERS AND DES

The DES cipher is a variant of the basic Feistel cipher described in Fig. 5.4, named after H. Feistel who worked at IBM and performed some of the earliest non-military research on encryption algorithms. The interesting property of a Feistel cipher is that the round function is invertible regardless of the choice of the function in the box marked F. To see this notice that each encryption round is given by

$$L_i = R_{i-1},$$
$$R_i = L_{i-1} \oplus F(K_i, R_{i-1}).$$

Hence, the decryption can be performed via

$$R_{i-1} = L_i,$$
$$L_{i-1} = R_i \oplus F(K_i, L_i).$$

Fig. 5.4 Basic operation of a Feistel cipher

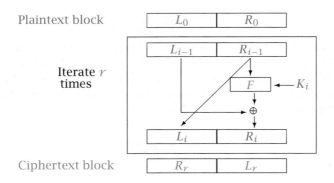

This means that in a Feistel cipher we have simplified the design somewhat, since

- we can choose any function for the function F, and we will still obtain an encryption function which can be inverted using the secret key,

- the same code/circuitry can be used for the encryption and decryption functions. We only need to use the round keys in the reverse order for decryption.

Of course to obtain a secure cipher we still need to take care with

- how the round keys are generated,

- how many rounds to take,

- how the function F is defined.

Work on DES was started in the early 1970s by a team in IBM which included Feistel. It was originally based on an earlier cipher of IBM's called Lucifer, but some of the design was known to have been amended by the National Security Agency, NSA. For many years this led the conspiracy theorists to believe that the NSA had placed a trapdoor into the design of the function F. However, it is now widely accepted that the modifications made by the NSA were done to make the cipher more secure. In particular, the changes made by the NSA made the cipher resistant to differential cryptanalysis, a technique that was not discovered in the open research community until the 1980s.

DES is also known as the Data Encryption Algorithm DEA in documents produced by the American National Standards Institute, ANSI. The International Standards Organisation ISO refers to DES by the name DEA-1. It has been a world-wide standard for well over twenty years and stands as the first publicly available algorithm to have an 'official status'. It therefore marks an important step on the road from cryptography being a purely military area to being a tool for the masses.

The basic properties of the DES cipher are that it is a variant of the Feistel cipher design with

- the number of rounds r is 16,

- the block length n is 64 bits,

- the key length is 56 bits,

- the round keys $K_1, \ldots, K_{16}$ are each 48 bits.

Note that a key length of 56 bits is insufficient for many modern applications, hence often one uses DES by using three keys and three iterations of the main cipher. Such a version is called Triple DES or 3DES, see Fig. 5.5. In 3DES the key length is equal to 168. There is another way of using DES three times, but using two keys instead of three giving rise to a key length of 112, see the exercises for further details.

Fig. 5.5 Triple DES

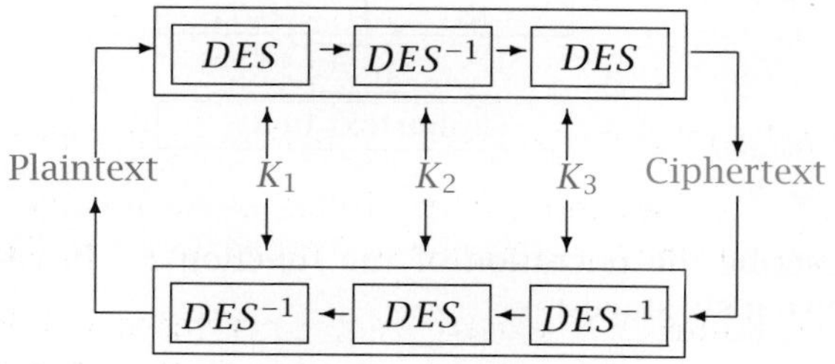

5.2.1 Overview of DES Operation

Basically DES is a Feistel cipher with 16 rounds, as depicted in Fig. 5.6, except that before and after the main Feistel iteration a permutation is performed. Notice how the two blocks are swapped around before being passed through the final inverse permutation. This permutation appears to produce no change to the security, and people have often wondered why it is there. One answer given by one of the original team members was that this permutation was there to make the original implementation easier to fit on the circuit board.

In summary the DES cipher operates on 64 bits of plaintext in the following manner:

- Perform an initial permutation.

- Split the blocks into left and right half.

- Perform 16 rounds of identical operations.

- Join the half blocks back together.

- Perform a final permutation.

The final permutation is the inverse of the initial permutation, this allows the same hardware/software to be used for encryption and decryption. The key schedule provides 16 round keys of 48 bits in length by selecting 48 bits from the 56-bit main key.

Fig. 5.6 DES as a Feistel cipher

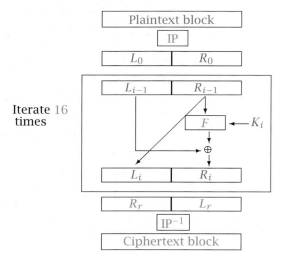

We shall now describe the operation of the function F. In each DES round this consists of the following six stages:

- **Expansion Permutation:** The right half of 32 bits is expanded and permuted to 48 bits. This helps the diffusion of any relationship of input bits to output bits. The expansion permutation (which is different from the initial permutation) has been chosen so that one bit of input affects two substitutions in the output, via the S-Boxes below. This helps spread dependencies and creates an avalanche effect (a small difference between two plaintexts will produce a very large difference in the corresponding ciphertexts).

- **Round Key Addition:** The 48-bit output from the expansion permutation is XORed with the round key, which is also 48 bits in length. Note, this is the only place where the round key is used in the algorithm.

- **Splitting:** The resulting 48-bit value is split into eight lots of six-bit values.

- **S-Box:** Each six-bit value is passed into one of eight different S-Boxes (Substitution Box) to produce a four-bit result. The S-Boxes represent the non-linear component in the DES algorithm and their design is a major contributor to the algorithms security. Each S-Box is a look-up table of four rows and sixteen columns. The six input bits specify which row and column to use. Bits 1 and 6 generate the row number, whilst bits $2, 3, 4$ and 5 specify the column number. The output of each S-Box is the value held in that element in the table.

- **P-Box:** We now have eight lots of four-bit outputs which are then combined into a 32-bit value and permuted to form the output of the function F.

The overall structure of DES is explained in Fig. 5.7.

Fig. 5.7 Structure of the DES function F

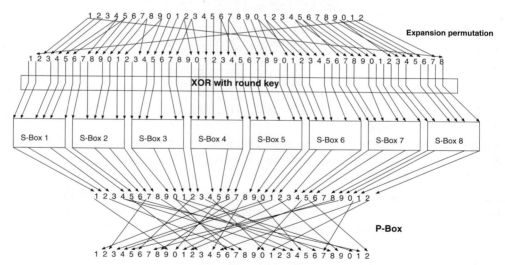

We now give details of each of the steps which we have not yet fully defined.

5.2.1.1 Initial Permutation, IP: The DES initial permutation is defined in the following table. Here the 58 in the first position means that the first bit of the output from the IP is the 58th bit of the input, and so on.

58	50	42	34	26	18	10	2
60	52	44	36	28	20	12	4
62	54	46	38	30	22	14	6
64	56	48	40	32	24	16	8
57	49	41	33	25	17	9	1
59	51	43	35	27	19	11	3
61	53	45	37	29	21	13	5
63	55	47	39	31	23	15	7

The inverse permutation is given in a similar manner by the following table.

40	8	48	16	56	24	64	32
39	7	47	15	55	23	63	31
38	6	46	14	54	22	62	30
37	5	45	13	53	21	61	29
36	4	44	12	52	20	60	28
35	3	43	11	51	19	59	27
34	2	42	10	50	18	58	26
33	1	41	9	49	17	57	25

5.2.1.2 Expansion Permutation, E: The expansion permutation is given in the following table. Each row corresponds to the bits which are input into the corresponding S-Box at the next stage. Notice how the bits which select a row of one S-Box (the first and last bit on each row) are also used to select the column of another S-Box.

32	1	2	3	4	5
4	5	6	7	8	9
8	9	10	11	12	13
12	13	14	15	16	17
16	17	18	19	20	21
20	21	22	23	24	25
24	25	26	27	28	29
28	29	30	31	32	1

5.2.1.3 S-Box: The details of the eight DES S-Boxes are given in the Fig. 5.8. Recall that each box consists of a table with four rows and sixteen columns.

5.2.1.4 The P-Box Permutation, P: The P-Box permutation takes the eight lots of four-bit nibbles, output of the S-Boxes, and produces a 32-bit permutation of these values as given by the following table.

16	7	20	21
29	12	28	17
1	15	23	26
5	18	31	10
2	8	24	14
32	27	3	9
19	13	30	6
22	11	4	25

Fig. 5.8 DES S-Boxes

S-Box 1

14	4	13	1	2	15	11	8	3	10	6	12	5	9	0	7
0	15	7	4	14	2	13	1	10	6	12	11	9	5	3	8
4	1	14	8	13	6	2	11	15	12	9	7	3	10	5	0
15	12	8	2	4	9	1	7	5	11	3	14	10	0	6	13

S-Box 2

15	1	8	14	6	11	3	4	9	7	2	13	12	0	5	10
3	13	4	7	15	2	8	14	12	0	1	10	6	9	11	5
0	14	7	11	10	4	13	1	5	8	12	6	9	3	2	15
13	8	10	1	3	15	4	2	11	6	7	12	0	5	14	9

S-Box 3

10	0	9	14	6	3	15	5	1	13	12	7	11	4	2	8
13	7	0	9	3	4	6	10	2	8	5	14	12	11	15	1
13	6	4	9	8	15	3	0	11	1	2	12	5	10	14	7
1	10	13	0	6	9	8	7	4	15	14	3	11	5	2	12

S-Box 4

7	13	14	3	0	6	9	10	1	2	8	5	11	12	4	15
13	8	11	5	6	15	0	3	4	7	2	12	1	10	14	9
10	6	9	0	12	11	7	13	15	1	3	14	5	2	8	4
3	15	0	6	10	1	13	8	9	4	5	11	12	7	2	14

S-Box 5

2	12	4	1	7	10	11	6	8	5	3	15	13	0	14	9
14	11	2	12	4	7	13	1	5	0	15	10	3	9	8	6
4	2	1	11	10	13	7	8	15	9	12	5	6	3	0	14
11	8	12	7	1	14	2	13	6	15	0	9	10	4	5	3

S-Box 6

12	1	10	15	9	2	6	8	0	13	3	4	14	7	5	11
10	15	4	2	7	12	9	5	6	1	13	14	0	11	3	8
9	14	15	5	2	8	12	3	7	0	4	10	1	13	11	6
4	3	2	12	9	5	15	10	11	14	1	7	6	0	8	13

S-Box 7

4	11	2	14	15	0	8	13	3	12	9	7	5	10	6	1
13	0	11	7	4	9	1	10	14	3	5	12	2	15	8	6
1	4	11	13	12	3	7	14	10	15	6	8	0	5	9	2
6	11	13	8	1	4	10	7	9	5	0	15	14	2	3	12

S-Box 8

13	2	8	4	6	15	11	1	10	9	3	14	5	0	12	7
1	15	13	8	10	3	7	4	12	5	6	11	0	14	9	2
7	11	4	1	9	12	14	2	0	6	10	13	15	3	5	8
2	1	14	7	4	10	8	13	15	12	9	0	3	5	6	11

5.2.2 DES Key Schedule

The DES key schedule takes the 56-bit key, which is actually input as a bitstring of 64 bits comprising of the key and eight parity bits, for error detection. These parity bits are in bit positions $8, 16, \ldots, 64$ and ensure that each byte of the key contains an odd number of bits.

We first permute the bits of the key according to the following permutation (which takes a 64-bit input and produces a 56-bit output, hence discarding the parity bits).

$$
\begin{array}{ccccccc}
57 & 49 & 41 & 33 & 25 & 17 & 9 \\
1 & 58 & 50 & 42 & 34 & 26 & 18 \\
10 & 2 & 59 & 51 & 43 & 35 & 27 \\
19 & 11 & 3 & 60 & 52 & 44 & 36 \\
63 & 55 & 47 & 39 & 31 & 23 & 15 \\
7 & 62 & 54 & 46 & 38 & 30 & 22 \\
14 & 6 & 61 & 53 & 45 & 37 & 29 \\
21 & 13 & 5 & 28 & 20 & 12 & 4
\end{array}
$$

The output of this permutation, called PC-1 in the literature, is divided into a 28-bit left half C_0 and a 28-bit right half D_0. Now for each round we compute

$$
C_i = C_{i-1} \lll p_i,
$$
$$
D_i = D_{i-1} \lll p_i,
$$

where $x \lll p_i$ means perform a cyclic shift on x to the left by p_i positions. If the round number i is $1, 2, 9$ or 16 then we shift left by one position, otherwise we shift left by two positions.

Finally the two portions C_i and D_i are joined back together and are subject to another permutation, called PC-2, to produce the final 48-bit round key. The permutation PC-2 is described below.

$$
\begin{array}{cccccc}
14 & 17 & 11 & 24 & 1 & 5 \\
3 & 28 & 15 & 6 & 21 & 10 \\
23 & 19 & 12 & 4 & 26 & 8 \\
16 & 7 & 27 & 20 & 13 & 2 \\
41 & 52 & 31 & 37 & 47 & 55 \\
30 & 40 & 51 & 45 & 33 & 48 \\
44 & 49 & 39 & 56 & 34 & 53 \\
46 & 42 & 50 & 36 & 29 & 32
\end{array}
$$

5.3 RIJNDAEL

The AES winner was decided in fall 2000 to be the Rijndael algorithm designed by Daemen and Rijmen. Rijndael is a block cipher which does not rely on the basic design of the Feistel cipher. However, Rijndael does have a number of similarities with DES. It uses a repeated number of rounds to obtain security and each round consists of substitutions and permutations, plus a key addition phase. Rijndael in addition has a strong mathematical structure, as most of its operations are based on arithmetic in the field $\mathbb{F}_{2^8}$. However, unlike DES the encryption and decryption operations are distinct.

Recall that elements of $\mathbb{F}_{2^8}$ are stored as bit vectors (or bytes) representing binary polynomials. For example the byte given by $0x83$ in hexadecimal, gives the bit pattern

$$1, 0, 0, 0, 0, 0, 1, 1$$

since

$$0x83 = 8 \cdot 16 + 3 = 131$$

in decimal. One can obtain the bit pattern directly by noticing that 8 in binary is $1, 0, 0, 0$ and 3 in 4-bit binary is $0, 0, 1, 1$ and one simply concatenates these two bit strings together. The bit pattern itself then corresponds to the binary polynomial

$$x^7 + x + 1.$$

So we say that the hexadecimal number $0x83$ represents the binary polynomial

$$x^7 + x + 1.$$

Arithmetic in $\mathbb{F}_{2^8}$ is performed using polynomial arithmetic modulo the irreducible polynomial

$$m(x) = x^8 + x^4 + x^3 + x + 1.$$

Rijndael identifies 32-bit words with polynomials in $\mathbb{F}_{2^8}[X]$ of degree three. This is done in a big-endian format, in that the smallest index corresponds to the least important coefficient. Hence, the word

$$a_0 \| a_1 \| a_2 \| a_3$$

will correspond to the polynomial

$$a_3 X^3 + a_2 X^2 + a_1 X + a_0.$$

Arithmetic is performed on polynomials in $\mathbb{F}_{2^8}[X]$ modulo the reducible polynomial

$$M(X) = X^4 + 1.$$

Hence, arithmetic is done on these polynomials in a ring rather than a field, since $M(X)$ is reducible.

Rijndael is a parametrized algorithm in that it can operate on block sizes of 128, 192 or 256 bits, it can also accept keys of size 128, 192 or 256 bits. For each combination of block and key size a different number of rounds is specified. To make our discussion simpler we shall consider the simpler, and probably more used, variant which uses a block size of 128 bits and a key size of 128 bits, in which case 10 rounds are specified. From now on our discussion is only of this simpler version.

Rijndael operates on an internal four-by-four matrix of bytes, called the state matrix

$$S = \begin{pmatrix} s_{0,0} & s_{0,1} & s_{0,2} & s_{0,3} \\ s_{1,0} & s_{1,1} & s_{1,2} & s_{1,3} \\ s_{2,0} & s_{2,1} & s_{2,2} & s_{2,3} \\ s_{3,0} & s_{3,1} & s_{3,2} & s_{3,3} \end{pmatrix},$$

which is usually held as a vector of four 32-bit words, each word representing a column. Each round key is also held as a four-by-four matrix

$$K_i = \begin{pmatrix} k_{0,0} & k_{0,1} & k_{0,2} & k_{0,3} \\ k_{1,0} & k_{1,1} & k_{1,2} & k_{1,3} \\ k_{2,0} & k_{2,1} & k_{2,2} & k_{2,3} \\ k_{3,0} & k_{3,1} & k_{3,2} & k_{3,3} \end{pmatrix}.$$

5.3.1 Rijndael Operations

The Rijndael round function operates using a set of four operations which we shall first describe.

5.3.1.1 SubBytes: There are two types of S-Boxes used in Rijndael: One for the encryption rounds and one for the decryption rounds, each one being the inverse of the other. We shall describe the encryption S-Box, the decryption one will follow immediately. The S-Boxes of DES were chosen by searching through a large space of possible S-Boxes, so as to avoid attacks such as differential cryptanalysis. The S-Box of Rijndael is chosen to have a simple mathematical structure, which allows one to formally argue how resilient the cipher is from differential and linear cryptanalysis. Not only does this mathematical structure help protect against differential cryptanalysis, but it also convinces users that it has not been engineered with some hidden trapdoor.

Each byte $s = [s_7, \ldots, s_0]$ of the Rijndael state matrix is taken in turn and considered as an element of $\mathbb{F}_{2^8}$. The S-Box can be mathematically described in two steps:

1. The multiplicative inverse in $\mathbb{F}_{2^8}$ of s is computed to produce a new byte $x = [x_7, \ldots, x_0]$. For the element $[0, \ldots, 0]$ which has no multiplicative inverse one uses the convention that this is mapped to zero.

2. The bit-vector x is then mapped, via the following affine $\mathbb{F}_2$ transformation, to the bit-vector y:

$$
\begin{pmatrix} y_0 \\ y_1 \\ y_2 \\ y_3 \\ y_4 \\ y_5 \\ y_6 \\ y_7 \end{pmatrix} = \begin{pmatrix} 1 & 0 & 0 & 0 & 1 & 1 & 1 & 1 \\ 1 & 1 & 0 & 0 & 0 & 1 & 1 & 1 \\ 1 & 1 & 1 & 0 & 0 & 0 & 1 & 1 \\ 1 & 1 & 1 & 1 & 0 & 0 & 0 & 1 \\ 1 & 1 & 1 & 1 & 1 & 0 & 0 & 0 \\ 0 & 1 & 1 & 1 & 1 & 1 & 0 & 0 \\ 0 & 0 & 1 & 1 & 1 & 1 & 1 & 0 \\ 0 & 0 & 0 & 1 & 1 & 1 & 1 & 1 \end{pmatrix} \cdot \begin{pmatrix} x_0 \\ x_1 \\ x_2 \\ x_3 \\ x_4 \\ x_5 \\ x_6 \\ x_7 \end{pmatrix}.
$$

The new byte is given by y. The decryption S-Box is obtained by first inverting the affine transformation and then taking the multiplicative inverse. These byte substitutions can either be implemented using table look-up or by implementing circuits, or code, which implement the inverse operation in $\mathbb{F}_{2^8}$ and the affine transformation.

5.3.1.2 ShiftRows: The ShiftRows operation in Rijndael performs a cyclic shift on the state matrix. Each row is shifted by different offsets. For the version of Rijndael we are considering this is given by

$$
\begin{pmatrix} s_{0,0} & s_{0,1} & s_{0,2} & s_{0,3} \\ s_{1,0} & s_{1,1} & s_{1,2} & s_{1,3} \\ s_{2,0} & s_{2,1} & s_{2,2} & s_{2,3} \\ s_{3,0} & s_{3,1} & s_{3,2} & s_{3,3} \end{pmatrix} \longmapsto \begin{pmatrix} s_{0,0} & s_{0,1} & s_{0,2} & s_{0,3} \\ s_{1,1} & s_{1,2} & s_{1,3} & s_{1,0} \\ s_{2,2} & s_{2,3} & s_{2,0} & s_{2,1} \\ s_{3,3} & s_{3,0} & s_{3,1} & s_{3,2} \end{pmatrix}.
$$

The inverse of the ShiftRows operation is simply a similar shift but in the opposite direction. The ShiftRows operation ensures that the columns of the state matrix 'interact' with each other over a number of rounds.

5.3.1.3 MixColumns: The MixColumns operation ensures that the rows in the state matrix 'interact' with each other over a number of rounds; combined with the ShiftRows operation it ensures each byte of the output state depends on each byte of the input state.

We consider each column of the state in turn and consider it as a polynomial of degree 3 with coefficients in $\mathbb{F}_{2^8}$. The new column $[b_0, b_1, b_2, b_3]$ is produced by taking this polynomial

$$a(X) = a_0 + a_1 X + a_2 X^2 + a_3 X^3$$

and multiplying it by the polynomial

$$c(X) = 0x02 + 0x01 \cdot X + 0x01 \cdot X^2 + 0x03 \cdot X^3$$

modulo

$$M(X) = X^4 + 1.$$

This operation is conveniently represented by the following matrix operation in $\mathbb{F}_{2^8}$,

$$\begin{pmatrix} b_0 \\ b_1 \\ b_2 \\ b_3 \end{pmatrix} = \begin{pmatrix} 0x02 & 0x03 & 0x01 & 0x01 \\ 0x01 & 0x02 & 0x03 & 0x01 \\ 0x01 & 0x01 & 0x02 & 0x03 \\ 0x03 & 0x01 & 0x01 & 0x02 \end{pmatrix} \cdot \begin{pmatrix} a_0 \\ a_1 \\ a_2 \\ a_3 \end{pmatrix}.$$

In $\mathbb{F}_{2^8}$ the above matrix is invertible, hence the inverse of the MixColumns operation can also be implemented using a matrix multiplication such as that above.

5.3.1.4 AddRoundKey: The round key addition is particularly simple. One takes the state matrix and XORs it, byte by byte, with the round key matrix. The inverse of this operation is clearly the same operation.

5.3.2 Round Structure

The Rijndael algorithm can now be described using the following pseudo-code:

```
AddRoundKey(S,K[0]);
for (i=1; i<=9; i++)
   { SubBytes(S);
     ShiftRows(S);
     MixColumns(S);
     AddRoundKey(S,K[i]);
   }
SubBytes(S);
ShiftRows(S);
AddRoundKey(S,K[10])
```

The message block to encrypt is assumed to be entered into the state matrix S, the output encrypted block is also given by the state matrix S. Notice that the final round does not perform a MixColumns operation. The decryption operation is described by the following pseudo-code:

```
AddRoundKey(S,K[10]);
InverseShiftRows(S);
InverseSubBytes(S);
for (i=9; i>=1; i--)
  { AddRoundKey(S,K[i]);
    InverseMixColumns(S);
    InverseShiftRows(S);
    InverseSubBytes(S);
  }
AddRoundKey(S,K[0]);
```

5.3.3 Key Schedule

The only thing left to describe is how Rijndael computes the round keys from the main key. Recall that the main key is 128 bits long, and we need to produce 11 round keys $K_0, \ldots, K_{11}$ all of which consist of four 32-bit words. Each word corresponding to a column of a matrix as described above. The key schedule makes use of a round constant which we shall denote by

$$RC_i = x^i \pmod{x^8 + x^4 + x^3 + x + 1}.$$

We label the round keys as $(W_{4i}, W_{4i+1}, W_{4i+2}, W_{4i+3})$ where i is the round. The initial main key is first divided into four 32-bit words (k_0, k_1, k_2, k_3). The round keys are then computed via the following algorithm, where RotBytes is the function which rotates a word to the left by a single byte, and SubBytes applies the Rijndael encryption S-Box to every byte in a word.

```
W[0]=K[0]; W[1]=K[1]; W[2]=K[2]; W[3]=K[3];
for (i=1; i<=10; i++)
  { T=RotBytes(W[4*i-1]);
    T=SubBytes(T);
    T=T^RC[i];
    W[4*i]=W[4*i-4]^T;
    W[4*i+1]=W[4*i-3]^W[4*i];
    W[4*i+2]=W[4*i-2]^W[4*i+1];
    W[4*i+3]=W[4*i-1]^W[4*i+2];
  }
```

5.4 MODES OF OPERATION

A block cipher like DES or Rijndael can be used in a variety of ways to encrypt a data string. Soon after DES was standardized another US Federal standard appeared giving four *recommended* ways of using DES for data encryption. These modes of operation have since been standardized internationally and can be used with any block cipher. The four modes are

- **ECB Mode:** This is simple to use, but suffers from possible deletion and insertion attacks. A one-bit error in ciphertext gives one whole block error in the decrypted plaintext.

- **CBC Mode:** This is the best mode to use as a block cipher since it helps protect against deletion and insertion attacks. In this mode a one-bit error in the ciphertext gives not only a one-block error in the corresponding plaintext block but also a one-bit error in the next decrypted plaintext block.

- **OFB Mode:** This mode turns a block cipher into a stream cipher. It has the property that a one-bit error in ciphertext gives a one-bit error in the decrypted plaintext.

- **CFB Mode:** This mode also turns a block cipher into a stream cipher. A single bit error in the ciphertext affects both this block and the next, just as in CBC mode.

We shall now describe each of these modes in detail.

5.4.1 ECB Mode

Electronic Code Book Mode, or ECB Mode, is the simplest way to use a block cipher. The data to be encrypted m is divided into blocks of n bits:

$$m_1, m_2, \ldots, m_q$$

with the last block padded if needed. The ciphertext blocks $c_1, \ldots, c_q$ are then defined as follows

$$c_i = e_k(m_i),$$

as described in Fig. 5.9. Decipherment is simply the reverse operation as explained in Fig. 5.10.

Fig. 5.9 ECB encipherment

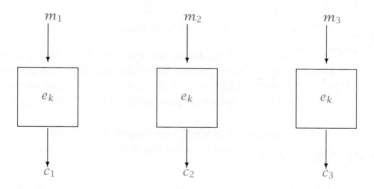

ECB Mode has a number of problems: the first is due to the property that if $m_i = m_j$ then we have $c_i = c_j$, i.e. the same input block always generates the same output block. This is a problem since stereotyped beginnings and ends of messages are common. The second problem comes because we could simply delete blocks from the message and no one would know. Thirdly we could replay known blocks from other messages. By extracting ciphertext corresponding to a known piece of plaintext we can then amend other transactions to contain this known block of text.

Fig. 5.10 ECB decipherment

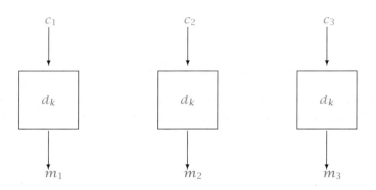

To see all these problems suppose our block cipher is rather simple and encrypts each English word as a block. Suppose we obtained the encryption of the sentences

Pay Alice one hundred pounds,
Don't pay Bob two hundred pounds,

which encrypted were

the horse has four legs,
stop the pony hasn't four legs.

We can now make the recipient pay Alice two hundred pounds by sending her the message

the horse hasn't four legs,

in other words we have replaced a block from one message by a block from another message. Or we could stop the recipient paying Alice one hundred pounds by inserting the encryption stop of don't onto the front of the original message to Alice. Or we can make the recipient pay Bob two hundred pounds by deleting the first block of the message sent to him.

These threats can be countered by adding checksums over a number of plaintext blocks, or by using a mode of operation which adds some 'context' to each ciphertext block.

5.4.2 CBC Mode

One way of countering the problems with ECB Mode is to chain the cipher, and in this way add context to each ciphertext block. The easiest way of doing this is to use Cipher Block Chaining Mode, or CBC Mode.

Again, the plaintext must first be divided into a series of blocks

$$m_1, \ldots, m_q,$$

and as before the final block may need padding to make the plaintext length a multiple of the block length. Encryption is then performed via the equations

$$c_1 = e_k(m_1 \oplus IV),$$
$$c_i = e_k(m_i \oplus c_{i-1}) \text{ for } i > 1,$$

see also Fig. 5.11.

Notice that we require an additional initial value IV to be passed to the encryption function, which can be used to make sure that two encryptions of the same plaintext produce different ciphertexts. It is not necessary for the IV to be kept secret and in real life it is usually transmitted in the clear from the encryptor to the decryptor as part of the message.

Fig. 5.11 CBC encipherment

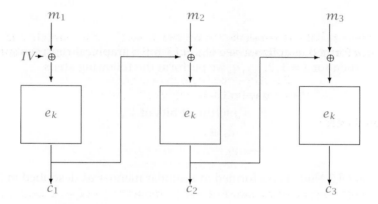

Decryption also requires the IV and is performed via the equations,

$$m_1 = d_k(c_1) \oplus IV,$$
$$m_i = d_k(c_i) \oplus c_{i-1} \text{ for } i > 1,$$

see Fig. 5.12.

With ECB Mode a single bit error in transmission of the ciphertext will result in a whole block being decrypted wrongly, whilst in CBC Mode we see that not only will we decrypt a block incorrectly but the error will also affect a single bit of the next block.

5.4.3 OFB Mode

Output Feedback Mode, or OFB Mode enables a block cipher to be used as a stream cipher. We need to choose a variable j ($1 \le j \le n$) which will denote the number of bits output by the keystream generator on each iteration. We use the block cipher to create the keystream, j bits at a time. It is however usually recommended to take $j = n$ as that makes the expected cycle length of the keystream generator larger.

Again we divide plaintext into a series of blocks, but this time each block is j-bits, rather than n-bits long:

$$m_1, \ldots, m_q.$$

Fig. 5.12 CBC decipherment

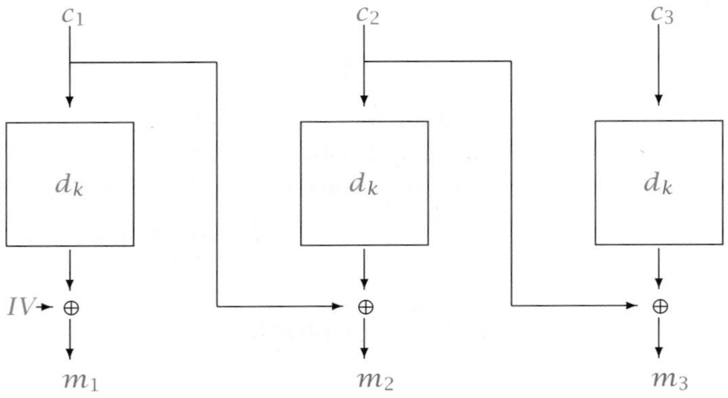

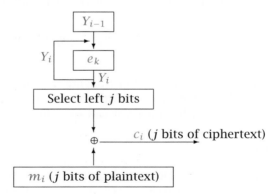

Encryption is performed as follows, see Fig. 5.13 for a graphical representation. First we set $X_1 = IV$, then for $i = 1, 2, \ldots, q$, we perform the following steps,

$$Y_i = e_k(X_i),$$
$$E_i = j \text{ leftmost bits of } Y_i,$$
$$c_i = m_i \oplus E_i,$$
$$X_{i+1} = Y_i.$$

Decipherment in OFB Mode is performed in a similar manner as described in Fig. 5.14.

Fig. 5.13 OFB encipherment

Y_{i-1}

Y_i e_k

Y_i

Select left j bits

$\oplus$ —— c_i (j bits of ciphertext)

m_i (j bits of plaintext)

5.4.4 CFB Mode

The final mode we consider is called Cipher FeedBack Mode, or CFB Mode. This is very similar to OFB Mode in that we use the block cipher to produce a stream cipher. Recall

Fig. 5.14 OFB decipherment

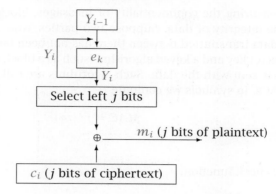

that in OFB Mode the keystream was generated by encrypting the IV and then iteratively encrypting the output from the previous encryption. In CFB Mode the keystream output is produced by the encryption of the ciphertext, as in Fig. 5.15, by the following steps,

$$Y_0 = IV,$$
$$Z_i = e_k(Y_{i-1}),$$
$$E_i = j \text{ leftmost bits of } Z_i,$$
$$Y_i = m_i \oplus E_i.$$

We do not present the decryption steps, but leave these as an exercise for the reader.

Fig. 5.15 CFB encipherment

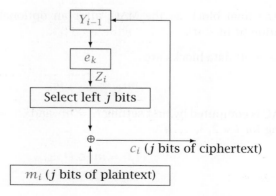

5.5 MACS

Apart from ensuring the confidentiality of messages, block ciphers can also be used to protect the integrity of data. Suppose two parties, who share a secret key, wish to ensure that data transmitted between them has not been tampered with. They can use the shared secret key and a keyed algorithm (such as a block cipher) to produce a check-value, which is sent with the data. Such algorithms are called Message Authentication Codes, or MACs. In symbols we compute

$$MAC = f_k(m)$$

where

- f is the check function,
- k is the secret key,
- m is the message.

Note we do not assume that the message is secret, we are trying to protect data integrity and not confidentiality. If we wish our message to remain confidential then we should encrypt it after applying the MAC. After computing the MAC and performing the encryption, the user transmits

$$e_k(m\|MAC(m)).$$

There are various types of MAC schemes, but the best known and most widely used by far are the CBC-MACs. These are generated by a block cipher in CBC Mode. CBC-MACs are the subject of various international standards dating back to the early 1980s. These early standards specify the use of DES in CBC mode to produce a MAC, although one could really use any block cipher in place of DES.

Using an n-bit block cipher to give an m-bit MAC, where $m \leq n$, is done as follows:

- The data is padded to form a series of n-bit blocks.

- The blocks are encrypted using the block cipher in CBC Mode.

- Take the final block as the MAC, after an optional postprocessing stage and truncation (if $m < n$).

Hence, if the n-bit data blocks are

$$m_1, m_2, \ldots, m_q$$

then the MAC is computed by first setting $I_1 = m_1$ and $O_1 = e_k(I_1)$ and then performing the following for $i = 2, 3, \ldots, q$

$$I_i = m_i \oplus O_{i-1},$$
$$O_i = e_k(I_i).$$

The final value O_q is then subject to an optional processing stage. The result is then truncated to m bits to give the final MAC. This is all summarized in Fig. 5.16.

Fig. 5.16 CBC-MAC: Flow diagram

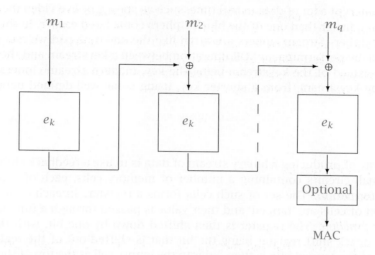

With a CBC-MAC one needs to be very careful as to how the initial padding is performed. There are three possible padding methods proposed in the standards:

- **Method 1:** Add as many zeros as necessary to make a whole number of blocks. This method has a number of problems associated to it as it does not allow the detection of the addition or deletion of trailing zeros, unless the message length is known.

- **Method 2:** Add a single one to the message followed by as many zeros as necessary to make a whole number of blocks. The addition of the extra bit is used to signal the end of the message, in case the message ends with a string of zeros.

- **Method 3:** As method one but also add an extra block containing the length of the unpadded message.

The standards specify two possible optional post-processing steps, designed to make it more difficult for the cryptanalyst to perform an exhaustive key search.

1. Choose a key k_1 and compute

$$O_q = e_k \left(d_{k_1}(O_q) \right).$$

2. Choose a key k_1 and compute

$$O_q = e_{k_1}(O_q).$$

Another method for producing MACs is to use cryptographic hash functions, see Section 10.3. A simple possibility for this type of MAC is to concatenate a secret key to a message and input the result to a hash function, the output is then the MAC.

5.6 MODERN STREAM CIPHERS

If we wish to encrypt a lot of data in real time, such as speech or live video then we may need something faster than one of the block ciphers considered earlier. In this case we use a stream cipher. Stream ciphers are often like the one-time pad we met earlier in that they work by performing an XOR operation between a keystream and the message stream. But instead of the keystream being the key, modern stream ciphers work by generating the keystream, from a shorter key, using some well-defined deterministic algorithm.

5.6.1 LFSR

A standard way of producing a binary stream of data is to use a feedback shift register. These are small circuits containing a number of memory cells, each of which holds one bit of information. The set of such cells forms a register. In each cycle a certain predefined set of cells are 'tapped' and their value is passed through a function, called the *feedback function*. The register is then shifted down by one bit, with the output bit of the feedback shift register being the bit that is shifted out of the register. The combination of the tapped bits is then fed into the empty cell at the top of the register. This is explained in Fig. 5.17.

Fig. 5.17 Feedback shift register

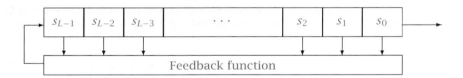

It is desirable, for reasons we shall see later, to use some form of non-linear function as the feedback function. However, this is often hard to do in practice hence usually one uses a linear feedback shift register, or LFSR for short, where the feedback function is a linear function of the tapped bits. In each cycle a certain predefined set of cells are 'tapped' and their value is XORed together. The register is then shifted down by one bit, with the output bit of the LFSR being the bit that is shifted out of the register. Again, the combination of the tapped bits is then fed into the empty cell at the top of the register.

Mathematically this can be defined as follows, where the register is assumed to be of length L. One defines a set of bits $[c_1, \ldots, c_L]$ which are set to one if that cell is tapped and set to zero otherwise. The initial internal state of the register is given by the bit sequence $[s_{L-1}, \ldots, s_1, s_0]$. The output sequence is then defined to be $s_0, s_1, s_2, \ldots, s_{L-1}, s_L, s_{L+1}, \ldots$ where for $j \geq L$ we have

$$s_j = c_1 \cdot s_{j-1} \oplus c_2 \cdot s_{j-2} \oplus \cdots \oplus c_L \cdot s_{j-L}.$$

Note, that for an initial state of all zeros the output sequence will be the zero sequence, but for a non-zero initial state the output sequence must be eventually periodic (since we must eventually return to a state we have already been in). The period of a sequence is defined to be the smallest integer N such that

$$s_{N+i} = s_i$$

for all sufficiently large i. In fact there are $2^L - 1$ possible non-zero states and so the most one can hope for is that an LFSR, for all non-zero initial states, produces an output stream whose period is of length exactly $2^L - 1$.

Fig. 5.18 Linear feedback shift register: $X^3 + X + 1$

The properties of the output sequence are closely tied up with the properties of the binary polynomial

$$C(X) = 1 + c_1 X + c_2 X^2 + \cdots + c_L X^L \in \mathbb{F}_2[X],$$

called the connection polynomial for the LFSR. As an example see Fig. 5.18 for an LFSR in which the connection polynomial is given by $X^3 + X + 1$ and Fig. 5.19 for an LFSR in which the connection polynomial is given by $X^{32} + X^3 + 1$.

Fig. 5.19 Linear feedback shift register: $X^{32} + X^3 + 1$

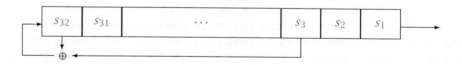

Of particular importance is when the connection polynomial is primitive.

Definition 5.1 *A binary polynomial $C(X)$ of degree L is primitive if it is irreducible and a root θ of $C(X)$ generates the multiplicative group of the field $\mathbb{F}_{2^L}$. In other words, since $C(X)$ is irreducible we already have*

$$\mathbb{F}_2[X]/(C(X)) = \mathbb{F}_2(\theta) = \mathbb{F}_{2^L},$$

but we also require

$$\mathbb{F}_{2^L}^* = \langle \theta \rangle.$$

The properties of the output sequence of the LFSR can then be deduced from the following cases.

- $c_L = 0$:
  In this case the sequence is said to be singular. The output sequence may not be periodic, but it will be eventually periodic.

- $c_L = 1$:
  Such a sequence is called non-singular. The output is always purely periodic, in that it satisfies $s_{N+i} = s_i$ for all i rather than for all sufficiently large values of i. Of the non-singular sequences of particular interest are those satisfying

  - $C(X)$ is irreducible:
    Every non-zero initial state will produce a sequence with period equal to the smallest value of N such that $C(X)$ divides $1 + X^N$. We have that N will divide $2^L - 1$.
  - $C(X)$ is primitive:
    Every non-zero initial state produces an output sequence which is periodic and of exact period $2^L - 1$.

We do not prove these results here, but proofs can be found in any good textbook on the application of finite fields to coding theory, cryptography or communications science. As an example consider the sequence generated by the LFSR with connection polynomial

$$1 + X + X^3.$$

This sequence is generated by the equation

$$s_j = s_{j-1} \oplus s_{j-3}.$$

We take the initial state as $[0, 0, 1]$ we will then obtain

Time	State	Output bit
0	[0,0,1]	–
1	[1,0,0]	1
2	[1,1,0]	0
3	[1,1,1]	0
4	[0,1,1]	1
5	[1,0,1]	1
6	[0,1,0]	1
7	[0,0,1]	0

Now as the internal state has returned to the initial state we see that the sequence will keep repeating itself every $7 = 2^3 - 1$ operations. This is because the polynomial $X^3 + X + 1$ is primitive.

Whilst there are algorithms to generate primitive polynomials for use in applications we shall not describe them here. We give some samples in the following list, where we give polynomials with a small number of taps for efficiency.

$$
\begin{array}{lll}
x^{31} + x^3 + 1 & x^{31} + x^6 + 1 & x^{31} + x^7 + 1 \\
x^{39} + x^4 + 1 & x^{60} + x + 1 & x^{63} + x + 1 \\
x^{71} + x^6 + 1 & x^{93} + x^2 + 1 & x^{137} + x^{21} + 1 \\
x^{145} + x^{52} + 1 & x^{161} + x^{18} + 1 & x^{521} + x^{32} + 1
\end{array}
$$

Although LFSRs efficiently produce bitstreams from a small key, especially when implemented in hardware, they are not usable on their own for cryptographic purposes. This is because they are essentially linear, which is after all why they are efficient.

We shall now show that if we know an LFSR has L internal registers, and we can determine $2L$ consecutive bits of the stream then we can determine the whole stream. First notice we need to determine L unknowns, the L values of the 'taps' c_i, since the L values of the initial state $s_0, \ldots, s_{L-1}$ are given to us. This type of data could be available in a known plaintext attack, where we obtain the ciphertext corresponding to a known piece of plaintext. Since the encryption operation is simply exclusive-or, we can determine as many bits of the keystream as we require.

Using the equation

$$s_j = \sum_{i=1}^{L} c_i \cdot s_{j-i} \pmod 2,$$

we obtain $2L$ linear equations, which we then solve via matrix techniques. We write our matrix equation as

$$\begin{pmatrix} s_{L-1} & s_{L-2} & \cdots & s_1 & s_0 \\ s_L & s_{L-1} & \cdots & s_2 & s_1 \\ \vdots & \vdots & & \vdots & \vdots \\ s_{2L-3} & s_{2L-4} & \cdots & s_{L-1} & s_{L-2} \\ s_{2L-2} & s_{2L-3} & \cdots & s_L & s_{L-1} \end{pmatrix} \begin{pmatrix} c_1 \\ c_2 \\ \vdots \\ c_{L-1} \\ c_L \end{pmatrix} = \begin{pmatrix} s_L \\ s_L \\ \vdots \\ s_{2L-2} \\ s_{2L-1} \end{pmatrix}.$$

As an example, suppose we see the output sequence

$$1, 1, 1, 1, 0, 1, 0, 1, 1, 0, 0, 1, 0, 0, 0, \ldots$$

and we are told that this sequence was the output of a four-bit LFSR. Using the above matrix equation, and solving it modulo 2, we would find that the connection polynomial was given by

$$X^4 + X + 1.$$

Hence, we can conclude that a stream cipher based solely on a single LFSR is insecure against a known plaintext attack.

An important measure of the cryptographic quality of a sequence is given by the linear complexity of the sequence.

Definition 5.2 (Linear complexity) *For an infinite binary sequence*

$$s = s_0, s_1, s_2, s_3, \ldots,$$

we define the linear complexity of s as $L(s)$ where

- *$L(s) = 0$ if s is the zero sequence,*

- *$L(s) = \infty$ if no LFSR generates s,*

- *$L(s)$ will be the length of the shortest LFSR to generate s.*

Since we cannot compute the linear complexity of an infinite set of bits we often restrict ourselves to a finite set s^n of the first n bits. The linear complexity satisfies the following properties for any sequence s.

- For all $n \geq 1$ we have $0 \leq L(s^n) \leq n$.

- If s is periodic with period N then $L(s) \leq N$.

- $L(s \oplus t) \leq L(s) + L(t)$.

For a random sequence of bits, which is what we want from a stream cipher's keystream generator, we should have that the expected linear complexity of s^n is approximately just larger than $n/2$. But for a keystream generated by an LFSR we know that we will have $L(s^n) = L$ for all $n \geq L$. Hence, an LFSR produces nothing at all like a random bit string.

We have seen that if we know the length of the LFSR then from the output bits we can generate the connection polynomial. To determine the length we use the linear complexity profile, this is defined to be the sequence $L(s^1), L(s^2), L(s^3), \ldots$. There is also an efficient algorithm called the Berlekamp–Massey algorithm which given a finite sequence s^n will compute the linear complexity profile $L(s^1), L(s^2), L(s^3), \ldots, L(s^n)$.

Hence, if we use an LFSR of size L to generate a keystream for a stream cipher and the adversary obtains at least $2L$ bits of this keystream then they can determine the exact LFSR used and so generate as much of the keystream as they wish. Therefore, one needs to find a way of using LFSRs in some non-linear way, which hides the linearity of the LFSRs and produces output sequences with high linear complexity.

5.6.2 Combining LFSRs

To use LFSRs in practice it is common for a number of them to be used, producing a set of output sequences $x_1^{(i)}, \ldots, x_n^{(i)}$. The key is then the initial state of all of the LFSRs and the keystream is produced from these n generators using a non-linear combination function $f(x_1, \ldots, x_n)$, as described in Fig. 5.20.

Fig. 5.20 Combining LFSRs

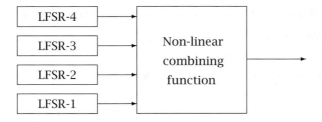

The combination function is a boolean function written as a sum of distinct products of variables, e.g.

$$f(x_1, x_2, x_3, x_4, x_5) = 1 \oplus x_2 \oplus x_3 \oplus x_4 \cdot x_5 \oplus x_1 \cdot x_2 \cdot x_3 \cdot x_5.$$

Suppose that one uses n LFSRs of maximal length (i.e. all with a primitive connection polynomial) and whose periods $L_1, \ldots, L_n$ are all distinct and greater than two. Then the linear complexity of the keystream generated by $f(x_1, \ldots, x_n)$ is equal to

$$f(L_1, \ldots, L_n)$$

where we replace $\oplus$ in f with integer addition and multiplication modulo two by integer multiplication and f is expressed in algebraic normal form.

There is a whole industry of people developing ways of combining LFSRs to produce stream ciphers. We leave it to the reader to investigate this matter further as we do not have the space to delve into this area ourselves.

5.6.3 RC4

RC stands for Ron's Cipher after Ron Rivest of MIT. You should not think that the RC4 cipher is a prior version of the block ciphers RC5 and RC6. It is in fact a very, very fast stream cipher. It is very easy to remember since it is surprisingly simple.

Given an array $S[0 \ldots 255]$ consisting of the integers $0, \ldots, 255$, permuted in some key-dependent way, the output of the RC4 algorithm is a keystream of bytes K which is XORed with the plaintext byte by byte. Since the algorithm works on bytes and not bits, and uses very simple operations it is particularly fast in software. We start by letting $i = 0$ and $j = 0$, we then repeat the following steps,

```
i=(i+1)%256;
j=(j+S[i])%256;
swap(S[i], S[j]);
t=(S[i]+S[j])%256;
K=s[t];
```

The security rests on the observation that even if the attacker knows K and i, he can deduce the value of $S[t]$, but this does not allow him to deduce anything about the internal state of the table. This follows from the observation that he cannot deduce the value of t, as he does not know $j, S[i]$ or $S[j]$.

It is a very tightly designed algorithm as each line of the code needs to be there to make the cipher secure.

- **i=(i+1)%256** : Makes sure every array element is used once after 256 iterations.

- **j=(j+S[i])%256** : Makes the output depend non-linearly on the array.

- **swap(S[i],S[j])** : Makes sure the array is evolved and modified as the iteration continues.

- **t=(S[i]+S[j])%256** : Makes sure the output sequence reveals little about the internal state of the array.

The initial state of the array S is determined from the key using the following method. The array is first initialized to $S[i] = i$. Then another array of 256 bytes is filled with the key, repeating the key as necessary. Then set $j = 0$ and run the following steps for $i = 0$ to 255,

```
j=(j+S[i]+K[i])%256;
swap(S[i],S[j]);
```

Chapter Summary

- Modern symmetric key ciphers come in two variants: block ciphers and stream ciphers.

- The most popular block cipher is DES, which is itself based on a general design called a Feistel cipher.

- A comparatively recent block cipher is the AES cipher, called Rijndael.

- Both DES and Rijndael obtain their security by repeated application of simple rounds consisting of substitution, permutation and key addition.

- To use a block cipher one needs to also specify a mode of operation. The simplest mode is ECB mode, which has a number of problems associated with it. Hence, it is common to use a more advanced mode such as CBC mode.

- Stream ciphers can be obtained by combining, in a non-linear way, simple bit generators called LFSRs. These provide very fast ciphers, suitable for implementation in hardware, which can encrypt real-time data such as voice or video.

Further Reading

The Rijndael algorithm, the AES process and a detailed discussion of attacks on block ciphers and Rijndael in particular can be found in the book by Daemen and Rijmen. Stinson's book is the best book to explain differential cryptanalysis for students. A book which covers an awful lot of other block and stream ciphers is the book by Schneier.

J. Daemen and V. Rijmen. *The Design of Rijndael: AES – The Advanced Encryption Standard.* Springer-Verlag, 2002.

D. Stinson. *Cryptography Theory and Practice.* CRC Press, 1995.

B. Schneier. *Applied Cryptography.* Wiley, 1996.

Review Exercises

5.1.1   What is Kerchhoff's principle?

5.1.2   Describe the operation of a Feistel cipher.

5.1.3   In what way does DES differ from a pure Feistel cipher?

5.1.4   What needs to change in a Feistel cipher between the encryption and decryption functions?

5.1.5   Describe the operation of triple DES.

5.1.6   Discuss the role of permutations and substitutions in the DES cipher. In which part of the DES algorithm are permutations used to increase security?

5.1.7   Discuss the role of permutations and substitutions in the Rijndael cipher.

5.1.8   What problems are associated with ECB Mode, and how does CBC Mode solve these issues?

5.1.9   What is a MAC? Give three examples of where one could use a MAC.

5.1.10   LFSRs are often used to make stream ciphers. What is an LFSR and why can they not be used directly to create a stream cipher?

Programming Exercises

5.2.1   Look at the code for a DES implementation available on the Internet. Compare the description of DES in the text with that actually implemented in the code. Explain why the programmers' changes to the DES algorithm are correct (in that they do not change the output of the function) and why these changes have been made.

5.2.2   Find out how to compute the linear complexity of a sequence and implement the resulting algorithm. Generate a number of sequences of bits using an LFSR and then compute the resulting linear complexity.

Standard Exercises

5.3.1   Let $\overline{a}$ denote the bitwise complement of a. Show that if

$$c = DES_k(m)$$

then

$$\overline{c} = DES_{\overline{k}}(\overline{m}).$$

Hint: Use the following identity $\overline{a \oplus b} = \overline{a} \oplus b$.

5.3.2   Consider the following composition of a block cipher with an n-bit key size

$$c = E_{k_1}(E_{k_2}(m)),$$

to produce a cipher with a key size of $2n$ bits. Show that there is a chosen plaintext attack on this composition which requires $O(2^n)$ memory and $O(2^n)$ encryptions/decryptions using E.

5.3.3   Consider triple DES but with two keys instead of three, i.e.

$$c = DES_{k_1}(DES_{k_2}^{-1}(DES_{k_1}(m))).$$

Describe a chosen plaintext attack on this two-key version of triple DES, which requires roughly 2^{56} steps and storage of 2^{56} encryptions under single DES.

5.3.4   Describe the decryption operation in CFB Mode.

5.3.5   Show that if the connection polynomial $C(X)$ of an LFSR is irreducible and has leading coefficient one, then the output sequence of an LFSR is purely periodic and each starting state gives rise to a sequence with period equal to the smallest value of N such that $C(X)$ divides $1 + X^N$.

Symmetric Key Distribution

Chapter Goals

- To understand the problems associated with managing and distributing secret keys.

- To learn about key distribution techniques based on symmetric key based protocols.

- To introduce the formal analysis of protocols.

6.1 KEY MANAGEMENT

To be able to use symmetric encryption algorithms such as DES or Rijndael we need a way for the two communicating parties to share the secret key. In this first section we discuss some issues related to how keys are managed, in particular

- key distribution,

- key selection,

- key lifetime,

- secret sharing.

But before we continue we need to distinguish between different types of keys. The following terminology will be used throughout this chapter and beyond:

- **Static (or long-term) Keys:** These are keys which are to be in use for a long time period. The exact definition of long will depend on the application, but this could mean from a few hours to a few years. The compromise of a static key is usually considered to be a major problem, with potentially catastrophic consequences.

- **Ephemeral, or Session (or short-term) Keys:** These are keys which have a short life-time, maybe a few seconds or a day. They are usually used to provide confidentiality for the given time period. The compromise of a session key should only result in the compromise of that session's secrecy and it should not affect the long-term security of the system.

6.1.1 Key Distribution

Key distribution is one of the fundamental problems with cryptography. There are a number of solutions to this problem; which one of these one chooses depends on the overall situation.

- **Physical Distribution:** Using trusted couriers or armed guards, keys can be distributed using traditional physical means. Until the 1970s this was in effect the only secure way of distributing keys at system setup. It has a large number of physical problems associated with it, especially scalability, but the main drawback is that security no longer rests with the key but with the courier. If we can bribe, kidnap or kill the courier then we have broken the system.

- **Distribution Using Symmetric Key Protocols:** Once some secret keys have been distributed between a number of users and a trusted central authority, we can use the trusted authority to help generate keys for any pair of users as the need arises. Protocols to perform this task will be discussed in this chapter. They are usually very efficient but have some drawbacks. In particular they usually assume that both the trusted authority and the two users who wish to agree on a key are both on-line. They also still require a physical means to set the initial keys up.

- **Distribution Using Public Key Protocols:** Using public key cryptography, two parties, who have never met or who do not trust any one single authority, can produce a shared secret key. This can be done in an on-line manner, using a key exchange protocol. Indeed this is the most common application of public key techniques for encryption. Rather than encrypting large amounts of data by public key techniques we agree a key by public key techniques and then use a symmetric cipher to actually do the encryption.

To understand the scale of the problem, if our system is to cope with n separate users, and each user may want to communicate securely with any other user, then we require

$$\frac{n(n-1)}{2}$$

separate secret keys. This soon produces huge key management problems; a small university with around $10\,000$ students would need to have around fifty million separate secret keys.

With a large number of keys in existence one finds a large number of problems. For example what happens when your key is compromised? In other words someone else has found your key. What can you do about it? What can they do? Hence, a large number of keys produces a large key management problem.

One solution is for each user to hold only one key with which it communicates with a central authority, hence a system with n users will only require n keys. When two users wish to communicate they generate a secret key which is only to be used for that message, a so-called session key. This session key can be generated with the help of the central authority using one of the protocols that appear later in this chapter.

6.1.2 Key Selection

The keys which one uses should be truly random, since otherwise an attacker may be able to determine information simply by knowing the more likely keys and the more likely messages, as we saw in a toy example in Chapter 4. All keys should be equally likely and really need to be generated using a true random number generator, however such a good source of entropy is hard to find.

Whilst a truly random key will be very strong, it is hard for a human to remember. Hence, many systems use a password or pass phrase to generate a secret key. But now one needs to worry even more about brute force attacks. As one can see from the following table, a typical PIN-like password of a number between 0 and 9999 is easy to mount a brute force attack against, but even using eight printable characters does not push us to the 2^{80} possibilities that we would like to ensure security.

Key size	Decimal digits	Printable characters
4	$10^4 \approx 2^{13}$	$10^7 \approx 2^{23}$
8	$10^8 \approx 2^{26}$	$10^{15} \approx 2^{50}$

One solution may be to use long pass phrases of 20–30 characters, but these are likely to lack sufficient entropy since we have already seen that natural language is not very random.

Short passwords based on names or words are a common problem in many large organizations. This is why a number of organizations now have automatic checking that passwords meet certain criteria such as

- at least one lower case letter,
- at least one upper case letter,
- at least one numeric character,
- at least one non-alpha-numeric character,
- at least eight characters in length.

But such rules, even though they eliminate the chance of a dictionary attack, still reduce the number of possible passwords from what they would be if they were chosen uniformly at random from all choices of eight printable characters.

6.1.3 Key Lifetime

One issue one needs to consider when generating and storing keys is the key lifetime. A general rule is that the longer the key is in use the more vulnerable it will be and the more valuable it will be to an attacker. We have already touched on this when mentioning the use of session keys. However, it is important to destroy keys properly after use. Relying on an operating system to delete a file by typing del/rm does not mean that an attacker cannot recover the file contents by examining the hard disk. Usually deleting a file does not destroy the file contents, it only signals that the file's location is now available for overwriting with new data. A similar problem occurs when deleting memory in an application.

6.1.4 Secret Sharing

As we have mentioned already the main problem is one of managing the secure distribution of keys. Even a system which uses a trusted central authority needs some way of getting the keys shared between the centre and each user out to the user.

One possible solution is key splitting (more formally called *secret sharing*) where we divide the key into a number of shares

$$K = k_1 \oplus k_2 \oplus \cdots \oplus k_r.$$

Each share is then distributed via separate routes. The beauty of this is that an attacker needs to attack all the routes so as to obtain the key. On the other hand attacking one route will stop the legitimate user from recovering the key.

A more complicated method, which does not have this last problem, is to use a form of threshold secret sharing scheme. The key is split up into a number of shares, say w, then if a certain threshold t of the shares get through then the legitimate user can recover the secret key. However, even if the adversary determines $t - 1$ of the shares then she cannot recover the key. Whilst not actually used much in practice for key distribution, we introduce this concept here since we shall see secret sharing schemes in a later chapter when we discuss a voting protocol.

An example of a threshold scheme is Shamir's secret sharing scheme. Suppose we wish to share a key k among w participants, so that we require t of them to come together to recover the key. Such a scheme is called a (t, w)-threshold scheme.

We take a prime p which is larger than $w + 1$. The key k is an element of $\mathbb{F}_p$. A trusted dealer chooses values x_i, for $i = 1, \ldots, w$, one value for each participant. Each participant is then given their value of x_i, and each such value is known to everyone else. To share the key k amongst the users the dealer computes $t - 1$ secret elements $a_1, \ldots, a_{t-1}$ and forms the polynomial

$$f(X) = k + \sum_{j=1}^{t-1} a_j X^j.$$

Then the shares y_i for each user are computed from

$$y_i = f(x_i) \text{ for } 1 \leq i \leq w,$$

and each share is given to each user.

To recover the secret key k the users use polynomial interpolation. Basically if l of them come together and divulge to each other y_i, for $i = 1, \ldots, l$, then they can try to recover the polynomial by solving the system of equations:

$$y_1 = k + a_1 x_1 + \cdots + a_{t-1} x_1^{t-1},$$

$$\vdots \qquad\qquad \vdots$$

$$y_l = k + a_1 x_l + \cdots + a_{t-1} x_l^{t-1},$$

If $l \geq t$ of them come together they can recover the polynomial $f(X)$ and so compute k. If $l \leq t - 1$ of them collude then they will not have enough information to determine any information about the key k.

Whilst the key can be recovered using polynomial interpolation, i.e. by solving the above linear system, in practice one can short-cut the linear equation solving by computing

$$b_j = \prod_{1 \le h \le t, h \ne j} \frac{x_h}{x_h - x_j}.$$

Then the key k is recovered from

$$k = \sum_{j=1}^{t} b_j y_j,$$

which is a method known as Lagrange interpolation.

6.2   SECRET KEY DISTRIBUTION

Recall, if we have n users each of whom wish to communicate securely with each other then we would require

$$\frac{n(n-1)}{2}$$

separate long-term key pairs. As remarked earlier this leads to huge key management problems and issues related to the distribution of the keys. We have already mentioned that it is better to use session keys and few long-term keys, but we have not explained how one deploys the session keys.

.   To solve this problem the community developed a number of protocols which make use of symmetric key cryptography to distribute secret session keys, some of which we shall describe in this section. Later on we shall look at public key techniques for this problem, which are often more elegant.

6.2.1   Notation

We first need to set up some notation to describe the protocols. Firstly we set up the names of the parties and quantities involved.

- **Parties/Principals:** A, B, S.
  Assume the two parties who wish to agree a secret are A and B, for Alice and Bob. We assume that they will use a trusted third party, or TTP, which we shall denote by S.

- **Shared Secret Keys:** K_{ab}, K_{bs}, K_{as}.
  K_{ab} will denote a secret key known only to A and B.

- **Nonces:** N_a, N_b.
  Nonces are numbers used only once, they should be random. The quantity N_a will denote a nonce originally produced by the principal A. Note, other notations for nonces are possible and we will introduce them as the need arises.

- **Timestamps:** T_a, T_b, T_s.
  The quantity T_a is a timestamp produced by A. When timestamps are used we

assume that the parties try to keep their clocks in synchronization using some other protocol.

The statement

$$A \longrightarrow B : M, A, B, \{N_a, M, A, B\}_{K_{as}},$$

means A sends to B the message to the right of the colon. The message consists of

- a nonce M,

- A the name of party A,

- B the name of party B,

- a message $\{N_a, M, A, B\}$ encrypted under the key K_{as} which A shares with S. Hence, the recipient B is unable to read the encrypted part of this message.

Before presenting our first protocol we need to decide the goals of key agreement and key transport, and what position the parties start from. We assume all parties, A and B say, only share secret keys, K_{as} and K_{bs} with the trusted third party S. They want to agree/transport a session key K_{ab} for a communication between themselves.

We also need to decide what capabilities an attacker has. As always we assume the worst possible situation in which an attacker can intercept any message flow over the network. She can then stop a message, alter it or change its destination. An attacker is also able to distribute her own messages over the network. With such a high-powered attacker it is often assumed that the attacker *is* the network.

This new session key should be fresh, i.e. it has not been used by any other party before and has been recently created. The freshness property will stop attacks whereby the adversary replays messages so as to use an old key again. Freshness also can be useful in deducing that the party with which you are communicating is still alive.

6.2.2 Wide-Mouth Frog Protocol

Our first protocol is the Wide-Mouth Frog protocol, which is a simple protocol invented by Burrows. The protocol transfers a key K_{ab} from A to B via S, it uses only two messages but has a number of drawbacks. In particular it requires the use of synchronized clocks, which can cause a problem in implementations. In addition the protocol assumes that A chooses the session key K_{ab} and then transports this key over to user B. This implies that user A is trusted by user B to be competent in making and keeping keys secret. This is a very strong assumption and the main reason that this protocol is not used much in real life. However, it is very simple and gives a good example of how to analyse a protocol formally, which we shall come to later in this chapter.

The protocol proceeds in the following steps, as illustrated in Fig. 6.1,

$$A \longrightarrow S : A, \{T_a, B, K_{ab}\}_{K_{as}},$$
$$S \longrightarrow B : \{T_s, A, K_{ab}\}_{K_{bs}}.$$

On obtaining the first message the trusted third party S decrypts the last part of the message and checks that the timestamp is recent. This decrypted message tells S he should forward the key to the party called B. If the timestamp is verified to be recent, S encrypts the key along with his timestamp and passes this encryption onto B.

Fig. 6.1 Wide-Mouth Frog protocol

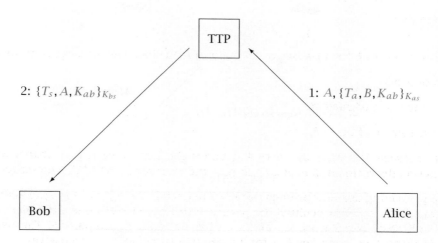

On obtaining this message B decrypts the message received and checks the time stamp is recent, then he can recover both the key K_{ab} and the name A of the person who wants to send data to him using this key.

The checks on the timestamps mean the session key should be recent, in that it left user A a short time ago. However, user A could have generated this key years ago and stored it on his hard disk, in which time Eve broke in and took a copy of this key.

We already said that this protocol requires that all parties need to keep synchronized clocks. However, this is not such a big problem since S checks or generates all the timestamps used in the protocol. Hence, each party only needs to record the difference between its clock and the clock owned by S. Clocks are then updated if a clock drift occurs which causes the protocol to fail.

This protocol is really too simple; much of the simplicity comes by assuming synchronized clocks and by assuming party A can be trusted with creating session keys.

6.2.3 Needham–Schroeder Protocol

We shall now look at more complicated protocols, starting with one of the most famous namely, the Needham–Schroeder protocol. This protocol was developed in 1978, and is one of most highly studied protocols ever; its fame is due to the fact that even a simple protocol can hide security flaws for a long time. The basic message flows are described as follows, as illustrated in Fig. 6.2,

$$A \longrightarrow S : A, B, N_a,$$
$$S \longrightarrow A : \{N_a, B, K_{ab}, \{K_{ab}, A\}_{K_{bs}}\}_{K_{as}},$$
$$A \longrightarrow B : \{K_{ab}, A\}_{K_{bs}},$$
$$B \longrightarrow A : \{N_b\}_{K_{ab}},$$
$$A \longrightarrow B : \{N_b - 1\}_{K_{ab}}.$$

Fig. 6.2 Needham–Schroeder protocol

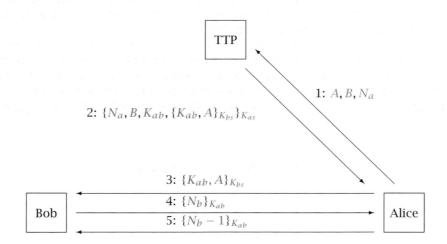

We now look at each message in detail, and explain what it does.

- The first message tells S that A wants a key to communicate with B.

- In the second message S generates the session key K_{ab} and sends it back to A. The nonce N_a is included so that A knows this was sent after her request of the first message. The session key is also encrypted under the key K_{bs} for sending to B.

- The third message conveys the session key to B.

- B needs to check that the third message was not a replay. So he needs to know if A is still alive, hence, in the fourth message he encrypts a nonce back to A.

- In the final message, to prove to B that she is still alive, A encrypts a simple function of B's nonce back to B.

The main problem with the Needham–Schroeder protocol is that B does not know that the key he shares with A is fresh, a fact which was not spotted until some time after the original protocol was published. An adversary who finds an old session transcript can, after finding the old session key by some other means, use the old session transcript in the last three messages involving B. Hence, the adversary can get B to agree to a key with the adversary, which B thinks he is sharing with A.

Note, A and B have their secret session key generated by S and so neither party needs to trust the other to produce 'good' keys. They of course trust S to generate good keys since S is an authority trusted by everyone. In some applications this last assumption is not valid and more involved algorithms, or public key algorithms, are required. In this chapter we shall assume everyone trusts S to perform correctly any action we require of him.

6.2.4 Otway–Rees Protocol

The Otway–Rees protocol from 1987 is not used that much, but again it is historically important. Like the Needham-Schroeder protocol it does not use synchronized clocks, but again it suffers from a number of problems.

As before two people wish to agree a key using a trusted server S. There are two nonces N_a and N_b used to flag certain encrypted components as recent. In addition a nonce M is used to flag that the current set of communications are linked. The Otway–Rees protocol is shorter than the Needham-Schroeder protocol since it only requires four messages, but the message types are very different. As before the server generates the key K_{ab} for the two parties.

Fig. 6.3 Otway–Rees protocol

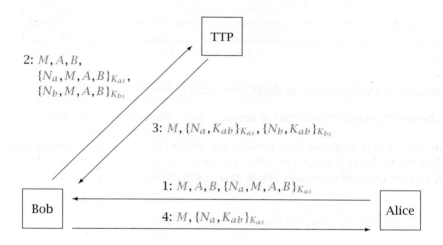

The message flows in the Otway–Rees protocol are as follows, as illustrated in Fig. 6.3,

$$A \longrightarrow B : M, A, B, \{N_a, M, A, B\}_{K_{as}},$$
$$B \longrightarrow S : M, A, B, \{N_a, M, A, B\}_{K_{as}}, \{N_b, M, A, B\}_{K_{bs}},$$
$$S \longrightarrow B : M, \{N_a, K_{ab}\}_{K_{as}}, \{N_b, K_{ab}\}_{K_{bs}},$$
$$B \longrightarrow A : M, \{N_a, K_{ab}\}_{K_{as}}.$$

Since the protocol does not make use of K_{ab} as an encryption key, neither party knows whether the key is known to each other. We say that Otway–Rees is a protocol which does not offer *key confirmation*. Let us see what the parties do know: A knows that B sent a message containing a nonce N_a which A knows to be fresh, since A originally generated the nonce. So B must have sent a message recently. On the other hand B has been told by the server that A used a nonce, but B has no idea whether this was a replay of an old message.

6.2.5 Kerberos

We end this section by looking at Kerberos. Kerberos is an authentication system based on symmetric encryption with keys shared with an authentication server; it is based on ideas underlying the Needham–Schroeder protocol. Kerberos was developed at MIT around 1987 as part of Project Athena. A modified version of this original version of Kerberos is now used in Windows 2000.

The network is assumed to consist of clients and a server, where the clients may be users, programs or services. Kerberos keeps a central database of clients including a secret key for each client, hence Kerberos requires a key space of size $O(n)$ if we have n clients. Kerberos is used to provide authentication of one entity to another and to issue session keys to these entities.

In addition Kerberos can run a ticket granting system to enable access control to services and resources. The division between authentication and access is a good idea which we shall see later echoed in SPKI. This division mirrors what happens in real companies. For example, in a company the personnel department administers who you are, whilst the computer department administers what resources you can use. This division is also echoed in Kerberos with an authentication server and a ticket generation server TGS. The TGS gives tickets to enable users to access resources, such as files, printers, etc.

Suppose A wishes to access a resource B. First A logs onto the authentication server using a password. The user A is given a ticket from this server encrypted under her password. This ticket contains a session key K_{as}. She now uses K_{as} to obtain a ticket from the TGS S to access the resource B. The output of the TGS is a key K_{ab}, a timestamp T_S and a lifetime L. The output of the TGS is used to authenticate A in subsequent traffic with B.

The flows look something like those given in Fig. 6.4,

$$A \longrightarrow S : A, B,$$
$$S \longrightarrow A : \{T_S, L, K_{ab}, B, \{T_S, L, K_{ab}, A\}_{K_{bs}}\}_{K_{as}},$$
$$A \longrightarrow B : \{T_S, L, K_{ab}, A\}_{K_{bs}}, \{A, T_A\}_{K_{ab}},$$
$$B \longrightarrow A : \{T_A + 1\}_{K_{ab}}.$$

- The first message is A telling S that she wants to access B.

- If S allows this access then a ticket $\{T_S, L, K_{ab}, A\}$ is created. This is encrypted under K_{bs} and sent to A for forwarding to B. The user A also gets a copy of the key in a form readable by her.

- The user A wants to verify that the ticket is valid and that the resource B is alive. Hence, she sends an encrypted nonce/timestamp T_A to B.

- The resource B sends back the encryption of $T_A + 1$, after checking that the timestamp T_A is recent, thus proving he knows the key and is alive.

We have removed the problems associated with the Needham–Schroeder protocol by using timestamps, but this has created the requirement for synchronized clocks.

Fig. 6.4   Kerberos

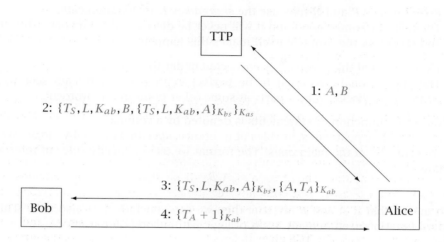

6.3   FORMAL APPROACHES TO PROTOCOL CHECKING

One can see that the above protocols are very intricate; spotting flaws in them can be a very subtle business. To try and make the design of these protocols more scientific a number of formal approaches have been proposed. The most influential of these is the BAN logic invented by Burrows, Abadi and Needham.

The BAN logic has a large number of drawbacks but was very influential in the design and analysis of symmetric key based key agreement protocols such as Kerberos and the Needham–Schroeder protocol. It has now been supplanted by more complicated logics and formal methods, but it is of historical importance and the study of the BAN logic can still be very instructive for protocol designers.

The main idea of BAN logic is that one should concentrate on what the parties believe is happening. It does not matter what is actually happening, we need to understand exactly what each party can logically deduce, from its own view of the protocol, as to what is actually happening. Even modern approaches to modelling PKI have taken this approach and so we shall now examine the BAN logic in more detail.

We first introduce the notation

- $P| \equiv X$ means P *believes* (or is entitled to believe) X.
  The principal P may act as though X is true.

- $P \triangleleft X$ means P *sees* X.
  Someone has sent a message to P containing X, so P can now read and repeat X.

- $P| \sim X$ means P *once said* X and P believed X when it was said.
  Note this tells us nothing about whether X was said recently or in the distant past.

- $P| \Rightarrow X$ means P has *jurisdiction* over X.
  This means P is an authority on X and should be trusted on this matter.

- #X means the formula X is *fresh*.
  This is usually used for nonces.

- $P \overset{K}{\leftrightarrow} Q$ means P and Q may use the *shared key K* to communicate.
  The key is assumed good and it will never be discovered by anyone other than P and Q, unless the protocol itself makes this happen.

- $\{X\}_K$, as usual this means X is *encrypted* under the key K.
  The encryption is assumed to be perfect in that X will remain secret unless deliberately disclosed by a party at some other point in the protocol.

In addition, conjunction of statements is denoted by a comma.

There are many postulates, or rules of inference, specified in the BAN logic. We shall only concentrate on the main ones. The format we use to specify rules of inference is as follows:

$$\frac{A, B}{C}$$

which means that if A and B are true then we can conclude C is also true. This is a standard notation used in many areas of logic within computer science.

Message Meaning Rule

$$\frac{A| \equiv A \overset{K}{\leftrightarrow} B, A \lhd \{X\}_K}{A| \equiv B| \sim X}.$$

In words, if both

- A believes she shares the key K with B,

- A sees X encrypted under the key K,

we can deduce that A believes that B once said X. Note that this implicitly assumes that A never said X.

Nonce Verification Rule

$$\frac{A| \equiv \#X, A| \equiv B| \sim X}{A| \equiv B| \equiv X}.$$

In words, if both

- A believes X is fresh (i.e. recent),

- A believes B once said X,

then we can deduce that A believes that B still believes X.

Jurisdiction Rule

$$\frac{A| \equiv B| \Rightarrow X, A| \equiv B| \equiv X}{A| \equiv X}.$$

In words, if both

- A believes B has jurisdiction over X, i.e. A trusts B on X,

- A believes B believes X,

then we conclude that A also believes X.

Other Rules

The belief operator and conjunction can be manipulated as follows:

$$\frac{P|\equiv X, P|\equiv Y}{P|\equiv(X,Y)}, \quad \frac{P|\equiv(X,Y)}{P|\equiv X}, \quad \frac{P|\equiv Q|\equiv(X,Y)}{P|\equiv Q|\equiv X}.$$

A similar rule also applies to the 'once said' operator

$$\frac{P|\equiv Q|\sim(X,Y)}{P|\equiv Q|\sim X}.$$

Note that $P|\equiv Q|\sim X$ and $P|\equiv Q|\sim Y$ does not imply $P|\equiv Q|\sim(X,Y)$, since that would imply X and Y were said at the same time. Finally, if part of a formula is fresh then so is the whole formula

$$\frac{P|\equiv\#X}{P|\equiv\#(X,Y)}.$$

We wish to analyse a key agreement protocol between A and B using the BAN logic. But what is the goal of such a protocol? The minimum we want to achieve is

$$A|\equiv A \overset{K}{\leftrightarrow} B \text{ and } B|\equiv A \overset{K}{\leftrightarrow} B,$$

i.e. both parties believe they share a secret key with each other.

However, we could expect to achieve more, for example

$$A|\equiv B|\equiv A \overset{K}{\leftrightarrow} B \text{ and } B|\equiv A|\equiv A \overset{K}{\leftrightarrow} B,$$

which is called key confirmation. In words, we may want to achieve that, after the protocol has run, A is assured that B knows he is sharing a key with A, and it is the same key A believes she is sharing with B.

Before analysing a protocol using the BAN logic we convert the protocol into logical statements. This process is called *idealization*, and is the most error prone part of the procedure since it cannot be automated. We also need to specify the assumptions, or axioms, which hold at the beginning of the protocol.

To see this in 'real life' we analyse the Wide-Mouth Frog protocol for key agreement using synchronized clocks.

6.3.1 Wide-Mouth Frog Protocol

Recall the Wide-Mouth Frog protocol

$$A \longrightarrow S : A, \{T_a, B, K_{ab}\}_{K_{as}},$$
$$S \longrightarrow B : \{T_s, A, K_{ab}\}_{K_{bs}}.$$

This becomes the idealized protocol

$$A \longrightarrow S : \{T_a, A \overset{K_{ab}}{\leftrightarrow} B\}_{K_{as}},$$
$$S \longrightarrow B : \{T_s, A|\equiv A \overset{K_{ab}}{\leftrightarrow} B\}_{K_{bs}}.$$

One should read the idealization of the first message as telling S that

- T_a is a timestamp/nonce,

- K_{ab} is a key which is meant as a key to communicate with B.

So what assumptions exist at the start of the protocol? Clearly A, B and S share secret keys which in BAN logic becomes

$$A| \equiv A \overset{K_{as}}{\leftrightarrow} S, \qquad S| \equiv A \overset{K_{as}}{\leftrightarrow} S,$$
$$B| \equiv B \overset{K_{bs}}{\leftrightarrow} S, \qquad S| \equiv B \overset{K_{bs}}{\leftrightarrow} S.$$

There are a couple of nonce assumptions,

$$S| \equiv \#T_a \text{ and } B| \equiv \#T_s.$$

Finally, we have the following three assumptions

- B trusts A to invent good keys,

$$B| \equiv (A| \Rightarrow A \overset{K_{ab}}{\leftrightarrow} B),$$

- B trusts S to relay the key from A,

$$B| \equiv (S| \Rightarrow A| \equiv A \overset{K_{ab}}{\leftrightarrow} B),$$

- A knows the session key in advance,

$$A| \equiv A \overset{K_{ab}}{\leftrightarrow} B.$$

Notice how these last three assumptions specify the problems we associated with this protocol in the earlier section.

Using these assumptions we can now analyse the protocol. Let us see what we can deduce from the first message

$$A \longrightarrow S : \{T_a, A \overset{K_{ab}}{\leftrightarrow} B\}_{K_{as}}.$$

- Since S sees the message encrypted under K_{as} he can deduce that A said the message.

- Since T_a is believed by S to be fresh he concludes the whole message is fresh.

- Since the whole message is fresh, S concludes that A currently believes the whole of it.

- S then concludes

$$S| \equiv A| \equiv A \overset{K_{ab}}{\leftrightarrow} B,$$

which is what we need to conclude so that S can send the second message of the protocol.

We now look at what happens when we analyse the second message

$$S \longrightarrow B : \{T_s, A| \equiv A \overset{K_{ab}}{\leftrightarrow} B\}_{K_{bs}}.$$

- Since B sees the message encrypted under K_{bs} he can deduce that S said the message.

- Since T_s is believed by B to be fresh he concludes the whole message is fresh.

- Since the whole message is fresh, B concludes that S currently believes the whole of it.

- So B believes that S believes the second part of the message.

- But B believes S has authority on whether A knows the key and B believes A has authority to generate the key.

So we conclude

$$B| \equiv A \overset{K_{ab}}{\leftrightarrow} B$$

and

$$B| \equiv A| \equiv A \overset{K_{ab}}{\leftrightarrow} B.$$

Combining with our axiom $A| \equiv A \overset{K_{ab}}{\leftrightarrow} B$ we conclude that the key agreement protocol is sound. The only requirement we have not met is that

$$A| \equiv B| \equiv A \overset{K_{ab}}{\leftrightarrow} B,$$

i.e. A does not achieve confirmation that B has received the key.

Notice what the application of the BAN logic has done is to make the axioms clearer, so it is easier to compare which assumptions each protocol needs to make it work. In addition it clarifies what the result of running the protocol is from all parties' points of view.

Chapter Summary

- Distributing secret keys used for symmetric ciphers can be a major problem.

- To distribute a key via a number of channels one can use a threshold secret sharing scheme.

- A number of key agreement protocols exist based on a trusted third party and symmetric encryption algorithms. These protocols require long-term keys to have been already established with the TTP, they may also require some form of clock synchronization.

- Various logics exist to analyse such protocols. The most influential of these has been the BAN logic. These logics help to identify explicit assumptions and problems associated with each protocol.

Further Reading

A nice introduction to more advanced secret sharing schemes can be found in Chapter 11 of Stinson. The paper by Burrows, Abadi and Needham is a very readable introduction to the BAN logic and a number of key agreement protocols, much of our treatment is based on this paper.

M. Burrows, M. Abadi and R. Needham. *A Logic of Authentication.* Digital Equipment Corporation, SRC Research Report 39, 1990.

D. Stinson. *Cryptography: Theory and Practice.* CRC Press, 1995.

Review Exercises

6.1.1   What is the key distribution problem?

6.1.2   What is a secret sharing scheme with threshold t?

6.1.3   How are nonces used in the protocols in this chapter? What security goals does the use of nonces allow us to guarantee?

6.1.4   In the BAN logic explain the meaning of the following symbols

$$P| \equiv X, P \lhd X \text{ and } P| \sim X.$$

6.1.5   Give explanations as to why the following rules of inference are valid as postulates.
Message Meaning Rule

$$\frac{A| \equiv A \overset{K}{\leftrightarrow} B, A \lhd \{X\}_K}{A| \equiv B| \sim X}.$$

Nonce Verification Rule

$$\frac{A| \equiv \#X, A| \equiv B| \sim X}{A| \equiv B| \equiv X}.$$

Jurisdiction Rule

$$\frac{A| \equiv B| \Rightarrow X, A| \equiv B| \equiv X}{A| \equiv X}.$$

6.1.6   Why in the Needham–Schroeder protocol do we not make the fifth message equal to

$$A \longrightarrow B : \{N_b\}_{K_{ab}}?$$

Standard Exercises

6.2.1   Formally go through our analysis of the Wide-Mouth Frog protocol using BAN logic and decide which postulates were used at which stage of the analysis.

6.2.2   Prove that the method of Lagrange interpolation actually recovers the secret key in the Shamir secret sharing scheme.

6.2.3   Alice and Bob know the one-time pad is totally secure, but do not wish to go through all the effort of distributing secret keys. They therefore come up with the following protocol based on the one-time pad to encrypt a message M from Alice to Bob. Both Alice and Bob compute a per message secret, known only to themselves, i.e. only Alice knows a and only Bob knows b.

$$A \longrightarrow B : A_1 = M \oplus a,$$
$$B \longrightarrow A : B_1 = A_1 \oplus b,$$
$$A \longrightarrow B : A_2 = B_1 \oplus a.$$

Show that after executing this protocol Bob can recover the message by computing

$$A_2 \oplus b.$$

Also show that Eve, the eavesdropper, can also recover the message M.

PART

III

Public Key Encryption and Signatures

Public key techniques were originally invented to solve the key distribution problem and to provide authenticity. They have many advantages over symmetric systems, the main one is that they do not require two communicating parties to know each other before encrypted communication can take place. In addition the use of digital signatures allows users to sign digital data such as electronic orders or money transfers. Hence, public key technology is one of the key enabling technologies for e-commerce and a digital society.

Basic Public Key Encryption Algorithms

Chapter Goals

- To learn about public key encryption and the hard problems on which it is based.

- To understand the RSA algorithm and the assumptions on which its security relies.

- To understand the ElGamal encryption algorithm and it assumptions.

- To learn about the Rabin encryption algorithm and its assumptions.

7.1 PUBLIC KEY CRYPTOGRAPHY

Recall that in symmetric key cryptography each communicating party needed to have a copy of the same secret key. This led to a very difficult key management problem. In public key cryptography we replace the use of identical keys with two keys, one public and one private.

The public key can be published in a directory along with the user's name. Anyone who then wishes to send a message to the holder of the associated private key will take the public key, encrypt a message under it and send it to the owner of the corresponding private key. The idea is that only the holder of the private key will be able to decrypt the message. More clearly, we have the transforms

$$\text{Message} + \text{Alice's public key} = \text{Ciphertext},$$
$$\text{Ciphertext} + \text{Alice's private key} = \text{Message}.$$

Hence anyone with Alice's public key can send Alice a secret message. But only Alice can decrypt the message, since only Alice has the corresponding private key.

Public key systems work because the two keys are linked in a mathematical way, such that knowing the public key tells you nothing about the private key. But knowing the private key allows you to unlock information encrypted with the public key. This may seem strange, and will require some thought and patience to understand. The concept was so strange it was not until 1976 that anyone thought of it. The idea was first presented in the seminal paper of Diffie and Hellman entitled *New Directions in Cryptography.* Although Diffie and Hellman invented the concept of public key cryptography it was not until a year or so later that the first (and most successful) system, namely RSA, was invented.

The previous paragraph is how the 'official' history of public key cryptography goes. However, in the late 1990s an unofficial history came to light. It turned out that in 1969, over five years before Diffie and Hellman invented public key cryptography, a cryptographer called James Ellis, working for the British government's communication headquarters GCHQ, invented the concept of public key cryptography (or non-secret encryption as he called it) as a means of solving the key distribution problem. Ellis, just like Diffie and Hellman, did not however have a system.

The problem of finding such a public key encryption system was given to a new recruit to GCHQ called Clifford Cocks in 1973. Within a day Cocks had invented what was essentially the RSA algorithm, although a full four years before Rivest, Shamir and Adleman. In 1974 another employee at GCHQ, Malcolm Williamson, invented the concept of Diffie–Hellman key exchange, which we shall return to in Chapter 10. Hence, by 1974 the British security services had already discovered the main techniques in public key cryptography.

There is a surprisingly small number of ideas behind public key encryption algorithms, which may explain why once Diffie and Hellman or Ellis had the concept of public key encryption, an invention of essentially the same cipher, i.e. RSA, came so quickly. There are so few ideas because we require a mathematical operation which is easy to do one way, i.e. encryption, but which is hard to do the other way, i.e. decryption, without some special secret information, namely the private key. Such a mathematical function is called a trapdoor one-way function, since it is effectively a one-way function unless one knows the key to the trapdoor.

Luckily there are a number of possible one-way functions which have been well studied, such as factoring integers, computing discrete logarithms or computing square roots modulo a composite number. In the next section we shall study such one-way functions, before presenting some public key encryption algorithms later in the chapter. However, these are only computational one-way functions in that given enough computing power one can invert these functions faster than exhaustive search.

7.2   CANDIDATE ONE-WAY FUNCTIONS

The most important one-way function used in public key cryptography is that of factoring integers. By factoring an integer we mean finding its prime factors, for example

$$10 = 2 \cdot 5$$
$$60 = 2^2 \cdot 3 \cdot 5$$
$$2^{113} - 1 = 3391 \cdot 23\,279 \cdot 65\,993 \cdot 1\,868\,569 \cdot 1\,066\,818\,132\,868\,207$$

Finding the factors is an expensive computational operation. To measure the complexity of algorithms to factor an integer N we often use the function

$$L_N(\alpha, \beta) = \exp\left((\beta + o(1))(\log N)^\alpha (\log \log N)^{1-\alpha}\right).$$

Notice that if an algorithm to factor an integer has complexity $O(L_N(0, \beta))$, then it runs in polynomial time (recall the input size of the problem is $\log N$). However, if an algorithm to factor an integer has complexity $O(L_N(1, \beta))$ then it runs in exponential time. Hence, the function $L_N(\alpha, \beta)$ for $0 < \alpha < 1$ interpolates between polynomial and exponential time. An algorithm with complexity $O(L_N(\alpha, \beta))$ for $0 < \alpha < 1$ is said to have sub-exponential behaviour. Notice that multiplication, which is the inverse algorithm to factoring, is a very simple operation requiring time less than $O(L_N(0, 2))$.

There are a number of methods to factor numbers of the form

$$N = p \cdot q,$$

some of which we shall discuss in a later chapter. For now we just summarize the most well-known techniques.

- **Trial Division:** Try every prime number up to $\sqrt{N}$ and see if it is a factor of N. This has complexity $L_N(1, 1)$, and is therefore an exponential algorithm.

- **Elliptic Curve Method:** This is a very good method if $p < 2^{50}$, its complexity is $L_p(1/2, c)$, which is sub-exponential. Notice that the complexity is given in terms of the size of the unknown value p. If the number is a product of two primes of very unequal size then the elliptic curve method may be the best at finding the factors.

- **Quadratic Sieve:** This is probably the fastest method for factoring integers of between 80 and 100 decimal digits. It has complexity $L_N(1/2, 1)$.

- **Number Field Sieve:** This is currently the most successful method for numbers with more than 100 decimal digits. It can factor numbers of the size of $10^{155} \approx 2^{512}$ and has complexity $L_N(1/3, 1.923)$.

There are a number of other hard problems related to factoring which can be used to produce public key cryptosystems. Suppose you are given N but not its factors p and q, there are four main problems which one can try to solve:

- **FACTORING:** Find p and q.

- **RSA:** Given e such that

$$\gcd(e, (p-1)(q-1)) = 1$$

and c, find m such that

$$m^e = c \pmod{N}.$$

- **QUADRES:** Given a, determine whether a is a square modulo N.

- **SQRROOT:** Given a such that

$$a = x^2 \pmod{N},$$

find x.

Another important class of problems are those based on the discrete logarithm problem or its variants. Let $(G, \cdot)$ be a finite abelian group, such as the multiplicative group of a finite field or the set of points on an elliptic curve over a finite field. The discrete logarithm problem, or DLOG problem, in G is given $g, h \in G$, find an integer x (if it exists) such that

$$g^x = h.$$

For some groups G this problem is easy. For example if we take G to be the integers modulo a number N under addition then given $g, h \in \mathbb{Z}/N\mathbb{Z}$ we need to solve

$$x \cdot g = h.$$

We have already seen in Chapter 1 that we can easily tell whether such an equation has a solution, and determine its solution when it does, using the extended Euclidean algorithm.

For certain other groups determining discrete logarithms is believed to be hard. For example in the multiplicative group of a finite field the best known algorithm for this task is the Number Field Sieve. The complexity of determining discrete logarithms in this case is given by

$$L_N(1/3, c)$$

for some constant c, depending on the type of the finite field, e.g. whether it is a large prime field or an extension field of characteristic two.

For other groups, such as elliptic curve groups, the discrete logarithm problem is believed to be even harder. The best known algorithm for finding discrete logarithms on a general elliptic curve defined over a finite field $\mathbb{F}_q$ is Pollard's Rho method which has complexity

$$\sqrt{q} = L_q(1, 1/2).$$

Hence, this is a fully exponential algorithm. Since determining elliptic curve discrete logarithms is harder than in the case of multiplicative groups of finite fields we are able to use smaller groups. This leads to an advantage in key size. Elliptic curve cryptosystems often have much smaller key sizes (say 160 bits) compared with those based on factoring or discrete logarithms in finite fields (where for both the 'equivalent' recommended key size is about 1024 bits).

Just as with the FACTORING problem, there are a number of related problems associated to discrete logarithms; again suppose we are given a finite abelian group $(G, \cdot)$ and $g \in G$.

- **DLP:** This is the discrete logarithm problem considered above. Namely given $g, h \in G$ such that $h = g^x$, find x.

- **DHP:** This is the Diffie–Hellman problem. Given $g \in G$ and

$$a = g^x \text{ and } b = g^y,$$

  find c such that

$$c = g^{xy}.$$

- **DDH:** This is the decision Diffie–Hellman problem. Given $g \in G$ and

$$a = g^x, b = g^y \text{ and } c = g^z,$$

  determine if $z = x \cdot y$.

When giving all these problems it is important to know how they are all related. This is done by giving complexity theoretic reductions from one problem to another. This allows us to say that 'Problem A is no harder than Problem B'. We do this by assuming an oracle (or efficient algorithm) to solve Problem B. We then use this oracle to give an efficient algorithm for Problem A. Hence, we reduce the problem of solving Problem A to inventing an efficient algorithm to solve Problem B. The algorithms which perform these reductions should be efficient, in that they run in polynomial time, where we treat each oracle query as a single step.

We can also show *equivalence* between two problems A and B, by showing an efficient reduction from A to B and an efficient reduction from B to A. If the two reductions are both polynomial-time reductions then we say that the two problems are *polynomial-time equivalent*.

As an example we first show how to reduce solving the Diffie–Hellman problem to the discrete logarithm problem.

Lemma 7.1 *In an arbitrary finite abelian group G the DHP is no harder than the DLP.*

Proof
Suppose I have an oracle $\mathcal{O}_{\text{DLP}}$ which will solve the DLP for me, i.e. on input of $h = g^x$ it will return x. To solve the DHP on input of $a = g^x$ and $b = g^y$ we compute

1. $z = \mathcal{O}_{\text{DLP}}(a)$.

2. $c = b^z$.

3. Output c.

The above reduction clearly runs in polynomial time and will compute the true solution to the DHP, assuming the oracle returns the correct value, i.e.

$$z = x.$$

Hence, the DHP is no harder than the DLP.

Q.E.D.

In some groups there is a more complicated argument to show that the DHP is in fact equivalent to the DLP.

We now show how to reduce the solution of the decision Diffie–Hellman problem to the Diffie–Hellman problem, and hence using our previous argument to the discrete logarithm problem.

Lemma 7.2 *In an arbitrary finite abelian group G the DDH is no harder than the DHP.*

Proof
Now suppose we have an oracle $\mathcal{O}_{\text{DHP}}$ which on input of g^x and g^y computes the value of g^{xy}. To solve the DDH on input of $a = g^x, b = g^y$ and $c = g^z$ we compute

1. $d = \mathcal{O}_{\text{DHP}}(a, b)$.

2. If $d = c$ output YES.

3. Else output NO.

Again the reduction clearly runs in polynomial time, and assuming the output of the oracle is correct then the above reduction will solve the DDH.

Q.E.D.

So the decision Diffie–Hellman problem is no harder than the computational Diffie–Hellman problem. There are however some groups in which one can solve the DDH in polynomial time but the fastest known algorithm to solve the DHP takes sub-exponential time.

Hence, of our three DLOG based problems, the easiest is DDH, then comes DHP and finally the hardest problem is DLP.

We now turn to show reductions for the factoring based problems. The most important result is

Lemma 7.3 *The FACTORING and SQRROOT problems are polynomial-time equivalent.*

Proof

We first show how to reduce SQRROOT to FACTORING. Assume we are given a factoring oracle, we wish to show how to use this to extract square roots modulo a composite number N. Namely, given

$$z = x^2 \pmod{N}$$

we wish to compute x. First we factor N into its prime factors p_i using the factoring oracle. Then we compute

$$s_i = \sqrt{z} \pmod{p_i},$$

this can be done in expected polynomial time using Shank's Algorithm. Then we compute the value of x using the Chinese Remainder Theorem on the data

$$s_i = \sqrt{z} \pmod{p_i}.$$

One has to be a little careful if powers of p_i greater than one divide N, but this is easy to deal with and will not concern us here. Hence, finding square roots modulo N is no harder than factoring.

We now show that FACTORING can be reduced to SQRROOT. Assume we are given an oracle for extracting square roots modulo a composite number N. We shall assume for simplicity that N is a product of two primes, which is the most difficult case. The general case is only slightly more tricky mathematically, but it is computationally easier since factoring numbers with three or more prime factors is usually easier than factoring numbers with two prime factors.

We wish to use our oracle for the problem SQRROOT to factor the integer N into its prime factors, i.e. given $N = p \cdot q$ we wish to compute p. First we pick a random $x \in (\mathbb{Z}/N\mathbb{Z})^*$ and compute

$$z = x^2 \pmod{N}.$$

Now we compute

$$y = \sqrt{z} \pmod{N}$$

using the SQRROOT oracle. There are four such square roots, since N is a product of two primes. With 50 percent probability we obtain

$$y \neq \pm x \pmod{N}.$$

If we do not obtain this inequality then we simply repeat the method. We expect after an average number of two repetitions we will obtain the desired inequality.

Now, since $x^2 = y^2 \pmod{N}$, we see that N divides

$$x^2 - y^2 = (x - y)(x + y).$$

But N does not divide either $x - y$ or $x + y$, since $y \neq \pm x \pmod{N}$. So the factors of N must be distributed over these later two pairs of numbers. This means we can obtain a non-trivial factor of N by computing $\gcd(x - y, N)$

Clearly both of the above reductions can be performed in expected polynomial time. Hence, the problems FACTORING and SQRROOT are polynomial-time equivalent.

Q.E.D.

The above proof contains an important tool used in factoring algorithms, namely the construction of a difference of two squares. We shall return to this later in Chapter 8.

Before leaving the problem SQRROOT notice that QUADRES is easier than SQRROOT, since an algorithm to compute square roots modulo N can be used to determine quadratic residuosity.

Finally we end this section by showing that the RSA problem can be reduced to FACTORING. Recall the RSA problem is given $c = m^e \pmod{N}$, find m.

Lemma 7.4 *The RSA problem is no harder than the FACTORING problem.*

Proof

Using a factoring oracle we first find the factorization of N. We can now compute $\Phi = \phi(N)$ and then compute

$$d = 1/e \pmod{\Phi}.$$

Once d has been computed it is easy to recover m via

$$c^d = m^{ed} = m^{1 \pmod{\Phi}} = m \pmod{N}.$$

Hence, the RSA problem is no harder than FACTORING.

Q.E.D.

There is some evidence, although slight, that the RSA problem may actually be easier than FACTORING for some problem instances. It is a major open question as to how much easier it is.

7.3   RSA

The RSA algorithm was the world's first public key encryption algorithm, and it has stood the test of time remarkably well. The RSA algorithm is based on the difficulty of the RSA problem considered in the previous section, and hence it is based on the difficulty of finding the prime factors of large integers. We have seen that it may be possible to solve the RSA problem without factoring, hence the RSA algorithm is not based completely on the difficulty of factoring.

Suppose Alice wishes to enable anyone to send her secret messages, which only she can decrypt. She first picks two large secret prime numbers p and q. Alice then computes

$$N = p \cdot q.$$

Alice also chooses an encryption exponent e which satisfies

$$\gcd(e, (p-1)(q-1)) = 1.$$

It is common to choose $e = 3, 17$ or $65\,537$. Now Alice's public key is the pair (N, e), which she can publish in a public directory. To compute the private key Alice applies the extended Euclidean algorithm to e and $(p-1)(q-1)$ to obtain the decryption exponent d, which should satisfy

$$e \cdot d \equiv 1 \pmod{(p-1)(q-1)}.$$

Alice keeps secret her private key, which is the triple (d, p, q). Actually, she could simply throw away p and q, and retain a copy of her public key which contains the integer N, but we shall see later that this is not efficient.

Now suppose Bob wishes to encrypt a message to Alice. He first looks up Alice's public key and represents the message as a number m which is strictly less than the public modulus N. The ciphertext is then produced by raising the message to the power of the public encryption exponent modulo the public modulus, i.e.

$$c = m^e \pmod{N}.$$

Alice on receiving c can decrypt the ciphertext to recover the message by exponentiating by the private decryption exponent, i.e.

$$m = c^d \pmod{N}.$$

This works since the group $(\mathbb{Z}/N\mathbb{Z})^*$ has order

$$\phi(N) = (p-1)(q-1)$$

and so, by Lagrange's Theorem,

$$x^{(p-1)(q-1)} \equiv 1 \pmod{N},$$

for all $x \in (\mathbb{Z}/N\mathbb{Z})^*$. For some integer s we have

$$ed - s(p-1)(q-1) = 1,$$

and so

$$\begin{aligned}
c^d &= (m^e)^d \\
&= m^{ed} \\
&= m^{1+s(p-1)(q-1)} \\
&= m \cdot m^{s(p-1)(q-1)} \\
&= m.
\end{aligned}$$

To make things clearer let's consider a baby example. Choose $p = 7$ and $q = 11$, and so $N = 77$ and $(p-1)(q-1) = 6 \cdot 10 = 60$. We pick as the public encryption exponent

$e = 37$, since we have $\gcd(37, 60) = 1$. Then, applying the extended Euclidean algorithm we obtain $d = 13$ since

$$37 \cdot 13 = 481 = 1 \ (\text{mod } 60).$$

Suppose the message we wish to transmit is given by $m = 2$, then to encrypt m we compute

$$c = m^e \ (\text{mod } N) = 2^{37} \ (\text{mod } 77) = 51,$$

whilst to decrypt the ciphertext c we compute

$$m = c^d \ (\text{mod } N) = 51^{13} \ (\text{mod } 77) = 2.$$

7.3.1   RSA Encryption and the RSA Problem

The security of RSA on first inspection relies on the difficulty of finding the private encryption exponent d given only the public key, namely the public modulus N and the public encryption exponent e.

We have shown that the RSA problem is no harder than FACTORING, hence if we can factor N then we can find p and q and hence we can calculate d. Hence, if factoring is easy we can break RSA. Currently 500-bit numbers are the largest that have been factored and so it is recommended that one takes public moduli of size around 1024 bits to ensure medium-term security. For long-term security one would need to take a public modulus size of over 2048 bits.

In this chapter we shall consider security to be defined as being unable to recover the whole plaintext given the ciphertext. We shall argue in a later chapter that this is far too weak a definition of security for many applications. In addition in a later chapter we shall show that RSA, as we have described it, is not secure against a chosen ciphertext attack.

For a public key algorithm the adversary always has access to the encryption algorithm, hence she can always mount a chosen plaintext attack. RSA is secure against a chosen plaintext attack assuming our weak definition of security and that the RSA problem is hard. To show this we use the reduction arguments of the previous section. This example is rather trivial but we labour the point since these arguments are used over and over again in later chapters.

Lemma 7.5 *If the RSA problem is hard then the RSA system is secure under a chosen plaintext attack, in the sense that an attacker is unable to recover the whole plaintext given the ciphertext.*

Proof
We wish to give an algorithm which solves the RSA problem using an algorithm to break the RSA cryptosystem as an oracle. If we can show this then we can conclude that the breaking the RSA cryptosystem is no harder than solving the RSA problem.

Recall that the RSA problem is given $N = p \cdot q$, e and $y \in (\mathbb{Z}/N\mathbb{Z})^*$, compute an x such that $x^e \ (\text{mod } N) = y$. We use our oracle to break the RSA encryption algorithm to 'decrypt' the message corresponding to $c = y$, this oracle will return the plaintext message m. Then our RSA problem is solved by setting $x = m$ since, by definition,

$$m^e \ (\text{mod } N) = c = y.$$

So if we can break the RSA algorithm then we can solve the RSA problem.

Q.E.D.

7.3.2   Knowledge of the Private Exponent and Factoring

Whilst it is unclear whether breaking RSA, in the sense of inverting the RSA function, is equivalent to factoring, determining the private key d given the public information N and e is equivalent to factoring.

Lemma 7.6 *If one knows the RSA decryption exponent d corresponding to the public key (N, e) then one can efficiently factor N.*

Proof
Recall that for some integer s

$$ed - 1 = s(p - 1)(q - 1).$$

We pick an integer $x \neq 0$, this is guaranteed to satisfy

$$x^{ed-1} = 1 \ (\text{mod } N).$$

We now compute a square root y_1 of one modulo N,

$$y_1 = \sqrt{x^{ed-1}} = x^{(ed-1)/2},$$

which we can do since $ed - 1$ is known and will be even. We will then have the identity

$$y_1{}^2 - 1 \equiv 0 \ (\text{mod } N),$$

which we can use to recover a factor of N via computing

$$\gcd(y_1 - 1, N).$$

But this will only work when $y_1 \neq \pm 1 \ (\text{mod } N)$.

Now suppose we are unlucky and we obtain $y_1 = \pm 1 \ (\text{mod } N)$ rather than a factor of N. If $y_1 = -1 \ (\text{mod } N)$ we return to the beginning and pick another value of x. This leaves us with the case $y_1 = 1 \ (\text{mod } N)$, in which case we take another square root of one via,

$$y_2 = \sqrt{y_1} = x^{(ed-1)/4}.$$

Again we have

$$y_2{}^2 - 1 = y_1 - 1 = 0 \ (\text{mod } N).$$

Hence we compute

$$\gcd(y_2 - 1, N)$$

and see if this gives a factor of N. Again this will give a factor of N unless $y_2 = \pm 1$, if we are unlucky we repeat once more and so on.

This method can be repeated until either we have factored N or until $(ed - 1)/2^t$ is no longer divisible by 2. In this latter case we return to the beginning, choose a new random value of x and start again.

Q.E.D.

The algorithm in the above proof is an example of a Las Vegas Algorithm: It is probabilistic in nature in the sense that whilst it may not actually give an answer (or terminate), it is however guaranteed that when it does give an answer then that answer will always be correct.

We shall now present a small example of the previous method. Consider the following RSA parameters

$$N = 1\,441\,499, e = 17 \text{ and } d = 507\,905.$$

Recall we are assuming that the private exponent d is public knowledge. We will show that the previous method does in fact find a factor of N. Put

$$t_1 = (ed - 1)/2 = 4\,317\,192,$$
$$x = 2.$$

To compute y_1 we evaluate

$$y_1 = x^{(ed-1)/2},$$
$$= 2^{t_1},$$
$$= 1 \pmod{N}.$$

Since we obtain $y_1 = 1$ we need to set

$$t_2 = t_1/2 = (ed - 1)/4 = 2\,158\,596,$$
$$y_2 = 2^{t_2}.$$

We now compute y_2,

$$y_2 = x^{(ed-1)/4},$$
$$= 2^{t_2},$$
$$= 1 \pmod{N}.$$

So we need to repeat the method again, this time we obtain $t_3 = (ed-1)/8 = 1\,079\,298$. We compute y_3,

$$y_3 = x^{(ed-1)/8},$$
$$= 2^{t_3},$$
$$= 119\,533 \pmod{N}.$$

So

$$y_3{}^2 - 1 = (y_3 - 1)(y_3 + 1) \equiv 0 \pmod{N},$$

and we compute a prime factor of N by evaluating

$$\gcd(y_3 - 1, N) = 1423.$$

7.3.3   Knowledge of $\phi(N)$ and Factoring

We have seen that knowledge of d allows us to factor N. Now we will show that knowledge of $\Phi = \phi(N)$ also allows us to factor N.

Lemma 7.7 *Given an RSA modulus N and the value of $\Phi = \phi(N)$ one can efficiently factor N.*

Proof

We have
$$\Phi = (p-1)(q-1) = N - (p+q) + 1.$$

Hence, if we set $S = N + 1 - \Phi$, we obtain
$$S = p + q.$$

So we need to determine p and q from their sum S and product N. Define the polynomial
$$f(X) = (X - p) \cdot (X - q) = X^2 - SX + N.$$

So we can find p and q by solving $f(X) = 0$ using the standard formulae for extracting the roots of a quadratic polynomial,
$$p = \frac{S + \sqrt{S^2 - 4N}}{2},$$
$$q = \frac{S - \sqrt{S^2 - 4N}}{2}.$$

Q.E.D.

As an example consider the RSA public modulus $N = 18\,923$. Assume that we are given $\Phi = \phi(N) = 18\,648$. We then compute
$$S = p + q = N + 1 - \Phi = 276.$$

Using this we compute the polynomial
$$f(X) = X^2 - SX + N = X^2 - 276X + 18\,923$$

and find that its roots over the real numbers are
$$p = 149, q = 127$$

which are indeed the factors of N.

7.3.4 Use of a Shared Modulus

Since modular arithmetic is very expensive it can be very tempting for a system to be set up in which a number of users share the same public modulus N but use different public/private exponents, (e_i, d_i). One reason to do this could be to allow very fast hardware acceleration of modular arithmetic, specially tuned to the chosen shared modulus N. This is, however, a very silly idea since it can be attacked in one of two ways, either by a malicious insider or by an external attacker.

Suppose the bad guy is one of the internal users, say user number one. He can now compute the value of the decryption exponent for user number two, namely d_2. First user one computes p and q since they know d_1, via the algorithm in the proof of Lemma 7.6. Then user one computes $\phi(N) = (p-1)(q-1)$, and finally they can recover d_2 from
$$d_2 = \frac{1}{e_2} \ (\text{mod } \phi(N)).$$

Now suppose the attacker is not one of the people who share the modulus. Suppose Alice sends the same message m to two of the users with public keys

$$(N, e_1) \text{ and } (N, e_2),$$

i.e. $N_1 = N_2 = N$. Eve, the external attacker, sees the messages c_1 and c_2 where

$$c_1 = m^{e_1} \pmod{N},$$
$$c_2 = m^{e_2} \pmod{N}.$$

Eve can now compute

$$t_1 = e_1^{-1} \pmod{e_2},$$
$$t_2 = (t_1 e_1 - 1)/e_2,$$

and can recover the message m from

$$c_1^{t_1} c_2^{-t_2} = m^{e_1 t_1} m^{-e_2 t_2}$$
$$= m^{1 + e_2 t_2} m^{-e_2 t_2}$$
$$= m^{1 + e_2 t_2 - e_2 t_2}$$
$$= m^1 = m.$$

As an example of this external attack, take the public keys as

$$N = N_1 = N_2 = 18\,923, \ e_1 = 11 \text{ and } e_2 = 5.$$

Now suppose Eve sees the ciphertexts

$$c_1 = 1514 \text{ and } c_2 = 8189$$

corresponding to the same plaintext m. Then Eve computes $t_1 = 1$ and $t_2 = 2$, and recovers the message
$$m = c_1^{t_1} c_2^{-t_2} = 100 \pmod{N}.$$

7.3.5 Use of a Small Public Exponent

Fielded RSA systems often use a small public exponent e so as to cut down the computational cost of the sender. We shall now show that this can also lead to problems. Suppose we have three users all with different public moduli

$$N_1, N_2 \text{ and } N_3.$$

In addition suppose they all have the same small public exponent $e = 3$. Suppose someone sends them the same message m.

The attacker Eve sees the messages

$$c_1 = m^3 \pmod{N_1},$$
$$c_2 = m^3 \pmod{N_2},$$
$$c_3 = m^3 \pmod{N_3}.$$

Now the attacker, using the Chinese Remainder Theorem, computes the simultaneous solution to

$$X = c_i \pmod{N_i} \text{ for } i = 1, 2, 3,$$

to obtain

$$X = m^3 \pmod{N_1 N_2 N_3}.$$

But since $m^3 < N_1 N_2 N_3$ we must have $X = m^3$ identically over the integers. Hence we can recover m by taking the real cube root of X.

As a simple example of this attack take,

$$N_1 = 323, N_2 = 299 \text{ and } N_3 = 341.$$

Suppose Eve sees the ciphertexts

$$c_1 = 50, c_2 = 268 \text{ and } c_3 = 1,$$

and wants to determine the common value of m. Eve computes via the Chinese Remainder Theorem

$$X = 300\,763 \pmod{N_1 N_2 N_3}.$$

Finally, she computes over the integers

$$m = X^{1/3} = 67.$$

This attack and the previous one are interesting since we find the message without factoring the modulus. This is, albeit slight, evidence that breaking RSA is easier than factoring. The main lesson, however, from both these attacks is that plaintext should be randomly padded before transmission. That way the same 'message' is never encrypted to two different people. In addition one should probably avoid very small exponents for encryption, $e = 65\,537$ is the usual choice now in use. However, small public exponents for RSA signatures (see later) do not seem to have any problems.

7.4 ELGAMAL ENCRYPTION

The simplest encryption algorithm based on the discrete logarithm problem is the ElGamal encryption algorithm. In the following we shall describe the finite field analogue of ElGamal encryption, we leave it as an exercise to write down the elliptic curve variant.

Unlike the RSA algorithm, in ElGamal there are some public parameters which can be shared by a number of users. These are called the domain parameters and are given by

- p a 'large prime', by which we mean one with around 1024 bits, such that $p - 1$ is divisible by another 'medium prime' q of around 160 bits.

- g an element of $\mathbb{F}_p^*$ of order divisible by q, i.e.

$$g^{(p-1)/q} \pmod{p} \neq 1.$$

All the domain parameters do is create a public finite abelian group G of prime order q with generator g. Such domain parameters can be shared between a large number of users.

Once these domain parameters have been fixed, the public and private keys can then be determined. The private key is chosen to be an integer x, whilst the public key is given by

$$h = g^x \pmod{p}.$$

Notice that whilst each user in RSA needed to generate two large primes to set up their key pair (which is a costly task), for ElGamal each user only needs to generate a random number and perform a modular exponentiation to generate a key pair.

Messages are assumed to be non-zero elements of the field $\mathbb{F}_p^*$. To encrypt a message $m \in \mathbb{F}_p^*$ we

- generate a random ephemeral key k,

- set $c_1 = g^k$,

- set $c_2 = m \cdot h^k$,

- output the ciphertext as $c = (c_1, c_2)$.

Notice that since each message has a different ephemeral key, encrypting the same message twice will produce different ciphertexts.

To decrypt a ciphertext $c = (c_1, c_2)$ we compute

$$\frac{c_2}{c_1{}^x} = \frac{m \cdot h^k}{g^{xk}}$$
$$= \frac{m \cdot g^{xk}}{g^{xk}}$$
$$= m.$$

As an example of ElGamal encryption consider the following. We first need to set up the domain parameters. For our small example we choose

$$q = 101, \ p = 809 \text{ and } g = 3.$$

Note that q divides $p - 1$ and that g has order divisible by q in the multiplicative group of integers modulo p. The actual order of g is 808 since

$$3^{808} = 1 \pmod{p},$$

and no smaller power of g is equal to one. As a public private key pair we choose

- $x = 68$,

- $h = g^x = 65$.

Now suppose we wish to encrypt the message $m = 100$ to the user with the above ElGamal public key.

- We generate a random ephemeral key $k = 89$.

- Set $c_1 = g^k = 345$.

- Set $c_2 = m \cdot h^k = 517$.

- Output the ciphertext as $c = (345, 517)$.

The recipient can decrypt our ciphertext by computing

$$\frac{c_2}{c_1{}^x} = \frac{517}{345^{68}}$$
$$= 100.$$

This last value is computed by first computing 345^{68}, taking the inverse modulo p of the result and then multiplying this value by 517.

In a later chapter we shall see that ElGamal encryption as it stands is not secure against a chosen ciphertext attack, so usually a modified scheme is used. However, ElGamal is secure against a chosen plaintext attack, assuming the Diffie–Hellman problem is hard. Again, here we take a naive definition of what security means in that an encryption algorithm is secure if an adversary is unable to invert the encryption function.

Lemma 7.8 *Assuming the Diffie–Hellman problem (DHP) is hard then ElGamal is secure under a chosen plaintext attack, where security means it is hard for the adversary, given the ciphertext, to recover the whole of the plaintext.*

Proof
To see that ElGamal is secure under a chosen plaintext attack assuming the Diffie–Hellman problem is hard, we first suppose that we have an oracle $\mathcal{O}$ to break ElGamal. This oracle $\mathcal{O}(h, (c_1, c_2))$ takes as input a public key h and a ciphertext (c_1, c_2) and then returns the underlying plaintext. We will then show how to use this oracle to solve the DHP.
    Suppose we are given

$$g^x \text{ and } g^y$$

and we are asked to solve the DHP, i.e. we need to compute g^{xy}.
    We first set up an ElGamal public key which depends on the input to this Diffie–Hellman problem, i.e. we set

$$h = g^x.$$

Note, we do not know what the corresponding private key is. Now we write down the 'ciphertext'

$$c = (c_1, c_2),$$

where

- $c_1 = g^y$,

- c_2 is a random element of $\mathbb{F}_p^*$.

Now we input this ciphertext into our oracle which breaks ElGamal so as to produce the corresponding plaintext, $m = \mathcal{O}(h, (c_1, c_2))$. We can now solve the original Diffie-Hellman problem by computing

$$\begin{aligned}
\frac{c_2}{m} &= \frac{m \cdot h^y}{m} \quad \text{since } c_1 = g^y \\
&= h^y \\
&= g^{xy}.
\end{aligned}$$

Q.E.D.

7.5 RABIN ENCRYPTION

There is another system, due to Rabin, based on the difficulty of factoring large integers. In fact it is actually based on the difficulty of extracting square roots modulo $N = p \cdot q$. Recall that these two problems are known to be equivalent, i.e.

- knowing the factors of N means we can extract square roots modulo N,

- extracting square roots modulo N means we can factor N.

Hence, in some respects such a system should be considered more secure than RSA. Encryption in the Rabin encryption system is also much faster than almost any other public key scheme. Despite these plus points the Rabin system is not used as much as the RSA system. It is, however, useful to study for a number of reasons, both historical and theoretical. The basic idea of the system is also used in some higher level protocols.

We first choose prime numbers of the form

$$p \equiv q \equiv 3 \pmod{4}$$

since this makes extracting square roots modulo p and q very fast. The private key is then the pair (p, q). To compute the associated public key we generate a random integer $B \in \{0, \ldots, N-1\}$ and then the public key is

$$(N, B),$$

where N is the product of p and q.

To encrypt a message m, using the above public key, in the Rabin encryption algorithm we compute

$$c = m(m + B) \pmod{N}.$$

Hence, encryption involves one addition and one multiplication modulo N. Encryption is therefore much faster than RSA encryption, even when one chooses a small RSA encryption exponent.

Decryption is far more complicated, essentially we want to compute

$$m = \sqrt{\frac{B^2}{4} + c} - \frac{B}{2} \pmod{N}.$$

At first sight this uses no private information, but a moment's thought reveals that you need the factorization of N to be able to find the square root. There are however four possible square roots modulo N, since N is the product of two primes. Hence, on decryption you obtain four possible plaintexts. This means that we need to add redundancy to the plaintext before encryption in order to decide which of the four possible plaintexts corresponds to the intended one.

We still need to show why Rabin decryption works. Recall

$$c = m(m + B) \pmod{N},$$

then

$$\sqrt{\frac{B^2}{4} + c} - \frac{B}{2} = \sqrt{\frac{B^2 + 4m(m + B)}{4}} - \frac{B}{2}$$

$$= \sqrt{\frac{4m^2 + 4Bm + B^2}{4}} - \frac{B}{2}$$

$$= \sqrt{\frac{(2m + B)^2}{4}} - \frac{B}{2}$$

$$= \frac{2m + B}{2} - \frac{B}{2}$$

$$= m,$$

of course assuming the 'correct' square root is taken.

We end with an example of Rabin encryption at work. Let the public and private keys be given by

- $p = 127$ and $q = 131$,

- $N = 16\,637$ and $B = 12\,345$.

To encrypt $m = 4410$ we compute

$$c = m(m + B) \pmod{N} = 4633.$$

To decrypt we first compute

$$t = B^2/4 + c \pmod{N} = 1500.$$

We then evaluate the square root of t modulo p and q

$$\sqrt{t} \pmod{p} = \pm 22,$$
$$\sqrt{t} \pmod{q} = \pm 37.$$

Now we apply the Chinese Remainder Theorem to both

$$\pm 22 \pmod{p} \text{ and } \pm 37 \pmod{q}$$

so as to find the square root of t modulo N,

$$s = \sqrt{t} \pmod{N} = \pm 3705 \text{ or } \pm 14\,373.$$

The four possible messages are then given by the four possible values of

$$s - \frac{B}{2} = s - \frac{12\,345}{2}.$$

This leaves us with the four messages

$$4410, 5851, 15\,078, \text{ or } 16\,519.$$

Chapter Summary

- Public key encryption requires one-way functions. Examples of these are FACTORING, SQRROOT, DLP, DHP and DDH.

- There are a number of relationships between these problems. These relationships are proved by assuming an oracle for one problem and then using this in an algorithm to solve the other problem.

- RSA is the most popular public key encryption algorithm, but its security rests on the difficulty of the RSA problem and not quite on the difficulty of FACTORING.

- ElGamal encryption is a system based on the difficulty of the Diffie–Hellman problem (DHP).

- Rabin encryption is based on the difficulty of extracting square roots modulo a composite modulus. Since SQRROOT and FACTORING are polynomial-time equivalent this means that Rabin encryption is based on the difficulty of FACTORING.

Further Reading

Still the best quick introduction to the concept of public key cryptography can be found in the original paper of Diffie and Hellman. See also the original papers on ElGamal, Rabin and RSA encryption.

W. Diffie and M. Hellman. *New directions in cryptography*. IEEE Trans. on Info. Theory, **22**, 644-654, 1976.

T. ElGamal. *A public key cryptosystem and a signature scheme based on discrete logarithms*. IEEE Trans. Info. Theory, **31**, 469–472, 1985.

R.L. Rivest, A. Shamir and L.M. Adleman. *A method for obtaining digital signatures and public-key cryptosystems*. Comm. ACM, **21**, 120-126, 1978.

M. Rabin. *Digitized signatures and public key functions as intractable as factorization*. MIT/LCS/TR-212, MIT Laboratory for Computer Science, 1979.

Review Exercises

7.1.1   What is the current fastest factoring algorithm?

7.1.2   What is meant by the problems FACTORING, RSA and QUADRES? Put the problems in order of difficulty.

7.1.3   What is meant by the problems DLP, DHP and DDH? Put the problems in order of difficulty.

7.1.4   Describe the RSA encryption algorithm.

7.1.5   Could one ever have an RSA encryption exponent which was even?

7.1.6   Discuss the statements:
a) Knowing the RSA decryption exponent is equivalent to knowing the factors of the RSA modulus.
b) Breaking the RSA encryption algorithm is equivalent to factoring the RSA modulus.

7.1.7   ElGamal is a randomized encryption algorithm in that encrypting the same plaintext twice will produce different ciphertexts. Is this a good or bad property?

7.1.8   Describe two advantages that the Rabin encryption algorithm has over RSA. Are there any disadvantages of using Rabin encryption?

Programming Exercises

7.2.1   Implement programs to encrypt and decrypt messages in the RSA, ElGamal and Rabin algorithms. Which is the most efficient algorithm for encryption and which is the most efficient for decryption?

Standard Exercises

7.3.1   Let N denote an RSA exponent and let $\lambda(N) = \text{lcm}(p - 1, q - 1)$. If e is the encryption exponent, show that the decryption exponent d can be chosen so that
$$e \cdot d = 1 \ (\text{mod } \lambda(N)).$$

Hint: Show that $\lambda(N)$ is the largest order of an element in the group $(\mathbb{Z}/N\mathbb{Z})^*$.

7.3.2   Let N denote an RSA exponent and let $\lambda(N) = \text{lcm}(p-1, q-1)$. Suppose that the encryption exponent e has order k in $(\mathbb{Z}/\lambda(N)\mathbb{Z})^*$, show that

$$m^{e^k} \equiv m \ (\text{mod } N).$$

Hence, conclude that the order of e modulo $p - 1$ or modulo $q - 1$ should be large.

7.3.3   Write down an elliptic curve version of the ElGamal encryption scheme.

7.3.4   Show that if a user is stupid, and chooses a prime N as the modulus in the RSA scheme, the resulting system can be trivially broken.

7.3.5   Explain why, for large plaintexts, it is better practice to use public key encryption to transport a symmetric key, and then to use a symmetric encryption function to transmit the data.

7.3.6   Formally show that breaking the Rabin encryption algorithm is equivalent to factoring.

7.3.7   Examine the various lemmas in the text and assume the oracles only respond with the correct answer with a certain probability, for example it is only correct 1/10th of the time. Modify the statements and proofs of the results to take account of this. In which results can you 'amplify' the probability and obtain a reduction which works with high probability even though the oracle responds correctly with a lower probability?

Primality Testing and Factoring

Chapter Goals

- To explain the basics of primality testing.

- To describe the most used primality testing algorithm, namely Miller–Rabin.

- To explain various factoring algorithms.

- To sketch how the most successful factoring algorithm works, namely the Number Field Sieve.

8.1 PRIME NUMBERS

The generation of prime numbers is needed for almost all public key algorithms, for example

- In the RSA or the Rabin system we need to find primes p and q to compute the public key $N = p \cdot q$.

- In ElGamal encryption we need to find p and q with q dividing $p - 1$.

- In the elliptic curve variant of ElGamal we require an elliptic curve over a finite field, such that the order of the elliptic curve is divisible by a large prime q.

Luckily we shall see that testing a number for primality can be done very fast using very simple code, but with an algorithm which has a probability of error. By repeating this algorithm we can reduce the error probability to any value that we require.

Some of the more advanced primality testing techniques will produce a certificate which can be checked by a third party to prove that the number is indeed prime. Clearly one requirement of such a certificate is that it should be quicker to verify than it is to generate. Such a primality testing routine will be called a primality proving algorithm, and the certificate will be called a proof of primality. However, the main primality testing algorithm used in cryptographic systems only produces certificates of compositeness and not certificates of primality.

Before discussing these algorithms we need to look at some basic heuristics concerning prime numbers. A famous result in mathematics, conjectured by Gauss after extensive calculation in the early 1800s, is the Prime Number Theorem:

Theorem 8.1 (Prime Number Theorem) *The function $\pi(X)$ counts the number of primes less than X, where we have the approximation*

$$\pi(X) \approx \frac{X}{\log X}.$$

This means primes are quite common. For example the number of primes less than 2^{512} is about 2^{503}.

The Prime Number Theorem also allows us to estimate what the probability of a random number being prime is: if p is a number chosen at random then the probability it is prime is about

$$\frac{1}{\log p}.$$

So a random number p of 512 bits in length will be a prime with probability

$$\approx \frac{1}{\log p} \approx \frac{1}{177}.$$

So on average we need to select 177 numbers of size 2^{512} before we find one which is prime. Hence, it is practical to generate large primes, as long as we can test primality efficiently.

8.1.1   Trial Division

The naive test for testing a number p to be prime is one of Trial Division. We essentially take all numbers between 2 and $\sqrt{p}$ and see if they divide p, if not then p is prime. If such a number does divide p then we obtain the added bonus of finding a factor of the composite number p. Hence, Trial Division has the advantage (compared with more advanced primality testing/proving algorithms) that it either determines that p is a prime, or determines a non-trivial factor of p.

However, primality testing by using Trial Division is a terrible strategy. In the worst case, when p is a prime, the algorithm requires $\sqrt{p}$ steps to run, which is an exponential function in terms of the size of the input to the problem. Another drawback is that it does not produce a certificate for the primality of p, in the case when the input p is prime. When p is not prime it produces a certificate which can easily be checked to prove that p is composite, namely a non-trivial factor of p. But when p is prime the only way we can verify this fact again (say to convince a third party) is to repeat the algorithm once more.

Despite its drawbacks Trial Division is however the method of choice for numbers which are very small. In addition partial Trial Division, up to a bound Y, is able to eliminate all but a proportion

$$\prod_{p<Y} \left(1 - \frac{1}{p}\right)$$

of all composites. Naively this is what one would always do, since for example one would never check an even number greater than two for primality since it is obviously composite. Hence, many primality testing algorithms first do Trial Division with all primes up to say 100, so as to eliminate all but

$$\prod_{p<100} \left(1 - \frac{1}{p}\right) \approx 0.12$$

of composites.

8.1.2 Fermat's Test

Most advanced probabilistic algorithms for testing primality make use of the converse to Fermat's Little Theorem. Recall, if G is a multiplicative group of size $\#G$ then

$$a^{\#G} = 1$$

for a random $a \in G$, which was Lagrange's Theorem. So if G is the group of integers modulo n under multiplication then

$$a^{\phi(n)} = 1 \pmod{n}$$

for all $a \in (\mathbb{Z}/n\mathbb{Z})^*$. Fermat's Little Theorem was the case where $n = p$ is prime, in which case the above equality becomes

$$a^{p-1} = 1 \pmod{p}.$$

So if n is prime we have that

$$a^{n-1} = 1 \pmod{n}$$

always holds, whilst if n is not prime then we have that

$$a^{n-1} = 1 \pmod{n}$$

is unlikely to hold.

Since computing $a^{n-1} \pmod{n}$ is a very fast operation this gives us a very fast test for compositeness, called the Fermat test to the base a. Note, running the Fermat test can only convince us of the compositeness of n, it can never prove to us that a number is prime, only that it is not prime.

To see how it does not prove primality consider the case $n = 11 \cdot 31 = 341$ and the base $a = 2$, we have

$$a^{n-1} = 2^{340} = 1 \pmod{341}.$$

but n is clearly not prime. In such a case we say that n is a (Fermat) pseudo-prime to the base 2. There are infinitely many pseudo-primes to any given base, although the pseudo-primes are in fact rarer than the primes. It can be shown that if n is composite then, with probability greater than $1/2$, we obtain

$$a^{n-1} \neq 1 \pmod{n}.$$

This gives us the following algorithm to test n for primality

```
for (i=0; i<k; i++)
  { pick a from [2,...,n-1];
    b = a^{n-1} mod n;
    if (b!=1)
       { Output (Composite, a);
         exit;
       }
  }
Output ''Probably Prime''
```

If the above outputs `(Composite,a)` then we know

- n is definitely a composite number,

- a is a witness for this compositeness, in that one can verify that n is composite by using the value of a.

If the above algorithm outputs `Probably Prime` then

- n is a composite with probability at most $1/2^k$,

- n is either a prime or a so-called probable prime.

For example if we take

$$n = 43\,040\,357$$

then n is clearly a composite, with one witness given by $a = 2$ since

$$2^{n-1} \pmod{n} = 9\,888\,212.$$

As another example if we take

$$n = 2^{192} - 2^{64} - 1$$

then the algorithm outputs `Probably Prime` since we cannot find a witness for compositeness. Actually this n is a prime, so it is not surprising we did not find a witness.

However, there are composite numbers for which the Fermat test will output

Probably Prime

for every a coprime to n. These numbers are called Carmichael numbers, and to make things worse there are infinitely many of them. The first three are given by $561, 1105$ and 1729. Carmichael numbers have the following properties

- They are always odd.

- They have at least three prime factors.

- They are square free.

- If p divides a Carmichael number N then $p - 1$ divides $N - 1$.

To give you some idea of their density, if we look at all numbers less than

$$10^{16}$$

then there are about

$$2.7 \cdot 10^{14}$$

primes in this region, but only

$$246\,683 \approx 2.4 \cdot 10^5$$

Carmichael numbers in this region. Hence, Carmichael numbers are rare, but not rare enough to be ignored completely.

8.1.3 Miller–Rabin Test

Due to the existence of Carmichael numbers the Fermat test is usually avoided. However, there is a modification of the Fermat test, called the Miller–Rabin test, which avoids the problem of composites for which no witness exists. This does not mean it is easy to find a witness for each composite, it only means that a witness must exist. In addition the Miller–Rabin test has probability of 1/4 of accepting a composite as prime for each random base a, so again repeated application of the algorithm leads us to reduce the error probability down to any value we care to mention.

The Miller–Rabin test is given by the following pseudo-code

```
Write n-1 = 2^s m, with m odd;
for (j=0; j<k; j++)
  { pick a from [2,...,n-1];
    b = a^m mod n;
    if (b!=1)
      { flag=true;
        for (i=1; i<s; i++)
          { if (b==(n-1))
              { flag=false;
                break;
              }
            b=b^2 mod n;
          }
        if (flag==true)
          { Output (Composite, a);
            exit;
          }
      }
  }
Output ''Probable Prime'';
```

We do not show that the Miller–Rabin test works. If you are interested in the reason see any book on algorithmic number theory for the details, for example that by Cohen or Bach and Shallit mentioned in the Further Reading section of this chapter. Just as with the Fermat test we repeat the method k times with k different bases, to obtain an error probability of $1/4^k$ if the algorithm always returns Probably Prime. Hence, we expect that the Miller-Rabin test will output Probably Prime for values of $k \geq 20$ only when n is actually a prime.

If n is a composite then a is called a Miller-Rabin witness for the compositeness of n, and under the Generalized Riemann Hypothesis (GRH), a conjecture believed to be true by most mathematicians, there is a Miller-Rabin witness a for the compositeness of n with

$$a \leq O((\log n)^2).$$

8.1.4   Primality Proofs

Up to now we have only output witnesses for compositeness, and we can interpret such a witness as a proof of compositeness. In addition we have only obtained probable primes rather than numbers which are 100 percent guaranteed to be prime. In practice this seems to be all right, since the probability of a composite number passing the Miller-Rabin test for twenty bases is around 2^{-40} which should never really occur in practice. But theoretically (and maybe in practice if we are totally paranoid) this could be a problem. In other words we may want real primes and not just probable ones.

There are algorithms whose output is a witness for the primality of the number. Such a witness is called a proof of primality. In practice such programs are only called when one is morally certain that the number one is testing for primality is actually prime. In other words the number has already passed the Miller-Rabin test for a number of bases and all one now requires is a proof of the primality.

The most successful of these primality proving algorithms is one based on elliptic curves called ECPP (for Elliptic Curve Primality Prover). This itself is based on an older primality proving algorithm based on finite fields due to Pocklington and Lehmer, the elliptic curve variant is due to Goldwasser and Kilian. The ECPP algorithm is a randomized algorithm which is not mathematically guaranteed to always produce an output, i.e. a witness, when the input is a prime number. If the input is composite then the algorithm is not guaranteed to terminate at all. Although ECPP runs in polynomial time, i.e. it is quite efficient, the proofs of primality it produces can be verified even faster.

There is an algorithm due to Adleman and Huang which, unlike the ECPP method, is guaranteed to terminate with a proof of primality on input of a prime number. It is based on a generalization of elliptic curves called hyperelliptic curves and has never to my knowledge been implemented. The fact that it has never been implemented is not only due to the far more complicated mathematics involved, but is also due to the fact that while the hyperelliptic variant is mathematically guaranteed to produce a proof, the ECPP method will always do so in practice for less work effort.

8.2   FACTORING ALGORITHMS

Factoring methods are usually divided into Dark Age methods such as

- Trial division,

- $p - 1$ method,

- $p + 1$ method,

- Pollard rho method,

and modern methods

- Continued Fraction Method (CFRAC),

- Quadratic Sieve (QS),

- Elliptic Curve Method (ECM),

- Number Field Sieve (NFS).

We do not have the time or space to discuss all of these in detail so we shall look at a couple of Dark Age methods and explain the main ideas behind some of the modern methods.

Modern factoring algorithms lie somewhere between polynomial and exponential time, in an area called sub-exponential time. These algorithms have complexity measured by the function

$$L_N(\alpha, \beta) = \exp\left((\beta + o(1))(\log N)^\alpha (\log\log N)^{1-\alpha}\right).$$

Notice that

- $L_N(0, \beta) = (\log N)^{\beta + o(1)}$, i.e. polynomial time,

- $L_N(1, \beta) = N^{\beta + o(1)}$, i.e. exponential time.

So, as we remarked in Chapter 7, in some sense the function $L_N(\alpha, \beta)$ interpolates between polynomial and exponential time. To give some idea of the use of this function:

- The slowest factoring algorithm, Trial Division, has complexity

$$L_N(1, 1/2).$$

- Up to the early 1990s the fastest general purpose factoring algorithm was the Quadratic Sieve, which has complexity

$$L_N(1/2, c)$$

  for some constant c.

- The current fastest algorithm is the Number Field Sieve which has complexity

$$L_N(1/3, c)$$

  for some constant c.

8.2.1 Trial Division

The most elementary algorithm is Trial Division, which we have already met in the context of testing primality. Suppose N is the number we wish to factor, we proceed as follows:

```
for (p=1; p<sqrt(N); p++)
  { e=0;
    if ((N mod p)==0) then
      { while ((N mod p)==0)
          { e=e+1;
            N=N/p;
          }
        Output (p,e);
      }
  }
```

A moment's thought reveals that Trial Division takes time at worst

$$O(\sqrt{N}).$$

The input size to the algorithm is of size $\log_2 N$, hence this complexity is exponential. But just as in primality testing we should not ignore Trial Division, it is usually the method of choice for numbers less than 10^{12}.

8.2.2 Smooth Numbers

For larger numbers we would like to improve on the Trial Division algorithm. Almost all other factoring algorithms make use of other auxiliary numbers called smooth numbers. Essentially a smooth number is one which is easy to factor using Trial Division, the following definition makes this more precise.

Definition 8.2 (Smooth Number) *Let B be an integer. An integer N is called B-smooth if every prime factor p of N is less than B.*

For example

$$N = 2^{78} \cdot 3^{89} \cdot 11^3$$

is 12-smooth. Sometimes we say that the number is just smooth if the bound B is small compared with N.

The number of y-smooth numbers which are less than x is given by the function $\psi(x, y)$. This is a rather complicated function which is approximated by

$$\psi(x, y) \approx x\rho(u)$$

where ρ is the Dickman–de Bruijn function and

$$u = \frac{\log x}{\log y}.$$

The Dickman–de Bruijn function ρ is defined as the function which satisfies the following differential-delay equation

$$u\rho'(u) + \rho(u - 1) = 0$$

for $u > 1$. In practice we approximate $\rho(u)$ via the expression

$$\rho(u) \approx u^{-u}$$

which holds as $u \to \infty$. This leads to the following result, which is important in analysing advanced factoring algorithms.

Theorem 8.3 *The proportion of integers less than x, which are $x^{1/u}$-smooth, is asymptotically equal to u^{-u}.*

Now if we set

$$y = L_N(\alpha, \beta)$$

then

$$u = \frac{\log N}{\log y}$$

$$= \frac{1}{\beta} \left(\frac{\log N}{\log \log N} \right)^{1-\alpha}.$$

Hence, one can show

$$\frac{1}{N} \psi(N, y) \approx u^{-u}$$

$$= \exp(-u \log u)$$

$$\approx \frac{1}{L_N(1 - \alpha, y)},$$

for some constant y. Suppose we are looking for numbers less than N which are $L_N(\alpha, \beta)$-smooth. The probability that any number less than N is actually $L_N(\alpha, \beta)$-smooth is given by $1/L_N(1 - \alpha, y)$. This hopefully will explain intuitively why some of the modern method complexity estimates for factoring are around $L_N(0.5, c)$, since to balance the smoothness bound against the probability estimate we take $\alpha = \frac{1}{2}$. The number field sieve obtains a better complexity estimate only by using a more mathematically complex algorithm.

We shall also require, in discussing our next factoring algorithm, the notion of a number being B-power smooth:

Definition 8.4 (Power Smooth) *A number is said to be B-power smooth if every prime power dividing N is less than B.*

For example

$$N = 2^5 \cdot 3^3$$

is 33-power smooth.

8.2.3 Pollard's $P - 1$ Method

The most famous name in factoring algorithms in the late 20th century was John Pollard. Almost all the important advances in factoring were made by him, for example

- the $P - 1$ method,

- the Rho-method,

- the Number Field Sieve.

In this section we discuss the $P - 1$ method and in a later section we consider the Number Field Sieve method, the other methods we leave for the exercises at the end of the chapter.

Suppose the number we wish to factor is given by

$$N = p \cdot q.$$

In addition suppose we know (by some pure guess) an integer B such that $p - 1$ is B-power smooth, but that $q - 1$ is not B-power smooth. We can then hope that $p - 1$ divides $B!$, but that $q - 1$ is unlikely to divide $B!$.

Suppose that we compute

$$a = 2^{B!} \pmod{N}.$$

Imagine that we could compute this modulo p and modulo q, we would then have

$$a \equiv 1 \pmod{p},$$

since

- $p - 1$ divides $B!$,

- $a^{p-1} = 1 \pmod{p}$ by Fermat's Little Theorem.

But it is unlikely that we would have

$$a \equiv 1 \pmod{q}.$$

Hence,

- p will divide $a - 1$,

- q will not divide $a - 1$.

We can then recover p by computing

$$p = \gcd(a - 1, N).$$

In code this is given by

```
a=2;
for (j=2; j<=B; j++)
   { a=a^j mod N; }
p=gcd(a-1,N);
if (p!=1 and p!=N) then
    Output ''p is a factor of N'';
else
    Output ''No Result''
```

As an example, suppose we wish to factor

$$N = 15\,770\,708\,441.$$

We take $B = 180$ and running the above algorithm we obtain

$$a = 2^{B!} \pmod{N} = 1\,162\,022\,425.$$

Then we obtain

$$p = \gcd(a - 1, N) = 135\,979.$$

To see why this works in this example we see that the prime factorization of N is given by

$$N = 135\,979 \cdot 115\,979$$

and we have

$$p - 1 = 135\,978 - 1 = 2 \cdot 3 \cdot 131 \cdot 173,$$
$$q - 1 = 115\,978 - 1 = 2 \cdot 103 \cdot 563.$$

Hence $p - 1$ is indeed B-power smooth, whilst $q - 1$ is not B-power smooth.

One can show that the complexity of the $P - 1$ method is given by

$$O(B \log B (\log N)^2 + (\log N)^3).$$

So if we choose $B = O((\log N)^i)$, for some integer i, then this is a polynomial-time factoring algorithm, but it only works for numbers of a special form.

Due to the $P - 1$ method one often sees recommended that RSA primes are chosen to satisfy

$$p - 1 = 2p_1 \text{ and } q - 1 = 2q_1,$$

where p_1 and q_1 are both primes. In this situation the primes p and q are called safe primes. However, this is not really needed these days with the large RSA moduli we use in current applications. This is because the probability that for a random 512-bit prime p, the number $p - 1$ is B-power smooth for a small value of B is very small. Hence, choosing random 512-bit primes would in all likelihood render the $P - 1$ method useless.

8.2.4 Difference of Two Squares

A basic trick in factoring algorithms, known for many centuries, is to produce two numbers x and y, of around the same size as N, such that

$$x^2 = y^2 \pmod{N}.$$

Since then we have
$$x^2 - y^2 = (x - y)(x + y) = 0 \pmod{N}.$$

If $N = p \cdot q$ then we have four possible cases

1. p divides $x - y$ and q divides $x + y$.

2. p divides $x + y$ and q divides $x - y$.

3. p and q both divide $x - y$ but neither divide $x + y$.

4. p and q both divide $x + y$ but neither divide $x - y$.

All these cases can occur with equal probability, namely $\frac{1}{4}$. If we then compute

$$d = \gcd(x - y, N),$$

our previous four cases then divide into the cases

1. $d = p$.

2. $d = q$.

3. $d = N$.

4. $d = 1$.

Since all these cases occur with equal probability, we see that with probability $\frac{1}{2}$ we will obtain a non-trivial factor of N. The only problem is, how do we find x and y such that $x^2 = y^2 \pmod{N}$?

8.3 MODERN FACTORING METHODS

Most modern factoring methods have the following strategy based on the difference of two squares method described at the end of the last section.

- Take a smoothness bound B.

- Compute a *factorbase* F of all prime numbers p less than B.

- Find a large number of values of x and y, such that x and y are B-smooth and

$$x = y \pmod{N}.$$

  These are called *relations* on the factorbase.

- Using linear algebra modulo 2, find a combination of the relations to give an X and Y with

$$X^2 = Y^2 \pmod{N}.$$

- Attempt to factor N by computing $\gcd(X - Y, N)$.

The trick in all algorithms of this form is how to find the relations. All the other details of the algorithms are basically the same. Such a strategy can also be used to solve discrete logarithm problems as well, which we shall discuss in a later chapter. In this section we explain the parts of the modern factoring algorithms which are common and justify why they work.

One way of looking at such algorithms is in the context of computational group theory. We have already shown that knowing the order of the group $(\mathbb{Z}/N\mathbb{Z})^*$, for an RSA modulus N, is the same as knowing the prime factors of N. Hence, the problem is really one of computing a group order. The factorbase is essentially a set of generators of the group $(\mathbb{Z}/N\mathbb{Z})^*$, whilst the relations are relations between the generators of this group. Once a sufficiently large number of relations have been found then, since the group is a finite abelian group, standard group theoretic algorithms will compute the group structure and hence the group order. These general group theoretic algorithms could include computing the Smith Normal Form of the associated matrix. Hence, it should not be surprising that linear algebra is used on the relations so as to factor the integer N.

8.3.1 Combining Relations

The Smith Normal Form algorithm is far too complicated for factoring algorithms where a more elementary approach, still based on linear algebra, can be used, as we shall now explain. Suppose we have the relations

$$p^2 q^5 r^2 = p^3 q^4 r^3 \pmod{N},$$
$$pq^3 r^5 = pqr^2 \pmod{N},$$
$$p^3 q^5 r^3 = pq^3 r^2 \pmod{N},$$

where p, q and r are primes in our factorbase, $B = \{p, q, r\}$. Dividing one side by the other in each of our relations we obtain

$$p^{-1} q r^{-1} = 1 \pmod{N},$$
$$q^2 r^3 = 1 \pmod{N},$$
$$p^2 q^2 r = 1 \pmod{N}.$$

Multiplying the last two equations together we obtain

$$p^{0+2} q^{2+2} r^{3+1} \equiv 1 \pmod{N}.$$

In other words

$$p^2 q^4 r^4 \equiv 1 \pmod{N}.$$

Hence if $X = pq^2 r^2$ and $Y = 1$ then we obtain

$$X^2 = Y^2 \pmod{N}$$

as required and computing

$$\gcd(X - Y, N)$$

will give us a 50 percent chance of factoring N.

Whilst it was easy to see by inspection in the previous example how to combine the relations to obtain a square, in a real-life example our factorbase could consist of hundreds of thousands of primes and we would have hundreds of thousands of relations. We basically need a technique of automating this process of finding out how to combine relations into squares. This is where linear algebra can come to our aid.

We explain how to automate the process using linear algebra by referring to our previous simple example. Recall that our relations were equivalent to

$$p^{-1} q r^{-1} = 1 \pmod{N},$$
$$q^2 r^3 = 1 \pmod{N},$$
$$p^2 q^2 r = 1 \pmod{N}.$$

To find which equations to multiply together to obtain a square we take a matrix A with #F columns and number of rows equal to the number of equations. Each equation is coded into the matrix as a row, modulo two, which in our example becomes

$$A = \begin{pmatrix} -1 & 1 & 1 \\ 0 & 2 & 3 \\ 2 & 2 & 1 \end{pmatrix} = \begin{pmatrix} 1 & 1 & 1 \\ 0 & 0 & 1 \\ 0 & 0 & 1 \end{pmatrix} \pmod{2}.$$

We now try and find a binary vector z such that

$$zA = 0 \pmod{2}.$$

In our example we can take

$$z = (0, 1, 1)$$

since

$$\begin{pmatrix} 0 & 1 & 1 \end{pmatrix} \begin{pmatrix} 1 & 1 & 1 \\ 0 & 0 & 1 \\ 0 & 0 & 1 \end{pmatrix} = \begin{pmatrix} 0 & 0 & 0 \end{pmatrix} \pmod{2}.$$

This solution vector $z = (0, 1, 1)$ tells us that multiplying the last two equations together will produce a square modulo N.

Finding the vector z is done using a variant of Gaussian Elimination. Hence in general this means that we require more equations (i.e. relations) than elements in the factorbase. This relation combining stage of factoring algorithms is usually the hardest part since the matrices involved tend to be rather large. For example using the Number Field Sieve to factor a 100 decimal digit number may require a matrix of dimension over 100 000. This results in huge memory problems and requires the writing of specialist matrix code and often the use of specialized super computers.

The matrix will, for cryptographically interesting numbers, have around 500 000 rows and as many columns. As this is nothing but a matrix modulo 2 each entry could be represented by a single bit. If we used a dense matrix representation then the matrix alone would occupy around 29 gigabytes of storage. Luckily the matrix is very, very sparse and so the storage will not be so large.

As we said above we can compute the vector z such that $zA = 0$ using a variant of Gaussian Elimination over $\mathbb{Z}/2\mathbb{Z}$. But standard Gaussian Elimination would start with a sparse matrix and end up with an upper triangular dense matrix, so we would be back with the huge memory problem again. To overcome this problem very advanced matrix algorithms are deployed which try not to alter the matrix at all. We do not discuss these here but refer the interested reader to the book of Lenstra and Lenstra mentioned in the Further Reading section of this chapter.

The only thing we have not sketched is how to find the relations, a topic which we shall discuss in the next section.

8.4 NUMBER FIELD SIEVE

The Number Field Sieve is the fastest known factoring algorithm. The basic idea is to factor a number N by finding two integers x and y such that

$$x^2 \equiv y^2 \pmod{N};$$

we then expect (hope) that $\gcd(x - y, N)$ will give us a non-trivial factor of N.

To explain the basic method we shall start with the linear sieve and then show how this is generalized to the number field sieve. The linear sieve is not a very good algorithm but it does show the rough method.

8.4.1   The Linear Sieve

We let F denote a set of 'small' prime numbers which form the factorbase:

$$F = \{p : p \leq B\}.$$

A number which factorizes with all its factors in F is therefore B-smooth. The idea of the linear sieve is to find two integers a and λ such that

$$b = a + N\lambda$$

is B-smooth. If in addition we only select values of a which are 'small', then we would expect that a will also be B-smooth and we could write

$$a = \prod_{p \in F} p^{a_p}$$

and

$$b = a + N\lambda = \prod_{p \in F} p^{b_p}.$$

We would then have a relation in $\mathbb{Z}/N\mathbb{Z}$

$$\prod_{p \in F} p^{a_p} \equiv \prod_{p \in F} p^{b_p} \pmod{N}.$$

So the main question is how do we find such values of a and λ?

1. Fix a value of λ to consider.

2. Initialize an array of length $A + 1$ indexed by 0 to A with zeros.

3. For each prime $p \in F$ add $\log_2 p$ to every array location whose position is congruent to $-\lambda N \pmod{p}$.

4. Choose the a to be the position of those elements which exceed some threshold bound.

The reasoning behind this method is that a position of the array which has an entry exceeding some bound, will when added to λN have a good chance of being B-smooth as it likely to be divisible by many primes in F.

For example suppose we take $N = 1159$, $F = \{2, 3, 5, 7, 11\}$ and $\lambda = -2$. So we wish to find a smooth value of

$$a - 2N.$$

We initialize the sieving array as follows:

0	1	2	3	4	5	6	7	8	9
0.0	0.0	0.0	0.0	0.0	0.0	0.0	0.0	0.0	0.0

We now take the first prime in F, namely $p = 2$, and we compute

$$-\lambda N \pmod{p} = 0.$$

So we add $\log_2(2) = 1$ to every array location with index equal to 0 modulo 2. This results in our sieve array becoming:

0	1	2	3	4	5	6	7	8	9
1.0	0.0	1.0	0.0	1.0	0.0	1.0	0.0	1.0	0.0

We now take the next prime in F, namely $p = 3$, and compute

$$-\lambda N \ (\mathrm{mod}\ p) = 2.$$

So we add $\log_2(3) = 1.6$ onto every array location with index equal to 2 modulo 3. Our sieve array then becomes:

0	1	2	3	4	5	6	7	8	9
1.0	0.0	2.6	0.0	1.0	1.6	1.0	0.0	2.6	0.0

Continuing in this way with $p = 5, 7$ and 11, eventually the sieve array becomes:

0	1	2	3	4	5	6	7	8	9
1.0	2.8	2.6	2.3	1.0	1.6	1.0	0.0	11.2	0.0

Hence, the value $a = 8$ looks like it should correspond to a smooth value, and indeed it does, since we find

$$a - \lambda N = 8 - 2 \cdot 1159 = -2310 = -2 \cdot 3 \cdot 5 \cdot 7 \cdot 11.$$

So using the linear sieve we obtain a large collection of numbers a and b such that

$$a_i = \prod_{p_j \in F} p_j^{a_{i,j}} \equiv \prod_{p_j \in F} p_j^{b_{i,j}} = b_i \ (\mathrm{mod}\ N).$$

We assume that we have at least $|B| + 1$ such relations with which we then form a matrix with the rows

$$(a_{i,1}, \ldots, a_{i,t}, b_{i,1}, \ldots, b_{i,t}) \ (\mathrm{mod}\ 2).$$

We then find elements of the kernel of this matrix modulo 2. This will tell us how to multiply the a_i and the b_i together to obtain elements x^2 and y^2 such that $x, y \in \mathbb{Z}$ are easily calculated and

$$x^2 \equiv y^2 \ (\mathrm{mod}\ N).$$

We can then try and factor N, but if these values of x and y do not provide a factor we just find a new element in the kernel of the matrix and continue.

The basic linear sieve gives a very small yield of relations. There is a variant called the *large prime variation* which relaxes the sieving condition to allow through pairs a and b which are almost B-smooth, bar say a single 'large' prime in a and a single 'large' prime in b. These large primes then have to be combined in some way so that the linear algebra step can proceed as above. This is done by constructing a graph and using an algorithm which computes a basis for the set of cycles in the graph. The basic idea for the large prime variation originally arose in the context of the Quadratic Sieve algorithm, but it can be applied to any of the sieving algorithms used in factoring.

It is clear that the sieving could be carried out in parallel, hence the sieving can be parcelled out to lots of slave computers around the world. The slaves then communicate any relations they find to the central master computer which performs the linear algebra step. In such a way the Internet can be turned into a large parallel computer dedicated to factoring numbers. The final linear algebra step we have already remarked needs to often be performed on specialized equipment with large amounts of disk space and RAM, so this final computation cannot be distributed over the Internet.

8.4.2 The Number Field Sieve

The linear sieve is simply not good enough to factor large numbers. Indeed the linear sieve was never proposed as a real factoring algorithm, its operation is however instructive for other algorithms of this type. The number field sieve uses the arithmetic of algebraic number fields to construct the desired relations between the elements of the factorbase. All that changes is the way the relations are found. The linear algebra step, the large prime variations and the slave/master approach all go over to NFS virtually unchanged. We now explain the NFS, but in a much simpler form than is actually used in real-life so as to aid the exposition. Those readers who do not know any algebraic number theory may wish to skip this section.

First we construct two monic, irreducible polynomials with integer coefficients f_1 and f_2, of degree d_1 and d_2 respectively, such that there exists an $m \in \mathbb{Z}$ such that

$$f_1(m) \equiv f_2(m) \equiv 0 \ (\mathrm{mod}\ N).$$

The number field sieve will make use of arithmetic in the number fields K_1 and K_2 given by

$$K_1 = \mathbb{Q}(\theta_1) \text{ and } K_2 = \mathbb{Q}(\theta_2),$$

where θ_1 and θ_2 are defined by $f_1(\theta_1) = f_2(\theta_2) = 0$. We then have two homomorphisms ϕ_1 and ϕ_2 given by

$$\phi_i : \begin{cases} \mathbb{Z}[\theta_i] \longrightarrow \mathbb{Z}/N\mathbb{Z} \\ \theta_i \longmapsto m. \end{cases}$$

We aim to use a sieve, just as in the linear sieve, to find a set

$$S \subset \{(a, b) \in \mathbb{Z}^2 : \gcd(a, b) = 1\}$$

such that

$$\prod_S (a - b\theta_1) = \beta^2$$

and

$$\prod_S (a - b\theta_2) = \gamma^2,$$

where $\beta \in K_1$ and $\gamma \in K_2$. If we found two such values of β and γ then we would have

$$\phi_1(\beta)^2 \equiv \phi_2(\gamma)^2 \pmod{N}$$

and hopefully

$$\gcd(N, \phi_1(\beta) - \phi_2(\gamma))$$

would be a factor of N.

This leads to three obvious problems

- How do we find the set S?

- Given $\beta^2 \in \mathbb{Q}[\theta_1]$, how do we compute β?

- How do we find the polynomials f_1 and f_2 in the first place?

8.4.2.1 How do we find the set S?: Similar to the linear sieve we can find such a set S using linear algebra provided we can find lots of a and b such that

$$a - b\theta_1 \text{ and } a - b\theta_2$$

are both 'smooth'. But what does it mean for these two objects to be smooth? It is here that the theory of algebraic number fields comes in, by generalizing our earlier definition of smooth integers to algebraic integers we obtain the definition:

Definition 8.5 *An algebraic integer is 'smooth' if and only if the ideal it generates is only divisible by 'small' prime ideals.*

Define $F_i(X, Y) = Y^{d_i} f_i(X/Y)$ then

$$N_{\mathbb{Q}(\theta_i)/\mathbb{Q}}(a - b\theta_i) = F_i(a, b).$$

We define two factorbases, one for each of the polynomials

$$\mathcal{F}_i = \{(p, r) : p \text{ a prime}, r \in \mathbb{Z} \text{ such that } f_i(r) \equiv 0 \pmod{p}\}.$$

Each element of $\mathcal{F}_i$ corresponds to a degree one prime ideal of $\mathbb{Z}[\theta_i]$, which is a sub-order of the ring of integers of $\mathcal{O}_{\mathbb{Q}(\theta_i)}$, given by

$$\langle p, \theta_i - r \rangle = p\mathbb{Z}[\theta_i] + (\theta_i - r)\mathbb{Z}[\theta_i].$$

Given values of a and b we can easily determine whether the ideal $\langle a - \theta_i b \rangle$ 'factorizes' over our factorbase. Note factorizes is in quotes as unique factorization of ideals may not hold in $\mathbb{Z}[\theta_i]$, whilst it will hold in $\mathcal{O}_{\mathbb{Q}(\theta_i)}$. It will turn out that this is not really a problem. To see why this is not a problem you should consult the book by Lenstra and Lenstra.

If $\mathbb{Z}[\theta_i] = \mathcal{O}_{\mathbb{Q}(\theta_i)}$ then the following method does indeed give the unique prime ideal factorization of $\langle a - \theta_i b \rangle$.

- Write

$$F_i(a, b) = \prod_{(p_j, r) \in \mathcal{F}_i} p_j^{s_j^{(i)}}.$$

- We have $(a : b) = (r : 1) \pmod{p}$, as an element in the projective space of dimension one over $\mathbb{F}_p$, if the ideal corresponding to (p, r) is included in a non-trivial way in the ideal factorization of $a - \theta_i b$.

- We have

$$\langle a - \theta_i b \rangle = \prod_{(p_j, r) \in \mathcal{F}_i} \langle p_j, \theta_i - r \rangle^{s_j^{(i)}}.$$

This leads to the following algorithm to sieve for values of a and b, such that $\langle a - \theta_i b \rangle$ is an ideal which factorizes over the factorbase. Just as with the linear sieve, the use of sieving allows us to avoid lots of expensive trial divisions when trying to determine smooth ideals. We end up only performing factorizations where we already know we have a good chance of being successful.

- Fix a.

- Initialize the sieve array for $-B \le b \le B$ by

$$S[b] = \log_2(F_1(a, b) \cdot F_2(a, b)).$$

- For every $(p, r) \in \mathcal{F}_i$ subtract $\log_2 p$ from every array element such that

$$a - rb \equiv 0 \pmod{p}.$$

- The bs we want are the ones such that $S[b]$ lies below some tolerance level.

If the tolerance level is set in a sensible way then we have a good chance that both $F_1(a, b)$ and $F_2(a, b)$ factor over the prime ideals in the factorbase, with the possibility of some large prime ideals creeping in. We keep these factorizations as a relation, just as we did with the linear sieve.

Then, after some linear algebra, we can find a subset S of all the pairs (a, b) we have found such that

$$\prod_{(a,b) \in S} \langle a - b\theta_i \rangle = \text{square of an } \textbf{ideal} \text{ in } \mathbb{Z}[\theta_i].$$

This is not however good enough, recall we want the product $\prod a - b\theta_i$ to be the square of an **element** of $\mathbb{Z}[\theta_i]$. To overcome this problem we need to add information from the 'infinite' places. This is done by adding in some quadratic characters, an idea introduced by Adleman. Let q be a rational prime (in neither $\mathcal{F}_1$ nor $\mathcal{F}_2$) such that there is an s_q with $f_i(s_q) \equiv 0 \pmod{q}$ and $f_i'(s_q) \ne 0 \pmod{q}$ for either $i = 1$ or $i = 2$. Then our extra condition is that we require

$$\prod_{(a,b) \in S} \left(\frac{a - bs_q}{q} \right) = 1,$$

where $(\frac{\cdot}{q})$ denotes the Legendre symbol. As the Legendre symbol is multiplicative this gives us an extra condition to put into our matrix. We need to add this condition for a number of primes q, hence we choose a set of such primes q and put the associated characters into our matrix as an extra column of 0s or 1s corresponding to:

$$\text{if } \left(\frac{a - bs_q}{q} \right) = \begin{cases} 1 & \text{then enter} \quad 0, \\ -1 & \text{then enter} \quad 1. \end{cases}$$

So after finding enough relations we hope to be able to find a subset S such that hopefully

$$\prod_S (a - b\theta_1) = \beta^2 \text{ and } \prod_S (a - b\theta_2) = \gamma^2.$$

8.4.2.2 How do we take the square roots?: We then need to be able to take the square root of β^2 to recover β, and similarly for γ^2. Each β^2 is given in the form

$$\beta^2 = \sum_{j=0}^{d_1-1} a_j \theta_1^j$$

where the a_j are huge integers. We want to be able to determine the solutions $b_j \in \mathbb{Z}$ to the equation

$$\left(\sum_{j=0}^{d_1-1} b_j \theta_1^j \right)^2 = \sum_{j=0}^{d_1-1} a_j \theta_1^j.$$

One way this is overcome, due to Couveignes, is by computing such a square root modulo a large number of very, very large primes p. We then perform Hensel lifting and Chinese remaindering to hopefully recover our square root. This is the easiest method to understand although more advanced methods are available, such as that by Nguyen.

8.4.2.3 Choosing the initial polynomials: This is the part of the method that is a black art at the moment. We require only the following conditions to be met

$$f_1(m) \equiv f_2(m) \equiv 0 \pmod{N}.$$

However there are good heuristic reasons why it also might be desirable to construct polynomials with additional properties such as

- The polynomials have small coefficients.

- f_1 and f_2 have 'many' real roots. Note, a random polynomial probably would have no real roots on average.

- f_1 and f_2 have 'many' roots modulo lots of small prime numbers.

- The Galois groups of f_1 and f_2 are 'small'

It is often worth spending a few weeks trying to find a good couple of polynomials before one starts to attempt the factorization algorithm proper. There are a number of search strategies used for finding these polynomials. Once a few candidates are found some experimental sieving is performed to see which appear to be the most successful, in that they yield the most relations. Then once a decision has been made one can launch the sieving stage 'for real'.

8.4.3 Example

I am grateful to Richard Pinch for allowing me to include the following example. It is taken from his lecture notes from a course at Cambridge in the mid-1990s. Suppose we wish to factor the number $N = 290^2 + 1 = 84\,101$. We take $f_1(x) = x^2 + 1$ and $f_2(x) = x - 290$ with $m = 290$. Then

$$f_1(m) \equiv f_2(m) \equiv 0 \pmod{N}.$$

On one side we have the order $\mathbb{Z}[i]$ which is the ring of integers of $\mathbb{Q}(i)$ and on the other side we have the order $\mathbb{Z}$.

We obtain the following factorizations:

x	y	$N(x - iy)$	Factors	$x - my$	Factors
-38	-1	1445	$(5)(17^2)$	252	$(2^2)(3^2)(7)$
-22	-19	845	$(5)(13^2)$	(5488)	$(2^4)(7^3)$

We then obtain the two factorizations, which are real factorizations of elements, as $\mathbb{Z}[i]$ is a unique factorization domain,

$$-38 + i = -(2 + i)(4 - i)^2, \quad -22 + 19i = -(2 + i)(3 - 2i)^2.$$

Hence, after a trivial bit of linear algebra, we obtain the following 'squares'

$$(-38 + i)(-22 + 19i) = (2 + i)^2(3 - 2i)^2(4 - i)^2 = (31 - 12i)^2$$

and

$$(-38 + m)(-22 + 19 \times m) = (2^6)(3^2)(7^4) = 1176^2.$$

We then apply the map ϕ_1 to $31 - 12i$ to obtain

$$\phi_1(31 - 12i) = 31 - 12 \times m = -3449.$$

But then we have

$$
\begin{aligned}
(-3449)^2 &= \phi_1(31 - 12i)^2 \\
&= \phi_1((31 - 12i)^2) \\
&= \phi_1((-38 + i)(-22 + 19i)) \\
&= \phi_1(-38 + i)\phi_1(-22 + 19i) \\
&\equiv (-38 + m)(-22 + 19 \times m) \pmod{N} \\
&= 1176^2.
\end{aligned}
$$

So we compute

$$\gcd(N, -3449 + 1176) = 2273$$

and

$$\gcd(N, -3449 - 1176) = 37.$$

Hence 37 and 2273 are factors of $N = 84\,101$.

Chapter Summary

- Prime numbers are very common and the probability that a random n-bit number is prime is around $1/n$.

- Numbers can be tested for primality using a probable prime test such as the Fermat or Miller–Rabin algorithms. The Fermat test has a problem in that certain composite numbers will always pass the Fermat test no matter how one chooses the possible witnesses.

- If one really needs to be certain that a number is prime then there are primality proving algorithms which run in polynomial time.

- Factoring algorithms are often based on the problem of finding the difference of two squares.

- Modern factoring algorithms run in two stages: In the first stage one collects a lot of relations on a factorbase by using a process called sieving, which can be done using thousands of computers on the Internet. In the second stage these relations are processed using linear algebra on a big central server. The final factorization is obtained by finding a difference of two squares.

Further Reading

The definitive reference work on computational number theory which deals with many algorithms for factoring and primality proving is the book by Cohen. The book by Bach and Shallit also provides a good reference for primality testing. The main book explaining the Number Field Sieve is the book by Lenstra and Lenstra.

E. Bach and J. Shallit. *Algorithmic Number Theory. Volume 1: Efficient Algorithms*. MIT Press, 1996.

H. Cohen. *A Course in Computational Algebraic Number Theory*. Springer-Verlag, 1993.

A. Lenstra and H. Lenstra. *The Development of the Number Field Sieve*. Springer-Verlag, 1993.

Review Exercises

8.1.1   When should one use Trial Division in primality testing?

8.1.2   What is the Fermat primality test and what is the main problem associated with it?

8.1.3   What is the main difference between a primality testing algorithm, like the Miller-Rabin algorithm, and a primality proving algorithm like ECPP?

8.1.4   What is meant by a smooth number and how can one use smooth numbers in factoring algorithms?

8.1.5   Describe the P − 1 factoring algorithm.

8.1.6   Why does finding two numbers x and y such that $x^2 = y^2 \pmod{N}$ allow us to factor N with probability at least $1/2$?

8.1.7   What is meant by a sieve and why are they used in modern factoring algorithms?

Programming Exercises

8.2.1   Implement the Fermat and Miller-Rabin primality tests described in the text. Give a witness for the compositeness of the number

$$2^{1024} - 3.$$

8.2.2   Implement the P − 1 factoring algorithm. How large a composite number N will your implementation always factor?

Standard Exercises

8.3.1   Show that if a composite number n passes the Fermat test to a base a, but fails the Miller-Rabin test for the same base then we can factor the number n.

The next three questions give another algorithm of Pollard to factor an integer N, called Pollard's Rho method. Define the sequence

$$x_0 = 2, \; x_{i+1} = x_i^2 + 1 \pmod{N}.$$

8.3.2   Show that if we find two values of the sequence with $x_i = x_j \pmod{p}$, with $i \neq j$, then we can factor N with high probability by computing

$$\gcd(x_i - x_j, N).$$

8.3.3   Argue that we must eventually find two indices $i \neq j$ such that $x_i = x_j \pmod{p}$.

8.3.4   Show how to find two such indices using a small amount of storage.

8.3.5   Pollard's P − 1 method is based on arithmetic in the finite field $\mathbb{F}_p^*$ and allows us to factor integers when $p - 1$ is smooth but $q - 1$ is not. Give a similar method using arithmetic in the finite field $\mathbb{F}_{p^2}$ which allows us to factor integers when $p + 1$ is smooth. This is Pollard's P + 1 factoring algorithm.

8.3.6   **[Hard]**. Generalize the P − 1 and P + 1 methods to elliptic curves in the following way. Consider an elliptic curve over the ring $\mathbb{Z}/N\mathbb{Z}$ and show that if $\#E(\mathbb{F}_p)$ is smooth but $\#E(\mathbb{F}_q)$ is not smooth then one can factor N using the elliptic curve group law. This is Lenstra's ECM factoring algorithm.

Discrete Logarithms

Chapter Goals

- To examine algorithms for solving the discrete logarithm problem.

- To introduce the Pohlig–Hellman algorithm.

- To introduce the Baby-Step/Giant-Step algorithm.

- To explain the methods of Pollard.

- To show how discrete logarithms can be solved in finite fields using algorithms like those used for factoring.

- To describe the known results on the elliptic curve discrete logarithm problem.

9.1 INTRODUCTION

In this chapter we survey the methods known for solving the discrete logarithm problem,

$$h = g^x$$

in various groups G. These algorithms fall into one of two categories, either the algorithms are generic and apply to any finite abelian group or the algorithms are specific to the special group under consideration.

We start with general purpose algorithms and then move onto special purpose algorithms later in the chapter.

9.2 POHLIG–HELLMAN

The first observation to make is that the discrete logarithm problem in a group G is only as hard as the discrete logarithm problem in the largest subgroup of prime order in G. This observation is due to Pohlig and Hellman, and it applies in an arbitrary finite abelian group.

To explain the Pohlig-Hellman algorithm, suppose we have a finite cyclic abelian group $G = \langle g \rangle$ whose order is given by

$$N = \#G = \prod_{i=1}^{t} p_i^{e_i}.$$

Now suppose we are given $h \in \langle g \rangle$, so there exists an integer x such that

$$h = g^x.$$

Our aim is to find x by first finding it modulo $p_i^{e_i}$ and then using the Chinese Remainder Theorem to recover it modulo N.

From basic group theory we know that there is a group isomorphism

$$\phi : G \longrightarrow C_{p_1^{e_1}} \times \cdots \times C_{p_t^{e_t}},$$

where C_{p^e} is a cyclic group of prime power order p^e. The projection of ϕ to the component C_{p^e} is given by

$$\phi_p : \begin{cases} G \longrightarrow C_{p^e} \\ f \longmapsto f^{N/p^e}. \end{cases}$$

Now the map ϕ_p is a group homomorphism so if we have $h = g^x$ in G then we will have $\phi_p(h) = \phi_p(g)^x$ in C_{p^e}. But the discrete logarithm in C_{p^e} is only determined modulo p^e. So if we could solve the discrete logarithm problem in C_{p^e}, then we would determine x modulo p^e. Doing this for all primes p dividing N would allow us to solve for x using the Chinese Remainder Theorem.

In summary suppose we had some oracle O(g,h,p,e) which for $g, h \in C_{p^e}$ will output the discrete logarithm of h with respect to g. We solve for x using the following algorithm

```
S={};
for all primes p dividing N
  { Compute the largest e such that T=p^e divides N;
    g1=g^{N/T};
    h1=h^{N/T};
    z=O(g1,h1,p,e);
    S = S + { (z,T) };
  }
x=CRT(S);
```

The only problem is that we have not shown how to solve the discrete logarithm problem in C_{p^e}. We shall now show how this is done, by reducing to solving e discrete logarithm problems in the group C_p. Suppose $g, h \in C_{p^e}$ and that there is an x such that

$$h = g^x.$$

Clearly x is only defined modulo p^e and we can write

$$x = x_0 + x_1 p + \cdots + x_{e-1} p^{e-1}.$$

We find $x_0, x_1, \ldots$ in turn, using the following inductive procedure. Suppose we know x', the value of x modulo p^t, i.e.

$$x' = x_0 + \cdots + x_{t-1} p^{t-1}.$$

We now wish to determine x_t and so compute x modulo p^{t+1}. We write

$$x = x' + p^t x'',$$

so we have that

$$h = g^{x'} (g^{p^t})^{x''}.$$

Hence, if we set

$$h' = h g^{-x'} \text{ and } g' = g^{p^t},$$

then

$$h' = g'^{x''}.$$

Now g' is an element of order p^{e-t} so to obtain an element of order p, and hence a discrete logarithm problem in C_p we need to raise the above equation to the power $s = p^{e-t-1}$. So setting

$$h'' = h'^s \text{ and } g'' = g'^s$$

we obtain the discrete logarithm problem in C_p given by

$$h'' = g''^{x_t}.$$

So assuming we can solve discrete logarithms in C_p we can find x_t and so find x.

We now illustrate this approach, assuming we can solve discrete logarithms in cyclic groups of prime order. We leave to the next two sections techniques to find discrete logarithms in cyclic groups of prime order, for now we assume that this is possible. As an example of the Pohlig-Hellman algorithm, consider the multiplicative group of the finite field $\mathbb{F}_{397}$, this has order

$$396 = 2^2 \cdot 3^2 \cdot 11$$

and a generator of $\mathbb{F}_{397}^*$ is given by

$$g = 5.$$

We wish to solve the discrete logarithm problem given by

$$h = 208 = 5^x \pmod{397}.$$

We first reduce to the three subgroups of prime power order, by raising the above equation to the power $396/p^e$. Hence, we obtain the three discrete logarithm problems

$$334 = h^{396/4} = g^{396/4 x_4} = 334^{x_4} \pmod{397},$$
$$286 = h^{396/9} = g^{396/9 x_9} = 79^{x_9} \pmod{397},$$
$$273 = h^{396/11} = g^{396/11 x_{11}} = 290^{x_{11}} \pmod{397}.$$

The value of x_4 is the value of x modulo 4, the value of x_9 is the value of x modulo 9 whilst the value of x_{11} is the value of x modulo 11. Clearly if we can determine these three values then we can determine x modulo 396.

9.2.1 Determining x_4

By inspection we see that $x_4 = 1$, but let us labour the point and show how the above algorithm will determine this for us. We write

$$x_4 = x_{4,0} + 2 \cdot x_{4,1},$$

where $x_{4,0}, x_{4,1} \in \{0, 1\}$. Recall that we wish to solve

$$h' = 334 = 334^{x_4} = g'^{x_4}.$$

We set $h'' = h'^2$ and $g'' = g'^2$ and solve the discrete logarithm problem

$$h'' = g''^{x_{4,0}}$$

in the cyclic group of order 2. We find, using our oracle for the discrete logarithm problem in cyclic groups, that $x_{4,0} = 1$. So we now have

$$\frac{h'}{g'} = g''^{x_{4,1}} \pmod{337}.$$

Hence we have

$$1 = 396^{x_{4,1}},$$

which is another discrete logarithm in the cyclic group of order two. We find $x_{4,1} = 0$ and so conclude, as expected, that

$$x_4 = x_{4,0} + 2 \cdot x_{4,1} = 1 + 2 \cdot 0 = 1.$$

9.2.2 Determining x_9

We write

$$x_9 = x_{9,0} + 3 \cdot x_{9,1},$$

where $x_{9,0}, x_{9,1} \in \{0, 1, 2\}$. Recall that we wish to solve

$$h' = 286 = 79^{x_9} = g'^{x_9}.$$

We set $h'' = h'^3$ and $g'' = g'^3$ and solve the discrete logarithm problem

$$h'' = 34 = g''^{x_{9,0}} = 362^{x_{9,0}}$$

in the cyclic group of order 3. We find, using our oracle for the discrete logarithm problem in cyclic groups, that $x_{9,0} = 2$. So we now have

$$\frac{h'}{g'^2} = g''^{x_{9,1}} \pmod{337}.$$

Hence we have

$$1 = 362^{x_{9,1}},$$

which is another discrete logarithm in the cyclic group of order two. We find $x_{9,1} = 0$ and so conclude that

$$x_9 = x_{9,0} + 3 \cdot x_{9,1} = 2 + 3 \cdot 0 = 2.$$

9.2.3 Determining x_{11}

We are already in a cyclic group of prime order, so applying our oracle to the discrete logarithm problem

$$273 = 290^{x_{11}} \pmod{397},$$

we find that $x_{11} = 6$.

So we have determined that if

$$208 = 5^x \pmod{397},$$

then x is given by

$$x = 1 \pmod 4,$$
$$x = 2 \pmod 9,$$
$$x = 6 \pmod{11}.$$

If we apply the Chinese Remainder Theorem to this set of three simultaneous equations then we obtain that the solution to our discrete logarithm problem is given by

$$x = 281.$$

9.3 BABY-STEP/GIANT-STEP METHOD

In our above discussion of the Pohlig–Hellman algorithm we assumed we had an oracle to solve the discrete logarithm problem in cyclic groups of prime order. We shall now describe a general method of solving such problems due to Shanks called the Baby-Step/Giant-Step method. Once again this is a generic method which applies to any cyclic finite abelian group.

Since the intermediate steps in the Pohlig–Hellman algorithm are quite simple, the difficulty of solving a general discrete logarithm problem will be dominated by the time required to solve the discrete logarithm problem in the cyclic subgroups of prime order. Hence, for generic groups the complexity of the Baby-Step/Giant-Step method will dominate the overall complexity of any algorithm. Indeed one can show that the following method is the best possible method, time-wise, for solving the discrete logarithm problem in an arbitrary group. Of course in any actual group there may be a special purpose algorithm which works faster, but in general the following is provably the best one can do.

Again we fix notation as follows: We have a public cyclic group $G = \langle g \rangle$, which we can now assume to have prime order p. We are also given an $h \in G$ and are asked to find the value of x modulo p such that

$$h = g^x.$$

We assume there is some fixed encoding of the elements of G, so in particular it is easy to store, sort and search a list of elements of G.

The idea behind the Baby-Step/Giant-Step method is a standard divide and conquer approach found in many areas of computer science. We first write

$$x = x_0 + x_1 \lceil \sqrt{p} \rceil.$$

Now, since $x \leq p$, we have that $0 \leq x_0, x_1 < \lceil \sqrt{p} \rceil$.
We first compute the Baby-Steps

$$g_i = g^i \text{ for } 0 \leq i < \lceil \sqrt{p} \rceil.$$

The pairs

$$(g_i, i)$$

are stored in a table so that one can easily search for items indexed by the first entry in the pair. This can be accomplished by sorting the table on the first entry or more efficiently by the use of hash-tables. To compute and store the Baby-Steps clearly requires

$$O(\lceil \sqrt{p} \rceil)$$

time, and a similar amount of storage.
We now compute the Giant-Steps

$$h_j = hg^{-j\lceil \sqrt{p} \rceil} \text{ for } 0 \leq j < \lceil \sqrt{p} \rceil.$$

We then try to find a match in the table of Baby-Steps, i.e. we try to find a value g_i such that $g_i = h_j$. If such a match occurs we have

$$x_0 = i \text{ and } x_1 = j$$

since, if $g_i = h_j$,

$$g^i = hg^{-j\lceil \sqrt{p} \rceil},$$

i.e.

$$g^{i+j\lceil \sqrt{p} \rceil} = h.$$

Notice that the time to compute the Giant-Steps is at most

$$O(\lceil \sqrt{p} \rceil).$$

Hence, the overall time and space complexity of the Baby-Step/Giant-Step method is

$$O(\sqrt{p}).$$

This means, combining with the Pohlig–Hellman algorithm, that if we wish a discrete logarithm problem in a group G to be as difficult as a work effort of 2^{80} operations, then we need the group G to have a prime order subgroup of order larger than 2^{160}.

As an example we take the subgroup of order 101 in the multiplicative group of the finite field $\mathbb{F}_{607}$, generated by $g = 64$. Suppose we are given the discrete logarithm problem

$$h = 182 = 64^x \pmod{607}.$$

We first compute the Baby-Steps

$$g_i = 64^i \pmod{607} \text{ for } 0 \leq i < \lceil \sqrt{101} \rceil = 11.$$

We compute

i	$64^i \pmod{607}$	i	$64^i \pmod{607}$
0	1	6	330
1	64	7	482
2	454	8	498
3	527	9	308
4	343	10	288
5	100		

Now we compute the Giant-Steps,

$$h_j = 182 \cdot 64^{-11j} \pmod{607} \text{ for } 0 \le j < 11,$$

and check when we obtain a Giant-Step which occurs in our table of Baby-Steps:

j	$182 \cdot 64^{-11j} \pmod{607}$	j	$182 \cdot 64^{-11j} \pmod{607}$
0	182	6	60
1	143	7	394
2	69	8	483
3	271	9	76
4	343	10	580
5	573		

So we obtain a match when $i = 4$ and $j = 4$, which means that

$$x = 4 + 11 \cdot 4 = 48,$$

which we can verify to be the correct answer to the earlier discrete logarithm problem by computing

$$64^{48} \pmod{607} = 182.$$

9.4 POLLARD TYPE METHODS

The trouble with the Baby-Step/Giant-Step method was that although its run time was bounded by $O(\sqrt{p})$ it also required $O(\sqrt{p})$ space. This space requirement is more of a hindrance in practice than the time requirement. Hence, one could ask whether one could trade the large space requirement for a smaller space requirement, but still obtain a time complexity of $O(\sqrt{p})$? Well we can, but we will now obtain only an expected running time rather than an absolute bound on the running time. There are a number of algorithms which achieve this reduced space requirement all of which are due to ideas of Pollard.

9.4.1 Pollard's Rho Algorithm

Suppose $f : S \rightarrow S$ is a random mapping between a set S and itself, where the size of S is n. Now pick a random value $x_0 \in S$ and compute

$$x_{i+1} = f(x_i) \text{ for } i \ge 0.$$

The values $x_0, x_1, x_2, \ldots$ we consider as a deterministic random walk. By this last statement we mean that each step $x_{i+1} = f(x_i)$ of the walk is a deterministic function of the current position x_i, but we are assuming that the sequence $x_0, x_1, x_2, \ldots$ *behaves as a random sequence would*. Another name for a deterministic random walk is a pseudo-random walk.

Since S is finite we must eventually obtain

$$x_i = x_j$$

and so

$$x_{i+1} = f(x_i) = f(x_j) = x_{j+1}.$$

Hence, the sequence $x_0, x_1, x_2, \ldots,$ will eventually become cyclic. If we 'draw' such a sequence then it looks like the Greek letter rho, i.e.

$$\rho.$$

In other words there is a cyclic part and an initial tail. One can show that for a random mapping the tail has expected length (i.e. the number of elements in the tail)

$$\sqrt{\pi n / 8},$$

whilst the cycle has expected length (i.e. the number of elements in the cycle)

$$\sqrt{\pi n / 8}.$$

The goal of many of Pollard's algorithms is to find a collision in a random mapping like the one above. A collision is finding two values x_i and x_j with $i \neq j$ such that

$$x_i = x_j.$$

From the birthday paradox we obtain a collision after an expected number of

$$\sqrt{\pi n / 2}$$

iterations of the map f. Hence, finding a collision using the birthday paradox in a naive way would require $O(\sqrt{n})$ time and $O(\sqrt{n})$ memory. But this is exactly the problem with the Baby-Step/Giant-Step method we were trying to avoid.

To find a collision, and make use of the rho shape of the random walk, we use Floyd's cycle finding algorithm: Given (x_1, x_2) we compute (x_2, x_4) and then (x_3, x_6) and so on, i.e. given the pair (x_i, x_{2i}) we compute

$$(x_{i+1}, x_{2i+2}) = (f(x_i), f(f(x_{2i}))).$$

We stop when we find

$$x_m = x_{2m}.$$

If the tail of the sequence $x_0, x_1, x_2, \ldots$ has length λ and the cycle has length μ then one can show that we obtain such a value of m when

$$m = \mu \left(1 + \lfloor \lambda / \mu \rfloor \right).$$

Since $\lambda < m \le \lambda + \mu$ we see that

$$m = O(\sqrt{n}),$$

and this will be an accurate complexity estimate if the mapping f behaves like an average random function. Hence, we can detect a collision with virtually no storage.

This is all very well, but we have not shown how to relate this to the discrete logarithm problem: Let G denote a group of order n and let the discrete logarithm problem be given by

$$h = g^x.$$

We partition the group into three sets S_1, S_2, S_3, where we assume $1 \notin S_2$, and then define the following random walk on the group G,

$$x_{i+1} = f(x_i) = \begin{cases} h \cdot x_i & x_i \in S_1, \\ x_i^2 & x_i \in S_2, \\ g \cdot x_i & x_i \in S_3. \end{cases}$$

In practice we actually keep track of three pieces of information

$$(x_i, a_i, b_i)$$

where

$$a_{i+1} = \begin{cases} a_i & x_i \in S_1, \\ 2a_i \ (\text{mod } n) & x_i \in S_2, \\ a_i + 1 \ (\text{mod } n) & x_i \in S_3, \end{cases}$$

and

$$b_{i+1} = \begin{cases} b_i + 1 \ (\text{mod } n) & x_i \in S_1, \\ 2b_i \ (\text{mod } n) & x_i \in S_2, \\ b_i & x_i \in S_3. \end{cases}$$

If we start with the triple

$$(x_0, a_0, b_0) = (1, 0, 0)$$

then we have, for all i,

$$\log_g(x_i) = a_i + b_i \log_g(h) = a_i + b_i x.$$

Applying Floyd's cycle finding algorithm we obtain a collision, and so find a value of m such that

$$x_m = x_{2m}.$$

This leads us to deduce the following equality of discrete logarithms

$$
\begin{aligned}
a_m + b_m x &= a_m + b_m \log_g(h) \\
&= \log_g(x_m) \\
&= \log_g(x_{2m}) \\
&= a_{2m} + b_{2m} \log_g(h) \\
&= a_{2m} + b_{2m} x.
\end{aligned}
$$

Rearranging we see that
$$(b_m - b_{2m})x = a_{2m} - a_m,$$
and so, if $b_m \neq b_{2m}$, we obtain
$$x = \frac{a_{2m} - a_m}{b_m - b_{2m}} \pmod{n}.$$

The probability that we have $b_m = b_{2m}$ is small enough, for large n, to be ignored.

If we assume the sequence $x_0, x_1, x_2, \ldots$ is produced by a random mapping from the group G to itself, then the above algorithm will find the discrete logarithm in expected time
$$O(\sqrt{n}).$$

As an example consider the subgroup G of $\mathbb{F}_{607}$ of order $n = 101$ generated by the element $g = 64$ and the discrete logarithm problem
$$h = 122 = 64^x.$$

We define the sets S_1, S_2, S_3 as follows:
$$S_1 = \{x \in \mathbb{F}_{607} : x \leq 201\},$$
$$S_2 = \{x \in \mathbb{F}_{607} : 202 \leq x \leq 403\},$$
$$S_3 = \{x \in \mathbb{F}_{607} : 404 \leq x \leq 606\}.$$

Applying Pollard's Rho method we obtain the following data

i	x_i	a_i	b_i	x_{2i}	a_{2i}	b_{2i}
0	1	0	0	1	0	0
1	122	0	1	316	0	2
2	316	0	2	172	0	8
3	308	0	4	137	0	18
4	172	0	8	7	0	38
5	346	0	9	309	0	78
6	137	0	18	352	0	56
7	325	0	19	167	0	12
8	7	0	38	498	0	26
9	247	0	39	172	2	52
10	309	0	78	137	4	5
11	182	0	55	7	8	12
12	352	0	56	309	16	26
13	76	0	11	352	32	53
14	167	0	12	167	64	6

So we obtain a collision, using Floyd's cycle finding algorithm, when $m = 14$. We see that
$$g^0 h^{12} = g^{64} h^6$$

which implies

$$12x = 64 + 6x \ (\text{mod } 101).$$

In other words

$$x = \frac{64}{12 - 6} \ (\text{mod } 101) = 78.$$

9.4.2 Pollard's Lambda Method

Pollard's Lambda method is like the Rho method in that one uses a deterministic random walk and a small amount of storage to solve the discrete logarithm problem. However, the Lambda method is particularly tuned to the situation where one knows that the discrete logarithm lies in a certain interval

$$x \in [a, \ldots, b].$$

In the Rho method we used one random walk, which turned into the shape of the Greek letter ρ, whilst in the Lambda method we use two walks which end up in the shape of the Greek letter lambda, i.e.

$$\lambda,$$

hence giving the method its name. Another name for this method is Pollard's Kangaroo method as it is originally described by the two walks being performed by kangaroos.

Let $w = b - a$ denote the length of the interval in which the discrete logarithm x is known to lie. We define a set

$$S = \{s_0, \ldots, s_{k-1}\}$$

of integers in non-decreasing order. The mean m of the set should be around $N = \sqrt{w}$. It is common to choose

$$s_i = 2^i \text{ for } 0 \leq i < k,$$

which implies that the mean of the set is

$$\frac{2^k}{k}$$

and so we choose

$$k \approx \frac{1}{2} \cdot \log_2(w).$$

We divide the group up into k sets S_i, for $i = 0, \ldots, k - 1$ and define the following deterministic random walk:

$$x_{i+1} = x_i \cdot g^{s_j} \text{ if } x_i \in S_j.$$

We first compute the deterministic random walk, starting from $g_0 = g^b$, by setting

$$g_i = g_{i-1} \cdot g^{s_j}$$

for $i = 1, \ldots, N$. We also set $c_0 = b$ and $c_{i+1} = c_i + s_j \ (\text{mod } q)$. We store g_N and notice that we have computed the discrete logarithm of g_N with respect to g,

$$c_N = \log_g(g_N).$$

We now compute our second deterministic random walk starting from the unknown point in the interval x; we set $h_0 = h = g^x$ and compute

$$h_{i+1} = h_i \cdot g^{s'_j}.$$

We also set $d_0 = 0$ and $d_{i+1} = d_i + s'_j \pmod{q}$. Notice that we have

$$\log_g(h_i) = x + d_i.$$

If the path of the h_i meets that of the path of the g_i then the h_i will carry on the path of the g_i and we will be able to find a value M where h_M equals our stored point g_N. At this point we have

$$c_N = \log_g(g_N) = \log_g(h_M) = x + d_M,$$

and so the solution to our discrete logarithm problem is given by

$$x = c_N - d_M \pmod{q}.$$

If we do not get a collision then we can increase N and continue both walks in a similar manner until a collision does occur.

The expected running time of this method is $\sqrt{w}$ and again the storage can be seen to be constant. The Lambda method can be used when the discrete logarithm is only known to lie in the full interval $[0, \ldots, q-1]$. But in this situation, whilst the asymptotic complexity is the same as the Rho method, the Rho method is better due to the implied constants.

As an example we again consider the subgroup G of $\mathbb{F}_{607}$ of order $n = 101$ generated by the element $g = 64$, but now we look at the discrete logarithm problem

$$h = 524 = 64^x.$$

We are given that the discrete logarithm x lies in the interval $[60, \ldots, 80]$. As our set of multipliers s_i we take $s_i = 2^i$ for $i = 0, 1, 2, 3$. The subsets $S_0, \ldots, S_3$ of G we define by

$$S_i = \{g \in G : g \pmod 4 = i\}.$$

We first compute the deterministic random walk g_i and the discrete logarithms $c_i = \log_g(g_i)$, for $i = 0, \ldots, N = 4$.

i	g_i	c_i
0	151	80
1	537	88
2	391	90
3	478	98
4	64	1

Now we compute the second deterministic random walk

i	h_i	$d_i = \log_g(h_i) - x$
0	524	0
1	151	1
2	537	9
3	391	11
4	478	19
5	64	23

Hence, we obtain the collision

$$h_5 = g_4$$

and so

$$x = 1 - 23 \ (\text{mod } 101) = 79.$$

Note that examining the above tables we see that we had earlier collisions between our two walks. However, we are unable to use these since we do not store g_0, g_1, g_2 or g_3. We have only stored the value of g_4.

9.4.3   Parallel Pollard's Rho

In real life when one uses random walk based techniques to solve discrete logarithm problems one uses a parallel version, so as to exploit the computing resources of a number of sites across the Internet. Suppose we are given the discrete logarithm problem

$$h = g^x$$

in a group G of prime order q. We first decide on an easily computable function

$$H : G \longrightarrow \{1, \ldots, k\},$$

where k is usually around 20. Then we define a set of multipliers m_i, these are produced by generating random integers $a_i, b_i \in [0, \ldots, q-1]$ and then setting

$$m_i = g^{a_i} h^{b_i}.$$

To start a deterministic random walk we pick random $s_0, t_0 \in [0, \ldots, q-1]$ and compute

$$g_0 = g^{s_0} h^{t_0},$$

the deterministic random walk is then defined on the triples (g_i, s_i, t_i) where

$$g_{i+1} = g_i \cdot m_{H(g_i)},$$
$$s_{i+1} = s_i + a_{H(g_i)} \ (\text{mod } q),$$
$$t_{i+1} = t_i + b_{H(g_i)} \ (\text{mod } q).$$

Hence, for every g_i we record the values of s_i and t_i such that

$$g_i = g^{s_i} h^{t_i}.$$

Suppose we have m processors, each processor starts a different deterministic random walk from a different starting position using the same algorithm to determine the next element in the walk. When two processors, or even the same processor, meet an element of the group that has been seen before then we obtain an equation

$$g^{s_i} h^{t_i} = g^{s_j} h^{t_j}$$

from which we can solve for the discrete logarithm x. Hence, we expect that after $O(\sqrt{\pi q/2}/m)$ iterations of these parallel walks we will find a collision and so solve the discrete logarithm problem.

However, as described this means that each processor needs to return every element in its computed deterministic random walk to a central server which then stores all the computed elements. This is highly inefficient as the storage requirements will be very large, namely $O(\sqrt{\pi q/2})$. We can reduce the storage to any required value as follows:
We define a function d on the group

$$d : G \longrightarrow \{0, 1\}$$

such that $d(g) = 1$ around $1/2^t$ of the time. The function d is often defined by returning $d(g) = 1$ if a certain subset of t of the bits representing g are set to zero for example. The elements in G for which $d(g) = 1$ will be called distinguished.
It is only the distinguished group elements which are now transmitted back to the central server. This means that one expects the deterministic random walks to need to continue another 2^t steps before a collision is detected between two deterministic random walks. Hence, the computing time now becomes

$$O\left(\sqrt{\pi q/2}/m + 2^t\right),$$

whilst the storage becomes

$$O\left(\sqrt{\pi q/2}/2^t\right).$$

This allows the storage to be reduced to any manageable amount, at the expense of a little extra computation. We do not give an example, since the method only really becomes useful as q becomes larger (say $q > 2^{20}$), but we leave it to the reader to construct their own examples.

9.5 SUB-EXPONENTIAL METHODS FOR FINITE FIELDS

There is a close relationship between the sub-exponential methods for factoring and the sub-exponential methods for solving the discrete logarithm problem in finite fields. We shall only consider the case of prime fields $\mathbb{F}_p$ but similar considerations apply to finite fields of characteristic two. The sub-exponential algorithms for finite fields are often referred to as index-calculus algorithms, for a reason which will become apparent as we explain the method.
We assume we are given $g, h \in \mathbb{F}_p^*$ such that

$$h = g^x.$$

We choose a factor base F of elements, usually small prime numbers, and then using one of the sieving strategies used for factoring we obtain a large number of relations of the form

$$\prod_{p_i \in F} p_i^{e_i} = 1 \ (\mathrm{mod} \ p).$$

These relations translate into the following equations for discrete logarithms,

$$\sum_{p_i \in F} e_i \log_g(p_i) = 0 \ (\mathrm{mod} \ p - 1).$$

Once enough equations like the one above have been found we can solve for the discrete logarithm of every element in the factor base, i.e. we can determine

$$x_i = \log_g(p_i).$$

The value of x_i is sometimes called the index of p_i with respect to g. This calculation is performed using linear algebra modulo $p - 1$, which is hence more complicated than the linear algebra modulo 2 performed in factoring algorithms. However, similar tricks, such as those deployed in the linear algebra stage of factoring algorithms, can be deployed to keep the storage requirements down to manageable levels. This linear algebra calculation only needs to be done once for each generator g, the results can then be used for many values of h.

When one wishes to solve a particular discrete logarithm problem

$$h = g^x,$$

we use a sieving technique, or simple trial and error, to write

$$h = \prod_{p_i \in F} p_i^{h_i} \ (\mathrm{mod} \ p),$$

i.e. we could compute

$$T = h \prod_{p_i \in F} p_i^{f_i} \ (\mathrm{mod} \ p)$$

and see if it factors in the form

$$T = \prod_{p_i \in F} p_i^{g_i}.$$

If it does then we have

$$h = \prod_{p_i \in F} p_i^{g_i - f_i} \ (\mathrm{mod} \ p).$$

We can then compute the discrete logarithm x from

$$x = \log_g(h) = \log_g \left(\prod_{p_i \in F} p_i^{h_i} \right)$$

$$= \sum_{p_i \in F} h_i \log_g(p_i) \ (\mathrm{mod} \ p - 1)$$

$$= \sum_{p_i \in F} h_i \cdot x_i \ (\mathrm{mod} \ p - 1).$$

This means that, once one discrete logarithm has been found, determining the next one is easier since we have already computed the values of the x_i.

The best of the methods to find the relations between the factorbase elements is the Number Field Sieve. This gives an overall running time of

$$O(L_p(1/3, c))$$

for some constant c. This is roughly the same complexity as the algorithms to factor large numbers, although the real practical problem is that the matrix algorithms now need to work modulo $p - 1$ and not modulo 2 as they did in factoring algorithms.

The upshot of these sub-exponential methods is that the size of p for finite field discrete logarithm based systems needs to be of the same order of magnitude as an RSA modulus, i.e. $p \geq 2^{1024}$.

Even though p has to be very large we still need to guard against generic attacks, hence $p - 1$ should have a prime factor q of order greater than 2^{160}. In fact for finite field based systems we usually work in the subgroup of $\mathbb{F}_p^*$ of order q.

9.6 SPECIAL METHODS FOR ELLIPTIC CURVES

For elliptic curves there are no known sub-exponential methods for the discrete logarithm problem, except in certain special cases. This means that the only method to solve the discrete logarithm problem in this setting is the parallel version of Pollard's Rho method.

Suppose the elliptic curve E is defined over the finite field $\mathbb{F}_q$. We set

$$\#E(\mathbb{F}_q) = h \cdot r$$

where r is a prime number. By Hasse's Theorem 2.3 the value of $\#E(\mathbb{F}_q)$ is close to q so we typically choose a curve with r close to q, i.e. we choose a curve E so that $h = 1, 2$ or 4.

The best known general algorithm for the elliptic curve discrete logarithm problem is the parallel Pollard's Rho method, which has complexity $O(\sqrt{r})$, which is about $O(\sqrt{q})$. Hence, to achieve the same security as an 80-bit block cipher we need to take $q \approx 2^{160}$, which is a lot smaller than the field size recommended for systems based on the discrete logarithm problems in a finite field. This results in the reduced bandwidth and computational times of elliptic curve systems.

However, there are a number of special cases which need to be avoided. We shall now give these special cases, but we shall not give the detailed reasons why they are to be avoided since the reasons are often quite mathematically involved. As usual we assume q is either a large prime or a power of 2.

- For any q we must choose curves for which there is no small number t such that r divides $q^t - 1$, where r is the large prime factor of $\#E(\mathbb{F}_q)$. This eliminates the supersingular curves and a few others. In this case there is a simple computable mapping from the elliptic curve discrete logarithm problem to the discrete logarithm problem in the finite field $\mathbb{F}_{q^t}$. Hence, in this case we obtain a sub-exponential method for solving the elliptic curve discrete logarithm problem.

- If $q = p$ is a large prime then we need to avoid the anomalous curves where $E(\mathbb{F}_p) = p$. In this case there is an algorithm which requires $O(\log p)$ elliptic curve operations.

- If $q = 2^n$ then we usually assume that n is prime to avoid the possibility of certain attacks based on the concept of 'Weil descent'.

One should treat these three special cases much like one treats the generation of large integers for the RSA algorithm. Due to the $P-1$ factoring method one often makes RSA moduli $N = p \cdot q$ such that p is a so-called safe prime of the form $2p_1 + 1$. Another special RSA based case is that we almost always use RSA with two prime factors, rather than three or four. This is because moduli with two prime factors appear to be the hardest to factor.

Chapter Summary

- Due to the Pohlig–Hellman algorithm a hard discrete logarithm problem should be set in a group whose order has a large prime factor.

- The generic algorithms such as the Baby-Step/Giant-Step algorithm mean that to achieve the same security as an 80-bit block cipher, the size of this large prime factor of the group order should be at least 160 bits.

- The Baby-Step/Giant-Step algorithm is a generic algorithm whose running time can be absolutely bounded by $\sqrt{q}$, where q is the size of the large prime factor of #G. However, the storage requirements of the Baby-Step/Giant-Step algorithm are $O(\sqrt{q})$.

- There are a number of techniques, due to Pollard, based on deterministic random walks in a group. These are generic algorithms which require little storage but which solve the discrete logarithm problem in expected time $O(\sqrt{q})$.

- For finite fields a number of index calculus algorithms exist which run in sub-exponential time. These mean that one needs to take large finite fields $\mathbb{F}_{p^t}$ with $p^t \geq 2^{1024}$ if one wants to obtain a hard discrete logarithm problem.

- For elliptic curves there are no sub-exponential algorithms known, except in very special cases. Hence, the only practical general algorithm to solve the discrete logarithm problem on an elliptic curve is the parallel Pollard's Rho method.

Further Reading

There are a number of good surveys on the discrete logarithm problem. I would recommend the ones by McCurley and Odlyzko. These articles only touch on the elliptic curve discrete logarithm problem though. For a treatment of what is known on the latter problem you could consult the survey by Koblitz et al.

N. Koblitz, A. Menezes and S. Vanstone. *The state of elliptic curve cryptography.* Designs Codes and Cryptography, **19**, 173–193, 2000.

K. McCurley. *The discrete logarithm problem.* In *Cryptology and Computational Number Theory*, Proc. Symposia in Applied Maths, Volume 42, 1990.

A. Odlyzko. *Discrete logarithms: The past and the future.* Designs Codes and Cryptography, **19**, 129–145, 2000.

Review Exercises

9.1.1   What cryptographic conclusion do we draw from the Pohlig–Hellman algorithm?

9.1.2   How does the Baby-Step/Giant-Step method work?

9.1.3   What are the practical problems associated with the Baby-Step/Giant-Step method, and how are these overcome when using the Pollard's Rho method?

9.1.4   What cryptographic conclusions can we draw from the existence of the Pollard's Rho method?

9.1.5   What cryptographic conclusions can we draw from the existence of the index-calculus algorithms in finite fields?

9.1.6   Discuss the statement that elliptic curves offer higher strength per bit than finite fields.

Programming Exercises

9.2.1   Implement the Pollard's Rho method and experiment with different definitions of deterministic random walks from those used in the text. What is the most efficient random walk you can come up with? (Efficient means it solves the discrete logarithm problem faster on average).

9.2.2   Implement the parallel Pollard method, using distinguished group elements, to solve discrete logarithm problems in a finite field. Using whatever computing resources you have available, how large a discrete logarithm problem can you reasonably solve within a time limit of 24 hours?

Standard Exercises

9.3.1   In the text we gave three deterministic random walks, one for the Rho, one for the Lambda and one for the parallel method. Can one use these walks in the different algorithms? What is the advantage/disadvantage of changing the deterministic random walks used?

9.3.2   Using only a pocket calculator, compute x such that

$$3^x = 5 \pmod{p}$$

where

$$p - 1 = 2 \cdot 3 \cdot 101 \cdot 103 \cdot 107^2.$$

Key Exchange, Signature Schemes and Hash Functions

Chapter Goals

- To introduce Diffie–Hellman key exchange.

- To introduce the need for digital signatures.

- To explain the two most used signature algorithms, namely RSA and DSA.

- To introduce and explain the need for cryptographic hash functions.

- To describe some other signature algorithms and key exchange techniques which have interesting properties.

10.1 DIFFIE–HELLMAN KEY EXCHANGE

Recall that the main drawback with the use of fast bulk encryption based on block or stream ciphers was the problem of key distribution. We have already seen a number of techniques to solve this problem, either using protocols which are themselves based on symmetric key techniques, or using a public key algorithm to transport a session key to the intended recipient. These, however, both have problems associated with them. For example, the symmetric key protocols were hard to analyse and required the use of already deployed long-term keys between each user and a trusted central authority.

A system is said to have forward secrecy, if the compromise of a long-term private key at some point in the future does not compromise the security of communications made using that key in the past. Key transport via public key encryption does not have *forward secrecy*. To see why this is important, suppose you bulk encrypt a video stream and then encrypt the session key under the recipient's RSA public key. Then suppose that some time in the future, the recipient's RSA private key is compromised. At that point your video stream is also compromised, assuming the attacker recorded this at the time it was transmitted.

In addition using key transport implies that the recipient trusts the sender to be able to generate, in a sensible way, the session key. Sometimes the recipient may wish to contribute some randomness of their own to the session key. However, this can only be done if both parties are online at the same moment in time. Key transport is more suited to the case where only the sender is online, as in applications like email for example.

The key distribution problem was solved in the same seminal paper by Diffie and Hellman as that in which they introduced public key cryptography. Their protocol for key distribution, called Diffie–Hellman Key Exchange, allows two parties to agree a secret key over an insecure channel without having met before. Its security is based on the DLOG problem in a finite abelian group G.

In the original paper the group is taken to be $G = \mathbb{F}_p^*$, but now more efficient versions can be produced by taking G to be an elliptic curve group, where the protocol is called EC-DH. The basic message flows for the Diffie–Hellman protocol are given in the following diagram:

$$
\begin{array}{ccc}
\text{Alice} & & \text{Bob} \\
a & g^a \longrightarrow & g^a \\
g^b & \longleftarrow g^b & b
\end{array}
$$

The two parties each have their own ephemeral secrets a and b. From these secrets both parties can agree on the same secret session key:

- Alice can compute $K = (g^b)^a$, since she knows a and was sent g^b by Bob,

- Bob can also compute $K = (g^a)^b$, since he knows b and was sent g^a by Alice.

Eve, the attacker, can see the messages

$$g^a \text{ and } g^b$$

and then needs to recover the secret key

$$K = g^{ab}$$

which is exactly the Diffie–Hellman problem considered in Chapter 7. Hence, the security of the above protocol rests not on the difficulty of solving the discrete logarithm problem, DLP, but on the difficulty of solving the Diffie–Hellman problem, DHP. Recall that it may be the case that it is easier to solve the DHP than the DLP, although no one believes this to be true for the groups that are currently used in real-life protocols.

Notice that the Diffie–Hellman protocol can be performed both online (in which case both parties contribute to the randomness in the shared session key) or offline, where one of the parties uses a long-term key of the form g^a instead of an ephemeral key. Hence, the Diffie–Hellman protocol can be used as a key exchange or as a key transport protocol.

The following is a very small example, in real life one takes $p \approx 2^{1024}$, but for our purposes we let the domain parameters be given by

$$p = 2\,147\,483\,659 \text{ and } g = 2.$$

Then the following diagram indicates a possible message flow for the Diffie–Hellman protocol:

Alice	Bob
$a = 12\,345$	$b = 654\,323$
$A = g^a = 428\,647\,416$ $\longrightarrow$	$A = 428\,647\,416$
$B = 450\,904\,856$ $\longleftarrow$	$B = g^b = 450\,904\,856$

The shared secret key is then computed via

$$A^b = 428\,647\,416^{654\,323} \pmod{p},$$
$$= 1\,333\,327\,162,$$
$$B^a = 450\,904\,856^{12\,345} \pmod{p},$$
$$= 1\,333\,327\,162.$$

Notice that group elements are transmitted in the protocol, hence when using a finite field such as $\mathbb{F}_p^*$ for the Diffie–Hellman protocol the communication costs are around 1024 bits in each direction, since it is prudent to choose $p \approx 2^{1024}$. However, when one uses an elliptic curve group $E(\mathbb{F}_q)$ one can choose $q \approx 2^{160}$, and so the communication costs are much less, namely around 160 bits in each direction. In addition the group exponentiation step for elliptic curves can be done more efficiently than that for finite prime fields.

As a baby example of EC-DH consider the elliptic curve

$$E : Y^2 = X^3 + X - 3$$

over the field $\mathbb{F}_{199}$. Let the base point be given by $G = (1, 76)$, then a possible message flow is given by

Alice	Bob
$a = 23$	$b = 86$
$A = [a]G = (2, 150)$ $\longrightarrow$	$A = (2, 150)$
$B = (123, 187)$ $\longleftarrow$	$B = [b]G = (123, 187)$

The shared secret key is then computed via

$$[b]A = [86](2, 150)$$
$$= (156, 75),$$
$$[a]B = [23](123, 187)$$
$$= (156, 75).$$

The shared key is then taken to be the x-coordinate 156 of the computed point. In addition, instead of transmitting the points, we transmit the compression of the point, which results in a significant saving in bandwidth.

So we seem to have solved the key distribution problem. But there is an important problem: you need to be careful *who* you are agreeing a key with. Alice has no assurance that she is agreeing a key with Bob, which can lead to the following (wo)man in the middle attack:

$$
\begin{array}{ccccc}
\text{Alice} & & \text{Eve} & & \text{Bob} \\
a & \longrightarrow & g^a & & \\
g^m & \longleftarrow & m & & \\
g^{am} & & g^{am} & & \\
& & n & \longrightarrow & g^n \\
& & g^b & \longleftarrow & b \\
& & g^{bn} & & g^{bn}
\end{array}
$$

In the man in the middle attack

- Alice agrees a key with Eve, thinking it is Bob she is agreeing a key with,

- Bob agrees a key with Eve, thinking it is Alice,

- Eve can now examine communications as they pass through her, she acts as a router. She does not alter the plaintext, so her actions go undetected.

So we can conclude that the Diffie–Hellman protocol on its own is not enough. For example how does Alice know who she is agreeing a key with? Is it Bob or Eve?

10.2   DIGITAL SIGNATURE SCHEMES

One way around the man in the middle attack on the Diffie–Hellman protocol is for Alice to sign her message to Bob and Bob to sign his message to Alice. In that way both parties know who they are talking to. Signatures are an important concept of public key cryptography, they also were invented by Diffie and Hellman in the same 1976 paper, but the first practical system was due to Rivest, Shamir and Adleman.

The basic idea behind public key signatures is as follows:

$$\text{Message} + \text{Alice's private key} = \text{Signature},$$
$$\text{Message} + \text{Signature} + \text{Alice's public key} = \text{YES/NO}.$$

The above is called a signature scheme with appendix, since the signature is appended to the message before transmission, the message needs to be input into the signature verification procedure. Another variant is the signature scheme with message recovery, where the message is output by the signature verification procedure, as described in

$$\text{Message} + \text{Alice's private key} = \text{Signature},$$
$$\text{Signature} + \text{Alice's public key} = \text{YES/NO} + \text{Message}.$$

The main idea is that only Alice can sign a message, which could only come from her since only Alice has access to the private key. On the other hand anyone can verify Alice's signature, since everyone can have access to her public key.

The main problem is how are the public keys to be trusted? How do you know a certain public key is associated to a given entity? You may think a public key belongs to Alice, but it may belong to Eve. Eve can therefore sign cheques etc., and you would think they come from Alice. We seem to have the same key management problem as in symmetric systems, albeit now the problem is not one of keeping the keys secret, but making sure they are authentic. We shall return to this problem later.

A digital signature scheme consists more formally of two transformations:

- a secret signing transform S,

- a public verification transform V.

In the following discussion, we assume a signature with message recovery. For an appendix based scheme a simple change to the following will suffice.

Alice, sending a message m, calculates

$$s = S(m)$$

and then transmits s, where s is the digital signature on the message m. Note, we are not interested in keeping the message secret here, since we are only interested in knowing who it comes from. If confidentiality of the message is important then the signature s could be encrypted using, for example, the public key of the receiver.

The receiver of the signature s applies the public verification transform V to s. The output is then the message m and a bit v. The bit v indicates valid or invalid, i.e. whether the signature is good or not. If v is valid the recipient gets a guarantee of three important security properties:

- message integrity – the message has not been altered in transit,

- message origin – the message was sent by Alice,

- non-repudiation – Alice cannot claim she did not send the message.

Note, the first two of these properties are also provided by message authentication codes, MACs. However, the last property of non-repudiation is not provided by MACs and has important applications in e-commerce. To see why non-repudiation is so important, consider what would happen if you could sign a cheque and then say you did not sign it.

The RSA encryption algorithm is particularly interesting since it can be used directly as a signature algorithm with message recovery.

- The sender applies the RSA decryption transform to generate the signature, by taking the message and raising it to the private exponent d

$$s = m^d \ (\text{mod } N).$$

- The receiver then applies the RSA encryption transform to recover the original message

$$m = s^e \ (\text{mod } N).$$

But this raises the question as to how do we check for validity of the signature? If the original message is in a natural language such as English then one can verify that the extracted message is also in the same natural language. But this is not a solution for all possible messages. Hence one needs to add redundancy to the message.

One way of doing this is as follows. Suppose the message D is t bits long and the RSA modulus N is k bits long, with $t < k - 32$. We first pad D to the right by zeros to produce a string of length a multiple of eight. We then add $(k - t)/8$ bytes to the left of D to produce a byte-string

$$m = 00\|01\|FF\|FF \ldots \|FF\|00\|D.$$

The signature is then computed via

$$m^d \pmod{N}.$$

When verifying the signature we ensure that the recovered value of m has the correct padding.

But not all messages will be so short so as to fit into the above method. Hence, naively to apply the RSA signature algorithm to a long message m we need to break it into blocks and sign each block in turn. This is very time consuming for long messages. Worse than this, we must add serial numbers and more redundancy to each message otherwise an attacker could delete parts of the long message without us knowing, just as happened when encrypting using a block cipher in ECB Mode. This problem arises because our signature model is one giving message recovery, i.e. the message is recovered from the signature and the verification process. If we used a system using a signature scheme with appendix then we could produce a hash of the message to be signed and then just sign the hash. However, not just any old hash function will do, we require hash functions with special properties as we shall now explain.

10.3   HASH FUNCTIONS

A cryptographic hash function h is a function which takes arbitrary length bit strings as input and produces a fixed length bit string as output, the output is often called a hashcode or hash value. Hash functions are used a lot in computer science, but the crucial difference between a standard hash function and a cryptographic hash function is that a cryptographic hash function should at least have the property of being one-way. In other words given any string y from the range of h, it should be computationally infeasible to find any value x in the domain of h such that

$$h(x) = y.$$

Another way to describe a hash function which has the one-way property is that it is preimage resistant. Using a cryptographic hash function h it is possible to make RSA into a signature scheme without message recovery, which is much more efficient for long messages.

Suppose we are given a long message m for signing, we first compute $h(m)$ and then apply the RSA signing transform to $h(m)$, i.e. the signature is given by

$$s = h(m)^d \pmod{N}.$$

The signature and message are then transmitted together as the pair (m, s). Verifying a message/signature pair (m, s) generated using a hash function involves three steps.

- 'Encrypt' s using the RSA encryption function to recover h', i.e.

$$h' = s^e \pmod{N}.$$

- Compute $h(m)$ from m.

- Check whether $h' = h(m)$. If they agree accept the signature as valid, otherwise the signature should be rejected.

Actually in practice one also needs padding, but here for example you can use the padding scheme given earlier when we discussed RSA with message recovery.

So why do we need to use a hash function which has the one-way property? The answer is that the one-way property stops a cryptanalyst from cooking up a message with a given signature. For example, suppose we are using the RSA scheme with appendix just described but with a hash function which does not have the one-way property. We then have the following attack.

- Eve computes

$$h' = r^e \pmod{N}$$

for some random integer r.

- Eve also computes the pre-image of h' under h (recall we are assuming that h does not have the one-way property) i.e. Eve computes

$$m = h^{-1}(h').$$

Eve now has your signature (m, r) on the message m. Such a forgery is called an existential forgery in that the attacker may not have any control over the contents of the message on which they have obtained a digital signature.

In practice we need something more than the one-way property. A hash function is called collision resistant if it is infeasible to find two distinct values x and x' such that

$$h(x) = h(x').$$

This is needed to avoid the following attack, which is performed by the legitimate signer.

- The signer chooses two messages m and m' with $h(m) = h(m')$.

- They sign m and output the signature (m, s).

- Later they repudiate this signature, saying it was really a signature on the message m'.

As a concrete example one could have that m is an electronic cheque for 1000 euros whilst m' is an electronic cheque for 10 euros.

It is harder to construct collision resistant hash functions than one-way hash functions due to the birthday paradox. To find a collision of a hash function f, we can keep computing

$$f(x_1), f(x_2), f(x_3), \ldots$$

until we get a collision. If the function has an output size of n bits then we expect to find a collision after $O(2^{n/2})$ iterations. This should be compared with the number of steps needed to find a preimage, which should be $O(2^n)$ for a well-designed hash function. Hence to achieve a security level of 80 bits for a collision resistant hash function we need roughly 160 bits of output.

But still that is not enough; a cryptographic hash function should also be second preimage resistant. This is the property that given m it should be hard to find an $m' \neq m$ with $h(m') = h(m)$. This property is needed to stop the following attack.

- An attacker obtains your signature (m, s) on a message m.

- The attacker finds another message m' with $h(m') = h(m)$.

- The attacker now has your signature (m', s) on the message m'.

In summary a cryptographic hash function needs to satisfy the following three properties:

1. **Preimage Resistant:** It should be hard to find a message with a given hash value.

2. **Collision Resistant:** It should be hard to find two messages with the same hash value.

3. **Second Preimage Resistant:** Given one message it should be hard to find another message with the same hash value.

But how are these properties related? Just as with public key encryption algorithms, we can relate these properties using reductions.

Lemma 10.1 *Assuming a function is preimage resistant is a weaker assumption than assuming it either collision resistant or second preimage resistant.*

Proof
Suppose h is a function and let $\mathcal{O}$ denote an oracle which on input of y finds an x such that $h(x) = y$, i.e. $\mathcal{O}$ is an oracle which breaks the preimage resistance of the function h.
   Using $\mathcal{O}$ we can then find a collision in h by pulling x at random and then computing $y = h(x)$. Passing y to the oracle $\mathcal{O}$ will produce a value x' such that $y = h(x')$. Since h is assumed to have infinite domain, it is unlikely that we have $x = x'$. Hence, we have found a collision in h.
   A similar argument applies to breaking the second preimage resistance of h.
                                                                                        Q.E.D.

Lemma 10.2 *Assuming a function is second preimage resistant is a weaker assumption than assuming it is collision resistant.*

Proof
Assume we are given an oracle $\mathcal{O}$ which on input of x will find x' such that $x \neq x'$ and $h(x) = h(x')$. We can clearly use $\mathcal{O}$ to find a collision in h by choosing x at random.
                                                                                        Q.E.D.

We would like to base our cryptographic schemes on the weakest assumptions possible. In this chapter we shall assume our cryptographic hash functions are collision resistant, which is a strong assumption. In later chapters we shall see cryptographic schemes which only require the hash function to be second preimage resistant.

Note, the security of any signature scheme which uses a cryptographic hash function, depends both on the security of the underlying hard mathematical problem, such as factoring or the discrete logarithm problem, and the security of the underlying hash function.

A collision-free cryptographic hash function can also be used as the basis of a MAC. One possibility to construct a MAC based on hash functions, is to concatenate the key with the message and then apply a hash function, i.e.

$$MAC = h(M\|k),$$

although this is not usually considered a good idea. A MAC, called HMAC, occurring in a number of standards documents works in this way, although slightly more complicated (for extra security),

$$HMAC = h(k\|p_1\|h(k\|p_2\|M)),$$

where p_1 and p_2 are strings used to pad out the input to the hash function to a full block.

Hash functions can also be considered as a special type of manipulation detection code, or MDC. For example a hash function can be used to protect the integrity of a large file, as used in some virus protection products. The hash value of the file contents is computed and then either stored in a secure place (e.g. on a floppy in a safe) or the hash value is put in a file of similar values which is then digitally signed to stop future tampering.

A basic design principle when designing a hash function is that its output should produce an avalanche effect, in other words a small change in the input produces a large and unpredictable change in the output. This is needed so that a signature on a cheque for 30 pounds cannot be altered into a signature on a cheque for 30 000 pounds, or vice versa.

To be effectively collision free a hash value should be at least 128 bits long, for applications with low security, but preferably its output should be 160 bits long.

10.3.1   The MD4 Family

Several hash functions are widely used, they are all iterative in nature. The three most widely deployed are MD5, RIPEMD-160 and SHA-1. The MD5 algorithm produces outputs of 128 bits in size, whilst RIPEMD-160 and SHA-1 both produce outputs of 160 bits in length. Recently NIST has proposed a new set of hash functions called SHA-256, SHA-384 and SHA-512 having outputs of 256, 384 and 512 bits respectively. All of these hash functions are derived from an earlier simpler algorithm called MD4.

The seven main algorithms in the MD4 family are

- **MD4**: This has 3 rounds of 16 steps and an output bitlength of 128 bits.

- **MD5**: This has 4 rounds of 16 steps and an output bitlength of 128 bits.

- **SHA-1**: This has 4 rounds of 20 steps and an output bitlength of 160 bits.

- **RIPEMD-160**: This has 5 rounds of 16 steps and an output bitlength of 160 bits.

- **SHA-256**: This has 64 rounds of single steps and an output bitlength of 256 bits.

- **SHA-384**: This is virtually identical to SHA-512 except the output is truncated to 384 bits.

- **SHA-512**: This has 80 rounds of single steps and an output bitlength of 512 bits.

We discuss MD4 in detail, the others are just more complicated versions of MD4, which we leave to the interested reader to look up in the literature. In MD4 there are three bit-wise functions of three 32-bit variables

$$f(u, v, w) = (u \wedge v) \vee ((\neg u) \wedge w),$$
$$g(u, v, w) = (u \wedge v) \vee (u \wedge w) \vee (v \wedge w),$$
$$h(u, v, w) = u \oplus v \oplus w.$$

Throughout the algorithm we maintain a current hash state

$$(H_1, H_2, H_3, H_4)$$

of four 32-bit values initialized with a fixed initial value,

$$H_1 = \text{0x67452301},$$
$$H_2 = \text{0xEFCDAB89},$$
$$H_3 = \text{0x98BADCFE},$$
$$H_4 = \text{0x10325476}.$$

There are various fixed constants (y_i, z_i, s_i), which depend on each round. We have

$$y_j = \begin{cases} 0 & 0 \le j \le 15, \\ \text{0x5A827999} & 16 \le j \le 31, \\ \text{0x6ED9EBA1} & 32 \le j \le 47, \end{cases}$$

and the values of z_i and s_i are given by following arrays,

$$z_{0...15} = [0, 1, 2, 3, 4, 5, 6, 7, 8, 9, 10, 11, 12, 13, 14, 15],$$
$$z_{16...31} = [0, 4, 8, 12, 1, 5, 9, 13, 2, 6, 10, 14, 3, 7, 11, 15],$$
$$z_{32...47} = [0, 8, 4, 12, 2, 10, 6, 14, 1, 9, 5, 13, 3, 11, 7, 15],$$
$$s_{0...15} = [3, 7, 11, 19, 3, 7, 11, 19, 3, 7, 11, 19, 3, 7, 11, 19],$$
$$s_{16...31} = [3, 5, 9, 13, 3, 5, 9, 13, 3, 5, 9, 13, 3, 5, 9, 13],$$
$$s_{32...47} = [3, 9, 11, 15, 3, 9, 11, 15, 3, 9, 11, 15, 3, 9, 11, 15].$$

The data stream is loaded 16 words at a time into $X[j]$ for $0 \le j < 16$. We then execute the following steps for each 16 words entered from the data stream.

```
(A,B,C,D) = (H[1],H[2],H[3],H[4]).
Execute Round 1.
Execute Round 2.
```

Execute Round 3.
(H[1],H[2],H[3],H[4]) = (H[1]+A, H[2]+B, H[3]+C, H[4]+D).

After all data has been read in, the output is the concatenation of the final value of

$$H_1, H_2, H_3, H_4.$$

The details of the rounds are given by the following descriptions, where $\lll$ denotes a bit-wise rotate to the left:

- **Round 1**
  For $j = 0$ to 15 do

  1. $t = A + f(B, C, D) + X[z_j] + y_j$.
  2. $(A, B, C, D) = (D, t \lll s_j, B, C)$.

- **Round 2**
  For $j = 16$ to 31 do

  1. $t = A + g(B, C, D) + X[z_j] + y_j$.
  2. $(A, B, C, D) = (D, t \lll s_j, B, C)$.

- **Round 3**
  For $j = 32$ to 47 do

  1. $t = A + h(B, C, D) + X[z_j] + y_j$.
  2. $(A, B, C, D) = (D, t \lll s_j, B, C)$.

10.3.2 Hash Functions and Block Ciphers

One can also make a hash function out of an n-bit block cipher, E_K. There are a number of ways of doing this, all of which make use of a constant public initial value IV. Some of the schemes also make use of a function g which maps n-bit inputs to keys.

We first pad the message to be hashed and divide it into blocks

$$x_0, x_1, \ldots, x_t,$$

of size either the block size or key size of the underlying block cipher, the exact choice of size depending on the exact definition of the hash function being created. The output hash value is then the final value of H_i in the following iteration

$$H_0 = IV,$$
$$H_i = f(x_i, H_{i-1}).$$

The exact definition of the function f depends on the scheme being used. We present just three, although others are possible.

- **Matyas–Meyer–Oseas Hash**

$$f(x_i, H_{i-1}) = E_{g(H_{i-1})}(x_i) \oplus x_i.$$

- **Davies–Meyer Hash**

$$f(x_i, H_{i-1}) = E_{x_i}(H_{i-1}) \oplus H_{i-1}.$$

- **Miyaguchi–Preneel Hash**

$$f(x_i, H_{i-1}) = E_{g(H_{i-1})}(x_i) \oplus x_i \oplus H_{i-1}.$$

10.4   DIGITAL SIGNATURE ALGORITHM

We have already presented one digital signature scheme RSA. You may ask why do we need another one?

- What if someone breaks the RSA algorithm or finds that factoring is easy?

- RSA is not suited to some applications since signature generation is a very costly operation.

- RSA signatures are very large, some applications require smaller signature footprints.

One algorithm which addresses all of these concerns is the Digital Signature Algorithm, or DSA. One sometimes sees this referred to as the DSS, or Digital Signature Standard. Although originally designed to work in the group $\mathbb{F}_p^*$, where p is a large prime, it is now common to see it used using elliptic curves, in which case it is called EC-DSA. The elliptic curve variants of DSA run very fast and have smaller footprints and key sizes than almost all other signature algorithms.

We shall first describe the basic DSA algorithm as it applies to finite fields. In this variant the security is based on the difficulty of solving the discrete logarithm problem in the field $\mathbb{F}_p$.

DSA is a signature with appendix algorithm and the signature produced consists of two 160-bit integers r and s. The integer r is a function of a 160-bit random number k called the ephemeral key which changes with every message. The integer s is a function of

- the message,

- the signer's private key x,

- the integer r,

- the ephemeral key k.

Just as with the ElGamal encryption algorithm there are a number of domain parameters which are usually shared amongst a number of users. The DSA domain parameters are all public information and are much like those found in the ElGamal encryption algorithm. First a 160-bit prime number q is chosen, one then selects a large prime number p such that

- p has between 512 and 2048 bits,

- q divides $p - 1$.

Finally we generate a random integer h less than p and compute

$$g = h^{(p-1)/q}.$$

If $g = 1$ then we pick a new value of h until we obtain $g \neq 1$. This ensures that g is an element of order q in the group $\mathbb{F}_p^*$, i.e.

$$g^q = 1 \pmod{p}.$$

After having decided on the domain parameters (p, q, g), each user generates their own private signing key x such that

$$0 < x < q.$$

The associated public key is y where

$$y = g^x \pmod{p}.$$

Notice that key generation for each user is much simpler than with RSA, since we only require a single modular exponentiation to generate the public key.

To sign a message m the user performs the following steps:

- Compute the hash value $h = H(m)$.
- Choose a random ephemeral key, $0 < k < q$.
- Compute
$$r = (g^k \pmod{p}) \pmod{q}.$$
- Compute
$$s = (h + xr)/k \pmod{q}.$$

The signature on m is then the pair (r, s), notice that this signature is therefore around 320 bits long.

To verify the signature (r, s) on the message m the verifier performs the following steps.

- Compute the hash value $h = H(m)$.
- $a = h/s \pmod{q}$.
- $b = r/s \pmod{q}$.
- Compute, where y is the public key of the sender,
$$v = (g^a y^b \pmod{p}) \pmod{q}.$$
- Accept the signature if and only if $v = r$.

As a baby example of DSA consider the following domain parameters

$$q = 13, \ p = 4q + 1 = 53 \text{ and } g = 16.$$

Suppose the public/private key pair of the user is given by $x = 3$ and

$$y = g^3 \pmod{p} = 15.$$

Now, if we wish to sign a message which has hash value $h = 5$, we first generate the ephemeral secret key $k = 2$ and then compute

$$r = (g^k \ (\text{mod } p)) \ (\text{mod } q) = 5,$$
$$s = (h + xr)/k \ (\text{mod } q) = 10.$$

To verify this signature the recipient computes

$$a = h/s \ (\text{mod } q) = 7,$$
$$b = r/s \ (\text{mod } q) = 7,$$
$$v = (g^a y^b \ (\text{mod } p)) \ (\text{mod } q) = 5.$$

Note $v = r$ and so the signature verifies correctly.

The DSA algorithm uses the subgroup of $\mathbb{F}_p^*$ of order q which is generated by g. Hence the DLOG problem really is in the cyclic group $\langle g \rangle$ of order q. For security we insisted that we have

- $p > 2^{512}$, although $p > 2^{1024}$ may be more prudent, to avoid attacks via the Number Field Sieve,

- $q > 2^{160}$ to avoid attacks via the Baby-Step/Giant-Step method.

Hence, to achieve the rough equivalent of 80 bits of DES strength we need to operate on integers of roughly 1024 bits in length. This makes DSA slower even than RSA, since the DSA operation is more complicated than RSA. The verification operation in RSA requires only one exponentiation modulo a 1024-bit number, and even that is an exponentiation by a small number. For DSA, verification requires two exponentiations modulo a 1024-bit number, rather than one as in RSA. In addition the signing operation for DSA is more complicated due to the need to compute the value of s.

The main problem is that the DSA algorithm really only requires to work in a finite abelian group of size 2^{160}, but since the integers modulo p are susceptible to an attack from the Number Field Sieve we are required to work with group elements of 1024 bits in size. This produces a significant performance penalty.

Luckily we can generalize DSA to an arbitrary finite abelian group in which the DLOG problem is hard. We can then use a group which provides a harder instance of the discrete logarithm problem, for example the group of points on an elliptic curve over a finite field.

We write $G = \langle g \rangle$ for a group generated by g, we assume that

- g has prime order $q > 2^{160}$,

- the discrete logarithm problem with respect to g is hard,

- there is a public function f such that

$$f : G \longrightarrow \mathbb{Z}/q\mathbb{Z}.$$

We summarize the different choices between DSA and EC-DSA in the following table:

Quantity	DSA	EC-DSA
G	$\langle g \rangle < \mathbb{F}_p^*$	$\langle P \rangle < E(\mathbb{F}_p)$
g	$g \in \mathbb{F}_p^*$	$P \in E(\mathbb{F}_p)$
y	g^x	$[x]P$
f	$\cdot \pmod{q}$	$x\text{-coord}(P) \pmod{q}$

For this generalized form of DSA each user again generates a secret signing key, x. The public key is again give by y where

$$y = g^x.$$

Signatures are computed via the steps

- Compute the hash value $h = H(m)$.

- Chooses a random ephemeral key, $0 < k < q$.

- Compute

$$r = f(g^k).$$

- Compute

$$s = (h + xr)/k \pmod{q}.$$

The signature on m is then the pair (r, s).

To verify the signature (r, s) on the message m the verifier performs the following steps.

- Compute the hash value $h = H(m)$.

- $a = h/s \pmod{q}$.

- $b = r/s \pmod{q}$.

- Compute, where y is the public key of the sender,

$$v = f(g^a y^b).$$

- Accept the signature if and only if $v = r$.

You should compare this signature and verification algorithm with that given earlier for DSA and spot where they differ. When used for EC-DSA the above generalization is written additively.

As a baby example of EC-DSA take the following elliptic curve

$$Y^2 = X^3 + X + 3,$$

over the field $\mathbb{F}_{199}$. The number of elements in $E(\mathbb{F}_{199})$ is equal to $q = 197$ which is a prime, the elliptic curve group is therefore cyclic and as a generator we can take

$$P = (1, 76).$$

As a private key let us take $x = 29$, and so the associated public key is given by

$$Y = [x]P = [29](1, 76) = (113, 191).$$

Suppose the holder of this public key wishes to sign a message with hash value $H(m)$ equal to 68. They first produce a random ephemeral key, which we shall take to be $k = 153$ and compute

$$
\begin{aligned}
r &= x\text{-coord}([k]P) \\
&= x\text{-coord}([153](1, 76)) \\
&= x\text{-coord}((185, 35)) \\
&= 185.
\end{aligned}
$$

Now they compute

$$
\begin{aligned}
s &= (H(m) + x \cdot r)/k \ (\text{mod } q) \\
&= (68 + 29 \cdot 185)/153 \ (\text{mod } 197) \\
&= 78.
\end{aligned}
$$

The signature is then the pair $(r, s) = (185, 78)$.

To verify this signature we compute

$$
\begin{aligned}
a &= H(m)/s \ (\text{mod } q) \\
&= 68/78 \ (\text{mod } 197) \\
&= 112, \\
b &= r/s \ (\text{mod } q) \\
&= 185/78 \ (\text{mod } 197) \\
&= 15.
\end{aligned}
$$

We then compute

$$
\begin{aligned}
Z &= [a]P + [b]Y \\
&= [112](1, 76) + [15](113, 191) \\
&= (111, 60) + (122, 140) \\
&= (185, 35).
\end{aligned}
$$

The signature now verifies since we have

$$r = 185 = x\text{-coord}(Z).$$

10.5 SCHNORR SIGNATURES

There are many variants of signature schemes based on discrete logarithms. A particularly interesting one is that of Schnorr signatures. We present the algorithm in the general case and allow the reader to work out the differences between the elliptic curve and finite field variants.

Suppose G is a public finite abelian group generated by an element g of prime order q. The public/private key pairs are just the same as in DSA, namely

- The private key is an integer x in the range $0 < x < q$.

- The public key is the element
$$y = g^x.$$

To sign a message m using the Schnorr signature algorithm we:

1. Choose an ephemeral key k in the range $0 < k < q$.

2. Compute the associated ephemeral public key
$$r = g^k.$$

3. Compute $e = h(m\|r)$. Notice how the hash function depends both on the message and the ephemeral public key.

4. Compute
$$s = k + x \cdot e \pmod{q}.$$

The signature is then given by the pair (e, s).

The verification step is very simple, we first compute
$$r = g^s y^{-e}.$$

The signature is accepted if and only if $e = h(m\|r)$.

As an example of Schnorr signatures in a finite field we take the domain parameters
$$q = 101, p = 607 \text{ and } g = 601.$$

As the public/private key pair we assume $x = 3$ and
$$y = g^x \pmod{p} = 391.$$

Then to sign a message we generate an ephemeral key $k = 65$ and compute
$$r = g^k \pmod{p} = 223.$$

We now need to compute the hash value
$$e = h(m\|r) \pmod{q}.$$

Let us assume that we compute $e = 93$, then the second component of the signature is given by

$$s = k + x \cdot e \pmod{q}$$
$$= 65 + 3 \cdot 93 \pmod{101}$$
$$= 41.$$

In a later chapter we shall see that Schnorr signatures are able to be proved to be secure, assuming that discrete logarithms are hard to compute, whereas no proof of security is known for DSA signatures.

Schnorr signatures have been suggested to be used for challenge response mechanisms in smart cards since the response part of the signature (the value of s) is particularly easy to evaluate since it only requires the computation of a single modular multiplication and a single modular addition. No matter what group we choose this final phase only requires arithmetic modulo a relatively small prime number.

To see how one uses Schnorr signatures in a challenge response situation we give the following scenario. A smart card wishes to authenticate you to a building or ATM machine. The card reader has a copy of your public key y, whilst the card has a copy of your private key x. Whilst you are walking around the card is generating commitments, which are ephemeral public keys of the form

$$r = g^k.$$

When you place your card into the card reader the card transmits to the reader the value of one of these precomputed commitments. The card reader then responds with a challenge message e. Your card then only needs to compute

$$s = k + xe \ (\text{mod } q),$$

and transmit it to the reader which then verifies the 'signature', by checking that

$$g^s = ry^e.$$

Notice that the only online computation needed by the card is the computation of the value of e and s, which are both easy to perform.

In more detail, if we let C denote the card and R denote the card reader then we have

$$C \longrightarrow R : r = g^k,$$
$$R \longrightarrow C : e,$$
$$C \longrightarrow R : s = k + xe \ (\text{mod } q).$$

The point of the initial commitment is to stop either the challenge being concocted so as to reveal your private key, or your response being concocted so as to fool the reader. A three-phase protocol consisting of

$$\text{commitment} \longrightarrow \text{challenge} \longrightarrow \text{response}$$

is a common form of authentication protocols, we shall see more protocols of this nature when we discuss zero-knowledge proofs in Chapter 13.

10.6 NYBERG–RUEPPEL SIGNATURES

What happens when we want to sign a general message which is itself quite short. It may turn out that the signature could be longer than the message. Recall that RSA can be used either as a scheme with appendix or as a scheme with message recovery. So far none of our discrete logarithm based schemes can be used with message recovery. We shall now give an example scheme which does have the message recovery property, called the Nyberg-Rueppel signature scheme, which is based on discrete logarithms in some public finite abelian group G.

All signature schemes with message recovery require a public redundancy function R. This function maps actual messages over to the data which is actually signed. This acts rather like a hash function does in the schemes based on signatures with appendix. However, unlike a hash function the redundancy function must be easy to invert. As a simple example we could take R to be the function

$$R : \begin{cases} \{0,1\}^{n/2} \longrightarrow \{0,1\}^n \\ \quad m \longmapsto m\|m. \end{cases}$$

We assume that the codomain of R can be embedded into the group G. In our description we shall use the integers modulo p, i.e. $G = \mathbb{F}_p^*$, and as usual we assume that a large prime q divides $p-1$ and that g is a generator of the subgroup of order q.

Once again the public/private key pair is given as a discrete logarithm problem

$$(y = g^x, x).$$

Nyberg-Rueppel signatures are then produced as follows:

1. Select a random $k \in \mathbb{Z}/q\mathbb{Z}$ and compute

$$r = g^k \pmod{p}.$$

2. Compute

$$e = R(m) \cdot r \pmod{p}.$$

3. Compute

$$s = x \cdot e + k \pmod{q}.$$

The signature is then the pair (e, s). From this pair, which is a group element and an integer modulo q, we need to

- verify that the signature comes from the user with public key y,

- recover the message m from the pair (e, s).

Verification for a Nyberg-Rueppel signature takes the signature (e, s) and the sender's public key $y = g^x$ and then computes

1. Set
$$u_1 = g^s y^{-e} = g^{s-ex} = g^k \pmod{p}.$$

2. Now compute
$$u_2 = e/u_1 \pmod{p}.$$

3. Verify that u_2 lies in the range of the redundancy function, e.g. we must have

$$u_2 = R(m) = m\|m.$$

If this does not hold then reject the signature.

4. Recover the message $m = R^{-1}(u_2)$ and accept the signature.

As an example we take the domain parameters

$$q = 101, p = 607 \text{ and } g = 601.$$

As the public/private key pair we assume $x = 3$ and

$$y = g^x \pmod{p} = 391.$$

To sign the message $m = 12$, where m must lie in $[0, \dots, 15]$, we compute an ephemeral key $k = 45$ and

$$r = g^k \pmod{p} = 143.$$

Suppose

$$R(m) = m + 2^4 \cdot m$$

then we have $R(m) = 204$. We then compute

$$e = R(m) \cdot r \pmod{p} = 36,$$
$$s = x \cdot e + k \pmod{q} = 52.$$

The signature is then the pair $(e, s) = (36, 52)$. We now show how this signature is verified and the message recovered. We first compute

$$u_1 = g^s y^{-e} = 143.$$

Notice how the verifier has computed u_1 to be the same as the value of r computed by the signer. The verifier now computes

$$u_2 = e/u_1 \pmod{p} = 204.$$

The verifier now checks that $u_2 = 204$ is of the form

$$m + 2^4 m$$

for some value of $m \in [0, \dots, 15]$. We see that u_2 is of this form and so the signature is valid. The message is then recovered by solving for m in

$$m + 2^4 m = 204,$$

from which we obtain $m = 12$.

10.7 AUTHENTICATED KEY AGREEMENT

Now we know how to perform digital signatures we can solve the problem with Diffie–Hellman key exchange. Recall that the man in the middle attack worked because each end did not know who they were talking to. We can now authenticate each end by requiring the parties to digitally sign their messages.

We will still obtain forward secrecy, since the long-term signing key is only used to provide authentication and is not used to perform a key transport operation.

We also have two choices of Diffie–Hellman protocol, namely one based on the discrete logarithms in a finite field DH and one based on elliptic curves EC-DH. There are also at least three possible signing algorithms RSA, DSA and EC-DSA. Assuming security sizes of 1024 bits for RSA, 1024 bits for the prime in DSA and 160 bits for the group order in both DSA and EC-DSA we obtain the following message sizes for our signed Diffie–Hellman protocol.

Algorithms	DH size	Signature size	Total size
DH+DSA	1024	320	1344
DH+RSA	1024	1024	2048
ECDH+RSA	160	1024	1184
ECDH+ECDSA	160	320	480

This is still an awfully large amount of overhead to simply agree what could be only a 128-bit session key.

To make the messages smaller Menezes, Qu and Vanstone invented the following protocol, called the MQV protocol based on the DLOG problem in a group G generated by g. One can use this protocol either in finite fields or in elliptic curves to obtain authenticated key exchange with message size of

Protocol	Message size
DL-MQV	1024
EC-MQV	160

Thus the MQV protocol gives us a considerable saving on the earlier message sizes. The protocol works by assuming that both parties, Alice and Bob, generate first a long-term public/private key pair which we shall denote by

$$(A = g^a, a) \text{ and } (B = g^b, b).$$

We shall assume that Bob knows that A is the authentic public key belonging to Alice and that Alice knows that B is the authentic public key belonging to Bob. This authentication of the public keys can be ensured by using some form of public key certification, described in a later chapter.

Assume Alice and Bob now want to agree on a secret session key to which they both contribute a random nonce. The use of the nonces provides them with forward secrecy and means that neither party has to trust the other in producing their session keys. So Alice and Bob now generate a public/private ephemeral key pair each

$$(C = g^c, c) \text{ and } (D = g^d, d).$$

They then exchange C and D. These are the only message flows in the MQV protocol, namely

$$\text{Alice} \longrightarrow \text{Bob} : g^c,$$
$$\text{Bob} \longrightarrow \text{Alice} : g^d.$$

Hence, to some extent this looks like a standard Diffie–Hellman protocol with no signing. However, the trick is that the final session key will also depend on the long-term public keys A and B.

Assume you are Alice, so you know

$$A, B, C, D, a \text{ and } c.$$

Let l denote half the bit size of the order of the group G, for example if we are using a group with order $q \approx 2^{160}$ then we set $l = 160/2 = 80$. To determine the session key, Alice now computes

1. Convert C to an integer i.
2. Put $s_A = (i \pmod{2^l}) + 2^l$.
3. Convert D to an integer j.
4. Put $t_A = (j \pmod{2^l}) + 2^l$.
5. Put $h_A = c + s_A a$.
6. Put $P_A = (DB^{t_A})^{h_A}$.

Bob runs the same protocol but with the roles of the public and private keys swapped around in the obvious manner, namely

1. Convert D to an integer i.
2. Put $s_B = (i \pmod{2^l}) + 2^l$.
3. Convert C to an integer j.
4. Put $t_B = (j \pmod{2^l}) + 2^l$.
5. Put $h_B = d + s_B b$.
6. Put $P_B = (CA^{t_B})^{h_B}$.

Then $P_A = P_B$ is the shared secret. To see why the P_A computed by Alice and the P_B computed by Bob are the same we notice that the s_A and t_A seen by Alice, are swapped when seen by Bob, i.e. $s_A = t_B$ and $s_B = t_A$. Setting $\log(P)$ to be the discrete logarithm of P to the base g, we see that

$$\begin{aligned}
\log(P_A) &= \log\left((DB^{t_A})^{h_A}\right) \\
&= (d + b t_A) h_A \\
&= d(c + s_A a) + b t_A (c + s_A a) \\
&= d(c + t_B a) + b s_B (c + t_B a) \\
&= c(d + s_B b) + a t_B (d + s_B b) \\
&= (c + a t_B) h_B \\
&= \log\left((CA^{t_B})^{h_B}\right) \\
&= \log(P_B).
\end{aligned}$$

Chapter Summary

- Diffie–Hellman key exchange can be used for two parties to agree on a secret key over an insecure channel. However, Diffie–Hellman is susceptible to the man in the middle attack and so requires some form of authentication of the communicating parties.

- Digital signatures provide authentication for both long-term and short-term purposes. They come in two variants either with message recovery or as a signature with appendix.

- The RSA encryption algorithm can be used in reverse to produce a public key signature scheme, but one needs to combine the RSA algorithm with a hash algorithm to obtain security for both short and long messages.

- Hash functions are required which are both one-way and collision resistant. This is to avoid a number of forgery attacks on the resulting signature algorithms. Due to the birthday paradox the output of the hash function should be at least twice the size of what one believes to be the limit of the computational ability of the attacker.

- DSA is a signature algorithm based on discrete logarithms, it has reduced bandwidth compared with RSA but is slower. EC-DSA is the elliptic curve variant of DSA, it also has the benefit of reduced bandwidth compared to DSA, but is more efficient than DSA.

- Other discrete logarithm based signature algorithms exist, all with different properties. Two we have looked at are Schnorr signatures and Nyberg–Rueppel signatures.

- Another way of using a key exchange scheme, without the need for digital signatures, is to use the MQV system. This has very small bandwidth requirements. It obtains implicit authentication of the agreed key, by combining the ephemeral exchanged key with the long-term static public key of each user, so as to obtain a new session key.

Further Reading

Details on more esoteric signature schemes such as one-time signatures, fail-stop signatures and undeniable signatures can be found in the books by Stinson and Schneier. These are also good places to look for further details about hash functions and message authentication codes, although by far the best reference in this area is *HAC*.

B. Schneier. *Applied Cryptography*. Wiley, 1996.

D. Stinson. *Cryptography: Theory and Practice*. CRC Press, 1995.

Review Exercises

10.1.1   Explain the man in the middle attack on the Diffie–Hellman key exchange algorithm.

10.1.2   Why do digital signature algorithms solve the problem raised by the man in the middle attack?

10.1.3   Why does a MAC not provide non-repudiation?

10.1.4   How does a hash function differ from a block cipher?

10.1.5   What is meant by the following properties of a hash function?

        a)   preimage resistant,
        b)   collision resistant,
        c)   second preimage resistant.

10.1.6   Describe the DSA signature algorithm, and describe where the security comes from.

10.1.7   What are the advantages of Schnorr signatures over DSA?

10.1.8   Explain the similarities and differences between the Diffie–Hellman protocol and the MQV protocol.

Programming Exercises

10.2.1   Implement the following signature algorithms; DSA, Schnorr and Nyberg–Rueppel.

10.2.2   Implement the MQV protocol and compare it with a standard signed Diffie–Hellman implementation. Clearly MQV is more efficient in terms of bandwidth, but is it more efficient in terms of computing time?

10.2.3   Implement elliptic curve variants of DSA, Schnorr, Nyberg–Rueppel, Diffie–Hellman and the MQV protocol. How much more efficient are your elliptic curve variants compared with the variants based on the discrete logarithm problem in a finite field?

Standard Exercises

10.3.1   Discuss the statement: 'Public key cryptography replaces the key distribution problem of securely distributing secret keys, with one of authentically distributing public keys'.

10.3.2   Show that if a user uses the same ephemeral key k to sign two different messages in the DSA algorithm then an attacker can recover their long-term private key.

10.3.3   Suppose that $H_1 : \{0,1\}^{2n} \rightarrow \{0,1\}^n$ is a collision resistant hash function. Define

$$H_2 : \begin{cases} \{0,1\}^{4n} \longrightarrow \{0,1\}^n \\ x_1 \| x_2 \longmapsto H_1(H_1(x_1) \| H_1(x_2)) \end{cases}$$

where $x_1, x_2 \in \{0,1\}^{2n}$. Show that H_2 is also collision resistant.

10.3.4   Fix an RSA key (N, e) and define the following hash function, $H(m) = h_k$, on a message of k blocks, $m = m_1 \ldots m_k$

$$h_i = \left(h_{i-1}^e \ (\bmod \ N) \right) \oplus m_i \text{ for } i = 2, \ldots, k,$$

where $h_1 = m_1$. Show how to find a collision in H.

10.3.5   Attacks on a MAC function of block and key size n should ideally require 2^n operations. Consider the following two hash based MAC functions and come up with attacks which can be performed in less than 2^n operations.

$$MAC = h(k \| M),$$
$$MAC = h(M \| k).$$

10.3.6   A key agreement scheme is said to have the key confirmation property if each party is given a guarantee that the other party shares the same key as it does. Describe how to add a key confirmation property to the MQV protocol.

CHAPTER 11

Implementation Issues

Chapter Goals

- To show how exponentiation algorithms are implemented.

- To explain how modular arithmetic can be implemented efficiently on large numbers.

- To show how certain tricks can be used to speed up RSA and DSA operations.

- To show how finite fields of characteristic two can be implemented efficiently.

11.1 INTRODUCTION

In this chapter we examine how one actually implements cryptographic operations. We shall mainly be concerned with public key operations since those are the most complex to implement. For example, in RSA or DSA we have to perform a modular exponentiation with respect to a modulus of a thousand or more bits. This means we need to understand the implementation issues involved with both modular arithmetic and exponentiation algorithms.

There is another reason to focus on public key algorithms rather than private key ones: in general public key schemes run much slower than symmetric schemes. In fact they can be so slow that their use can seriously slow down networks and web servers. Hence, efficient implementation is crucial unless one is willing to pay a large performance penalty.

Since RSA is the easiest system to understand we will concentrate on this, although where special techniques exist for other schemes we will mention these as well. The chapter focuses on algorithms used in software, for hardware based algorithms one often uses different techniques entirely, but these alternative techniques are related to those used in software, so an understanding of software techniques is important.

11.2 EXPONENTIATION ALGORITHMS

So far in this book we have assumed that computing

$$a^b \pmod{c}$$

is an easy operation. We need this operation both in RSA and in systems based on discrete logarithms such as ElGamal and DSA. In this section we concentrate on the exponentiation algorithms and assume that we can perform modular arithmetic efficiently. In a later section we shall discuss how to perform modular arithmetic.

As we have already stressed, the main operation in RSA and DSA is modular exponentiation

$$M = C^d \pmod{N}.$$

Firstly note it does not make sense to perform this via

- compute $R = C^d$,

- then compute $R \pmod{N}$.

To see this, consider

$$123^5 \pmod{511} = 28\,153\,056\,843 \pmod{511} = 359.$$

With this naive method one obtains a huge intermediate result, in our small case above this is

$$28\,153\,056\,843.$$

But in a real 1024-bit RSA multiplication this intermediate result would be in general

$$2^{1024} \cdot 1024$$

bits long. Such a number requires 10^{301} gigabytes simply to write down.

To stop this explosion in the size of any intermediate results we use the fact that we are working modulo N. But even here one needs to be careful, a naive algorithm would compute the above example by computing

$$x = 123,$$
$$x^2 = x \times x \pmod{511} = 310,$$
$$x^3 = x \times x^2 \pmod{511} = 316,$$
$$x^4 = x \times x^3 \pmod{511} = 32,$$
$$x^5 = x \times x^4 \pmod{511} = 359.$$

This requires four modular multiplications, which seems fine for our small example. But for a general RSA exponentiation by a 1024-bit exponent using this method would require around 2^{1024} modular multiplications. If each such multiplication could be done in under one millionth of a second we would still require 10^{294} years to perform an RSA decryption operation.

However, it is easy to see that, even in our small example, we can reduce the number of required multiplications by being a little more clever:

$$x = 123,$$
$$x^2 = x \times x \ (\text{mod } 511) = 310,$$
$$x^4 = x^2 \times x^2 \ (\text{mod } 511) = 32,$$
$$x^5 = x \times x^4 \ (\text{mod } 511) = 359.$$

Which only requires three modular multiplications rather than the previous four. To understand why we only require three modular multiplications notice that the exponent 5 has binary representation $0b101$ and so

- has bit length $t = 3$,

- has Hamming weight $h = 2$.

In the above example we required $1 = (h - 1)$ general multiplication and $2 = (t - 1)$ squarings. This fact holds in general, in that a modular exponentiation can be performed using

- $(h - 1)$ multiplications,

- $(t - 1)$ squarings,

where t is the bit length of the exponent and h is the Hamming weight. The average Hamming weight of an integer is $t/2$ so the number of multiplications and squarings is on average

$$t + t/2 - 1.$$

For a 1024-bit RSA modulus this means that the average number of modular multiplications needed to perform exponentiation by a 1024-bit exponent is at most 2048 and on average 1535.

The method used to achieve this improvement in performance is called the binary exponentiation method. This is because it works by reading each bit of the binary representation of the exponent in turn, starting with the least significant bit and working up to the most significant bit. To see how this is done we present some pseudo-code to compute

$$y = x^d \ (\text{mod } n)$$

where we assume x, y, d and n are given by a C, or Java, like big-integer data type:

```
y=1;
while (d<>0)
  { if ((d%2)!=0)
      { y=(y*x)%n;
        d=d-1;
      }
    d/=2;
    x=(x*x)%n;
  }
```

The above binary exponentiation algorithm has a number of different names, some authors call it the *square and multiply* algorithm, since it proceeds by a sequence of squarings and multiplications, other authors call it the *Indian exponentiation* algorithm. The above algorithm is called a *right to left* exponentiation algorithm since it processes the bits of d from the least significant bit up to the most significant bit.

One can also implement the square and multiply method using a recursive function call. The following Haskell code implements binary exponentiation modulo m. To compute a^n (mod m) one uses bin_pow a m n, where bin_pow is defined by

```
bin_pow :: Int -> Int -> Int -> Int
bin_pow a m n
  | n == 0          = 1
  | n 'mod' 2 == 0  = bin_pow ((a*a) 'mod' m) m (n 'div' 2)
  | otherwise       = (a*t) 'mod' m
      where t = bin_pow ((a*a) 'mod' m) m ((n-1) 'div' 2)
```

Most of the time it is faster to perform a squaring operation than a general multiplication. Hence to reduce time even more one tries to reduce the total number of modular multiplications even further. This is done using window techniques which trade off precomputations (i.e. storage) against the time in the main loop.

To understand window methods better we first examine the binary exponentiation method again. But this time instead of a right to left variant, we process the exponent from the most significant bit first, thus producing a *left to right* binary exponentiation algorithm. Again we assume we wish to compute

$$y = x^d \pmod{n}.$$

We first give a notation for the binary representation of the exponent

$$d = \sum_{i=0}^{t} d_i 2^i,$$

where $d_i \in \{0, 1\}$. The left to right binary exponentiation algorithm is now performed as follows.

```
y=1;
for (i=t; i>=0; i--)
  { y = (y*y)%n;
    if (d[i]==1)
      { y = (y*x)%n; }
  }
```

The above algorithm processes a single bit of the exponent on every iteration of the loop. Again the number of squarings is equal to t and the expected number of multiplications is equal to $t/2$.

In a window method we process w bits of the exponent at a time. We first precompute a table

$$x_i = x^i \pmod{n} \text{ for } i = 0, \ldots, 2^w - 1.$$

Then we write our exponent out, but this time taking w bits at a time,

$$d = \sum_{i=0}^{t/w} d_i 2^{iw},$$

where $d_i \in \{0, 1, 2, \ldots, 2^w - 1\}$. The window method then runs as follows

```
y=1;
for (i=t/w; i>=0; i--)
  { for (j=0; j<w; j++)
      { y = (y*y)%n; }
    j=d[i];
    y = (y*x[j])%n;
  }
```

Let us see this algorithm in action by computing

$$y = x^{215} \pmod{n}$$

with a window width of $w = 3$. We compute the d_i as

$$215 = 3 \cdot 2^6 + 2 \cdot 2^3 + 7.$$

Hence, our iteration to compute $x^{215} \pmod{n}$ computes in order

$$y = 1,$$
$$y = y \cdot x^3 = x^3,$$
$$y = y^8 = x^{24},$$
$$y = y \cdot x^2 = x^{26},$$
$$y = y^8 = y^{208},$$
$$y = y \cdot x^7 = x^{215}.$$

With a window method as above, we still perform t squarings but the number of multiplications reduces to t/w on average. One can do even better by adopting a sliding window method, where we now encode our exponent as

$$d = \sum_{i=0}^{l} d_i 2^{e_i}$$

where $d_i \in \{1, 3, 5, \ldots, 2^w - 1\}$ and $e_{i+1} - e_i \geq w$. By choosing only odd values for d_i and having a variable window width we achieve both decreased storage for the precomputed values and improved efficiency. Our code for the sliding window method now becomes, after precomputing $x[i] = x^i$ for $i = 1, 3, 5, \ldots, 2^w - 1$,

```
y=1;
for (i=l; i>=0; i--)
  { for (j=0; j<e[i+1]-e[i]; j++)
```

```
        { y = (y*y)%n; }
        j=d[i];
        y = (y*x[j])%n;
    }
for (j=0; j<e[0]; j++)
    { y = (y*y)%n; }
```

The number of squarings remains again at t, but now the number of multiplications reduces to l, which is about $t/(w+1)$ on average. In our example of computing $y = x^{215} \pmod{n}$ we have

$$215 = 3 \cdot 2^6 + 2^4 + 7,$$

and so we execute the steps

$$y = 1,$$
$$y = y \cdot x^3 = x^3,$$
$$y = y^4 = x^{12},$$
$$y = y \cdot x = x^{13},$$
$$y = y^{16} = x^{208},$$
$$y = y \cdot x^7 = x^{215}.$$

Notice that all of the above window algorithms apply to exponentiation in any abelian group and not just the integers modulo n. Hence, we can use these algorithms to compute

$$\alpha^d$$

in a finite field or to compute

$$[d]P$$

on an elliptic curve, in the latter case we call this point multiplication rather than exponentiation.

An advantage with elliptic curve variants is that negation comes for free, in that given P it is easy to compute $-P$. This leads to the use of signed binary and signed window methods. We only present the signed window method. We precompute

$$P_i = [i]P \text{ for } i = 1, 3, 5, \ldots, 2^{w-1} - 1,$$

which requires only half the storage of the equivalent sliding window method or one quarter of the storage of the equivalent standard window method. We now write our multiplicand d as

$$d = \sum_{i=0}^{l} d_i 2^{e_i}$$

where $d_i \in \{\pm 1, \pm 3, \pm 5, \ldots, \pm(2^{w-1} - 1)\}$. The signed sliding window method for elliptic curves is then given by the following pseudo-code.

```
Q=0;
for (i=l; i>=0; i--)
```

```
  { for (j=0; j<e[i+1]-e[i]; j++)
      { Q = [2] Q; }
    j=d[i];
    if (j>0)   { Q = Q + P[j]; }
    else       { Q = Q - P[-j]; }
  }
for (j=0; j<e[0]; j++)
  { Q = [2] Q; }
```

11.3 EXPONENTIATION IN RSA

To speed up RSA exponentiation even more, a number of tricks are used which are special to RSA. The tricks used are different depending on whether we are performing an encryption/verification operation with the public key or a decryption/signing operation with the private key.

11.3.1 RSA Encryption/Verification

As already remarked in earlier chapters one often uses a small public exponent, for example $e = 3, 17$ or $65\,537$. The reason for these particular values is that they have small Hamming weight, in fact the smallest possible for an RSA public key, namely two. This means that the binary method, or any other exponentiation algorithm, will require only one general multiplication, but it will still need k squarings where k is the bit size of the public exponent. For example

$$M^3 = M^2 \times M,$$
$$M^{17} = M^{16} \times M,$$
$$= (((M^2)^2)^2)^2 \times M.$$

11.3.2 RSA Decryption/Signing

In the case of RSA decryption or signing the exponent will be a general 1000-bit number. Hence, we need some way of speeding up the computation. Luckily, since we are considering a private key operation we have access to the private key, and hence the factorization of the modulus,

$$N = p \cdot q.$$

Supposing we are decrypting a message, we therefore wish to compute

$$M = C^d \pmod{N}.$$

We speed up the calculation by first computing M modulo p and q:

$$M_p = C^d \pmod{p} = C^{d \pmod{p-1}} \pmod{p},$$
$$M_q = C^d \pmod{q} = C^{d \pmod{q-1}} \pmod{q}.$$

Since p and q are 512-bit numbers, the above calculation requires two exponentiations modulo 512-bit moduli and 512-bit exponents. This is faster than a single exponentiation modulo a 1024-bit number with a 1024-bit exponent.

But we now need to recover M from M_p and M_q, which is done using the Chinese Remainder Theorem as follows: We compute $T = p^{-1} \pmod{q}$ and store it with the private key. The message M can then be recovered from M_p and M_q via

- $u = (M_q - M_p)T \pmod{q}$,

- $M = M_p + up$.

This is why in Chapter 7 we said that when you generate a private key it is best to store p and q even though they are not mathematically needed.

11.4 EXPONENTIATION IN DSA

Recall that in DSA verification one needs to compute

$$r = g^a y^b.$$

This can be accomplished by first computing g^a and then y^b and then multiplying the results together. However, often it is easier to perform the two exponentiations simultaneously. There are a number of techniques to accomplish this, using various forms of window techniques etc. But all are essentially based on the following idea, called Shamir's trick.

We first compute the following look-up table

$$G_i = g^{i_0} y^{i_1}$$

where $i = (i_1, i_0)$ is the binary representation of i, for $i = 0, 1, 2, 3$. We then compute an exponent array from the two exponents a and b. This is a 2 by t array, where t is the maximum bit length of a and b. The rows of this array are the binary representation of the exponents a and b. We then let I_j, for $j = 1, \ldots, t$, denote the integers whose binary representation is given by the columns of this array. The exponentiation is then computed by setting $r = 1$ and computing

$$r = r^2 \cdot G_{I_j}$$

for $j = 1$ to t.

As an example suppose we wish to compute

$$r = g^{11} y^7,$$

hence we have $t = 4$. We precompute

$$G_0 = 1, \ G_1 = g, \ G_2 = y, \ G_3 = g \cdot y.$$

Since the binary representation of 11 and 7 is given by 1011 and 111, our exponent array is given by

$$\begin{pmatrix} 1 & 0 & 1 & 1 \\ 0 & 1 & 1 & 1 \end{pmatrix}.$$

The integers I_j then become

$$I_1 = 1, I_2 = 2, I_3 = 3, I_4 = 3.$$

Hence, the four steps of our algorithm become

$$r = G_1 = g,$$
$$r = r^2 \cdot G_2 = g^2 \cdot y,$$
$$r = r^2 \cdot G_3 = (g^4 \cdot y^2) \cdot (g \cdot y) = g^5 \cdot y^3,$$
$$r = r^2 \cdot G_3 = (g^{10} \cdot y^6) \cdot (g \cdot y) = g^{11} \cdot y^7.$$

Note, elliptic curve analogues of Shamir's trick and its variants can be made which make use of signed representations for the exponent. We do not give these here, but leave them for the interested reader to investigate.

11.5 MULTI-PRECISION ARITHMETIC

We shall now explain how to perform modular arithmetic on 1024-bit numbers. We show how this is accomplished using modern processors, and why naive algorithms are usually replaced with a special technique due to Montgomery.

In a cryptographic application it is common to focus on a fixed length for the integers in use, for example 1024 bits in an RSA/DSA implementation or 200 bits for an ECC implementation. This leads to different programming choices than when one implements a general purpose multi-precision arithmetic library. For example one no longer needs to worry so much about dynamic memory allocation, and one can now concentrate on particular performance enhancements for the integer sizes one is dealing with.

It is common to represent all integers in little-wordian format. This means that if a large integer is held in memory locations, $x_0, x_1, \ldots, x_n$, then x_0 is the least significant word and x_n is the most significant word. For a 32-bit machine and 64-bit numbers we obtain would represent x and y as $[x_0, x_1]$ and $[y_0, y_1]$ where

$$x = x_1 2^{32} + x_0,$$
$$y = y_1 2^{32} + y_0.$$

11.5.1 Addition

Most modern processors have a carry flag which is set by any overflow from an addition operation. Also most have a special instruction, usually called something like **addc**, which adds two integers together and adds on the contents of the carry flag. So if we wish to add our two 64-bit integers given earlier then we need to compute

$$z = x + y = z_2 2^{64} + z_1 2^{32} + z_0.$$

The values of z_0, z_1 and z_2 are then computed via

```
z0 <- add   x0,y0
z1 <- addc  x1,y1
z2 <- addc  0,0
```

Note that the value held in z_2 is at most one, so the value of z could be a 65-bit integer. The above technique for adding two 64-bit integers can clearly be scaled to adding integers of any fixed length, and can also be made to work for subtraction of large integers.

11.5.2 School-book Multiplication

We now turn to the next simplest arithmetic operation, after addition and subtraction, namely multiplication. Notice that two 32 -bit words multiply together to form a 64-bit result, and so most modern processors have an instruction which will do this operation.

$$w_1 \cdot w_2 = (High, Low) = (H(w_1 \cdot w_2), L(w_1 \cdot w_2)).$$

When we use school-book long multiplication, for our two 64-bit numbers, we obtain something like

$$
\begin{array}{ccccc}
 & & & x_1 & x_0 \\
 & \times & & y_1 & y_0 \\
\hline
 & & H(x_0 \cdot y_0) & L(x_0 \cdot y_0) \\
 & H(x_0 \cdot y_1) & L(x_0 \cdot y_1) \\
 & H(x_1 \cdot y_0) & L(x_1 \cdot y_0) \\
H(x_1 \cdot y_1) & L(x_1 \cdot y_1)
\end{array}
$$

Then we add up the four rows to get the answer, remembering we need to take care of the carries. This then becomes, for

$$z = x \cdot y,$$

something like the following pseudo-code

```
(z1,z0) <- mul x0,y0
(z3,z2) <- mul x1,y1
(h,l)   <- mul x1,y0
z1      <- add z1,l
z2      <- addc z2,h
z3      <- addc z3,0
(h,l)   <- mul x0,y1
z1      <- add z1,l
z2      <- addc z2,h
z3      <- addc z3,0
```

If n denotes the bit size of the integers we are operating on, the above technique for multiplying large integers together clearly requires $O(n^2)$ bit operations, whilst it requires $O(n)$ bit operations to add or subtract integers. It is a natural question as to whether one can multiply integers faster than $O(n^2)$.

11.5.3 Karatsuba Multiplication

One technique to speed up multiplication is called Karatsuba multiplication. Suppose we have two n-bit integers x and y that we wish to multiply. We write these integers as

$$x = x_0 + 2^{n/2}x_1,$$
$$y = y_0 + 2^{n/2}y_2,$$

where $0 \le x_0, x_1, y_0, y_1 < 2^{n/2}$. We then multiply x and y by computing

$$A = x_0 \cdot y_0,$$
$$B = (x_0 + x_1) \cdot (y_0 + y_1),$$
$$C = x_1 \cdot y_1.$$

The product $x \cdot y$ is then given by

$$C2^n + (B - A - C)2^{n/2} + A = x_1y_12^n + (x_1y_0 + x_0y_1)2^{n/2} + x_0y_0$$
$$= (x_0 + 2^{n/2}x_1) \cdot (y_0 + 2^{n/2}y_1)$$
$$= x \cdot y.$$

Hence, this multiplication technique to multiply two n-bit numbers requires three $n/2$-bit multiplications, two $n/2$-bit additions and three n-bit additions/subtractions. If we denote the cost of an n-bit multiplication by $M(n)$ and the cost of an n-bit addition/subtraction by $A(n)$ then this becomes

$$M(n) = 3M(n/2) + 2A(n/2) + 3A(n).$$

Now if we make the approximation that $A(n) \approx n$ then

$$M(n) \approx 3M(n/2) + 4n.$$

If the multiplication of the $n/2$-bit numbers is accomplished in a similar fashion then to obtain the final complexity of multiplication we need to solve the above recurrence relation to obtain

$$M(n) \approx 9n^{\frac{\log(3)}{\log(2)}} \text{ as } n \longrightarrow \infty$$
$$= 9n^{1.58}.$$

So we obtain an algorithm with asymptotic complexity $O(n^{1.58})$. Karatsuba multiplication becomes faster than the $O(n^2)$ method for integers of sizes greater than a few hundred bits. However, one can do even better for very large integers since the fastest known multiplication algorithm takes time

$$O(n \log n \log \log n).$$

But neither this latter technique nor Karatsuba multiplication are used in many cryptographic applications. The reason for this will become apparent as we discuss integer division.

11.5.4 Division

After having looked at multiplication we are left with the division operation, which is the hardest of all the basic algorithms. Division is required in order to be able to compute the remainder on division, which is after all a basic operation in RSA. Given two large integers x and y we wish to be able to compute q and r such that

$$x = qy + r$$

where $0 \leq r < y$, such an operation is called a Euclidean division.

If we write our two integers x and y in the little-wordian format

$$x = (x_0, \ldots, x_n) \text{ and } y = (y_0, \ldots, y_t)$$

where the base for the representation is $b = 2^w$ then the Euclidean division can be performed by the following algorithm. We let t << v denote a large integer t shifted to the left by v words, in other words the result of multiplying t by b^v.

```
r=x;
/* Cope with the trivial case */
if (t>n)
   { q=0;   return; }
q=0; s=0;
/* Normalise the divisor */
while (y[t]<b/2)
   { y=y*2; r=r*2; s++; }
if (r[n+1]!=0) { n=n+1; }
/* Get the msw of the quotient */
while (r>=(y<<(n-t)))
   { q[n-t]=q[n-t]+1;
     r=r-(y<<n-t);
   }
/* Deal with the rest */
for (i=n; i>=t+1; i--)
   { if (r[i]==y[t])
       { q[i-t-1]=b-1; }
     else
       { q[i-t-1]=floor( (x[i]*b+r[i-1])/y[t] ); }

     if (t!=0) { rhs_m = y[t]*b+y[t-1]; }
     else      { rhs_m = y[t]*b; }
     rhs=q[i-t-1]*rhs_m;

     if (i!=1) { lhs = x[i]*b*b+r[i-1]*b+r[i-2]; }
     else      { lhs = x[i]*b*b+r[i-1]*b;        }

     while (rhs>lhs)
       { q[i-t-1]=q[i-t-1]-1;
         rhs=rhs-rhs_m;
       }
     r=r-(q[i-t-1]*y)<<(i-t-1);
     if (r<0)
       { r=r+(y<<i-t-1);
```

```
        q[i-t-1]=q[i-t-1]-1;
      }
    }
/* Renormalise */
for (i=0; i<s; i++) { r=r/2; }
```

As one can see this is a complex operation, hence one should try and avoid divisions as much as possible.

11.5.5 Montgomery Arithmetic

That division is a complex operation means our cryptographic operations run very slowly if we use standard division operations as above. Recall that virtually all of our public key systems make use of arithmetic modulo another number. What we require is the ability to compute remainders (i.e. to perform modular arithmetic) without having to perform any costly division operations. This at first sight may seem a state of affairs which is impossible to reach, but it can be achieved using a special form of arithmetic called Montgomery arithmetic.

Montgomery arithmetic works by using an alternative representation of integers, called the Montgomery representation. Let us fix some notation, we let b denote 2 to the power of the word size of our computer, for example $b = 2^{32}$ or 2^{64}. We then choose an integer R which satisfies

$$R = b^t > N.$$

Now instead of holding the value of the integer x in memory, we instead hold the value

$$x \cdot R \ (\mathrm{mod}\ N).$$

Again this is usually held in a little-wordian format. The value $x \cdot R \ (\mathrm{mod}\ N)$ is called the Montgomery representation of the integer $x \ (\mathrm{mod}\ N)$.

Adding two elements in Montgomery representation is easy. If

$$z = x + y \ (\mathrm{mod}\ N)$$

then given $x \cdot R \ (\mathrm{mod}\ N)$ and $y \cdot R \ (\mathrm{mod}\ N)$ we need to compute $z \cdot R \ (\mathrm{mod}\ N)$. This can be accomplished via the pseudo-code

```
zR = xR + yR
if (zR>=N) { zR-=N; }
```

Let us take a simple example with

$$N = 1\,073\,741\,827,$$
$$b = R = 2^{32} = 4\,294\,967\,296.$$

The following is the map from the normal to Montgomery representation of the integers 1, 2 and 3.

$$1 \longrightarrow 1 \cdot R \ (\mathrm{mod}\ N) = 1\,073\,741\,815,$$
$$2 \longrightarrow 2 \cdot R \ (\mathrm{mod}\ N) = 1\,073\,741\,803,$$
$$3 \longrightarrow 3 \cdot R \ (\mathrm{mod}\ N) = 1\,073\,741\,791.$$

We can now verify that addition works since we have in the standard representation

$$1 + 2 = 3$$

whilst this is mirrored in the Montgomery representation as

$$1\,073\,741\,815 + 1\,073\,741\,803 = 1\,073\,741\,791 \pmod{N}.$$

Now we look at multiplication in Montgomery arithmetic. If we simply multiply two elements in Montgomery representation we will obtain

$$(xR) \cdot (yR) = xyR^2 \pmod{N}$$

but we want $xyR \pmod{N}$. Hence, we need to divide the result of the standard multiplication by R. Since R is a power of 2 we hope this should be easy.

The process of given y and computing

$$z = y/R \pmod{N}$$

given the earlier choice of R, is called Montgomery reduction. We first precompute the integer $q = 1/N \pmod{R}$, which is simple to perform with no divisions using the binary Euclidean algorithm. Then, performing a Montgomery reduction is done using the following pseudo-code,

```
u=(-y*q)%R;
z=(y+u*N)/R;
if (z>=N) { z-=N; }
```

Note that the reduction modulo R in the first line is easy, we compute $y \cdot q$ using standard algorithms, the reduction modulo R being achieved by truncating the result. This latter trick works since R is a power of b. The division by R in the second line can also be simply achieved, since $y + u \cdot N = 0 \pmod{R}$, we simply shift the result to the right by t words, again since $R = b^t$.

As an example we again take

$$N = 1\,073\,741\,827,$$
$$b = R = 2^{32} = 4\,294\,967\,296.$$

We wish to compute $2 \cdot 3$ in Montgomery representation. Recall

$$2 \longrightarrow 2 \cdot R \pmod{N} = 1\,073\,741\,803 = x,$$
$$3 \longrightarrow 3 \cdot R \pmod{N} = 1\,073\,741\,791 = y.$$

We then compute, using a standard multiplication algorithm that

$$w = x \cdot y = 1\,152\,921\,446\,624\,789\,173 = 2 \cdot 3 \cdot R^2.$$

We now need to pass this value of w into our technique for Montgomery reduction, so as to find the Montgomery representation of $x \cdot y$. We find

$$w = 1\,152\,921\,446\,624\,789\,173,$$
$$q = (1/N) \pmod{R} = 1\,789\,569\,707,$$
$$u = -w \cdot q \pmod{R} = 3\,221\,225\,241,$$
$$z = (w + u \cdot N)/R = 1\,073\,741\,755.$$

So the multiplication of x and y in Montgomery arithmetic should be

$$1\,073\,741\,755.$$

We can check that this is the correct value by computing

$$6 \cdot R \pmod{N} = 1\,073\,741\,755.$$

Hence, we see that Montgomery arithmetic allows us to add and multiply integers modulo an integer N without the need for costly division algorithms.

Our above method for Montgomery reduction requires two full multi-precision multiplications. So to multiply two numbers in Montgomery arithmetic we require three full multi-precision multiplications. If we are multiplying 1024-bit numbers, this means the intermediate results can grow to be 2048-bit numbers. We would like to do better, and we can.

Suppose y is given in little-wordian format

$$y = (y_0, y_1, \ldots, y_{2t-2}, y_{2t-1}).$$

Then a better way to perform Montgomery reduction is to first precompute

$$N' = -1/N \pmod{b}$$

which is easy and only requires operations on word-sized quantities. Then the Montgomery reduction can be performed by

```
z=y;
for (i=0; i<t; i++)
  { u=(zi*N')%b;
    z+=u*N*b;
  }
z/=R;
if (z>=N) { z-=N; }
```

Note, since we are reducing modulo b in the first line of the for loop we can execute this initial multiplication using a simple word multiplication algorithm. The second step of the for loop requires a shift by one word (to multiply by b) and a single *word* × *bigint* multiply. Hence, we have reduced the need for large intermediate results in the Montgomery reduction step.

We can also interleave the multiplication with the reduction to perform a single loop to produce

$$Z = XY/R \pmod{N}.$$

So if $X = xR$ and $Y = yR$ this will produce

$$Z = (xy)R.$$

This procedure is called Montgomery multiplication and allows us to perform a multiplication in Montgomery arithmetic without the need for larger integers. The interleaved version is given by

```
Z=0;
for (i=0; i<t; i++)
  { u=((z0+Xi*Y0)*N')%b;
    Z=(Z+Xi*Y+u*N)/b;
  }
if (Z>=N) { Z-=N; }
```

Whilst Montgomery multiplication has complexity $O(n^2)$ as opposed to the $O(n^{1.58})$ of Karatsuba multiplication, it is still preferable to use Montgomery arithmetic since it deals more efficiently with modular arithmetic.

11.6   FINITE FIELD ARITHMETIC

Apart from the integers modulo a large prime p the other type of finite field used in cryptography are those based on fields of characteristic two. These occur in the Rijndael algorithm and in certain elliptic curve systems. In Rijndael the field is so small that one can use look-up tables or special circuits to perform the basic arithmetic tasks, so in this section we shall concentrate on fields of large degree over $\mathbb{F}_2$, like those used with elliptic curves. In addition we shall concern ourselves with software implementations only. Fields of characteristic two can have special types of hardware implementations based on things called optimal normal bases, but we shall not concern ourselves with these.

Recall that to define a finite field of characteristic two we first pick an irreducible polynomial $f(x)$ over $\mathbb{F}_2$ of degree n. The field is defined to be

$$\mathbb{F}_{2^n} = \mathbb{F}_2[x]/f(x),$$

i.e. we look at binary polynomials modulo $f(x)$. Elements of this field are usually represented as bit strings, which represent a binary polynomial. For example the bit string

$$101010111$$

represents the polynomial

$$x^8 + x^6 + x^4 + x^2 + x + 1.$$

Addition and subtraction of elements in $\mathbb{F}_{2^n}$ is accomplished by simply performing a bitwise XOR between the two bitstrings. Hence, the difficult tasks are multiplication and division.

It turns out that division, although slower than multiplication, is easier to describe, so we start with division. To compute

$$\alpha/\beta,$$

where $\alpha, \beta \in \mathbb{F}_{2^n}$, we first compute

$$\beta^{-1}$$

and then perform the multiplication

$$\alpha \cdot \beta^{-1}.$$

So division is reduced to multiplication and the computation of β^{-1}. One way of computing β^{-1} is to use Lagrange's Theorem which tells us for $\beta \neq 0$ that we have

$$\beta^{2^n - 1} = 1.$$

But this means that

$$\beta \cdot \beta^{2^n - 2} = 1,$$

or in other words

$$\beta^{-1} = \beta^{2^n - 2} = \beta^{2(2^{n-1} - 1)}.$$

Another way of computing β^{-1} is to use the binary Euclidean algorithm. We take the polynomial f and the polynomial b which represents β and then perform the following version of the binary Euclidean algorithm, where lsb(b) refers to the least significant bit of b (in other words the coefficient of x^0),

```
  a=f;
  B=0;
  D=1;
/* At least one of a and b now has a constant term
    on every execution of the loop.
*/
  while (a != 0) do
    { while (lsb(a)=0)
        { a=a>>1;
          if (lsb(B)!=0) { B=B^f; }
          B=B>>1;
        }
      while (lsb(b)=0)
        { b=b>>1;
          if (lsb(D)!=0) { D=D^f; }
          D=D>>1;
        }
/*  Now both a and b have a constant term */
        if (deg(a)>=deg(b))
          { a=(a^b);
            B=B^D;
          }
        else
          { b=(a^b);
            D=D^B;
          }
    }
  return D;
```

We now turn to the multiplication operation. Unlike the case of integers modulo N or p, where we use a special method of Montgomery arithmetic, in characteristic two we have the opportunity to choose a polynomial $f(x)$ which has 'nice' properties. Any irreducible polynomials of degree n can be used to implement the finite field $\mathbb{F}_{2^n}$, we just need to select the best one.

Almost always one chooses a value of $f(x)$ which is either a trinomial

$$f(x) = x^n + x^k + 1$$

or a pentanomial

$$f(x) = x^n + x^{k_3} + x^{k_2} + x^{k_1} + 1.$$

It turns out that for all fields of degree less than $10\,000$ we can always find such a trinomial or pentanomial to make the multiplication operation very efficient. Table 11.1 at the end of this chapter gives a list for all values of n between 2 and 500 of an example pentanomial or trinomial which defines the field $\mathbb{F}_{2^n}$. In all cases where a trinomial exists we give one, otherwise we present a pentanomial.

Now to perform a multiplication of α by β we first multiply the polynomials representing α and β together to form a polynomial $y(x)$ of degree at most $2n - 2$. Then we reduce this polynomial by taking the remainder on division by the polynomial $f(x)$.

We show how this remainder on division is efficiently performed for trinomials, and leave the pentanomial case for the reader. We write

$$y(x) = y_1(x)x^n + y_0(x).$$

Hence, $\deg(y_1(x)), \deg(y_0(x)) \le n - 1$. We can then write

$$y(x) \ (\mathrm{mod} \ f(x)) = y_0(x) + (x^k + 1)y_1(x).$$

The right-hand side of this equation can be computed from the bit operations

$$\delta = y_0 \oplus y_1 \oplus (y_1 \ll k).$$

Now δ, as a polynomial, will have degree at most $n - 1 + k$. So we need to carry out this procedure again by first writing

$$\delta(x) = \delta_1(x)x^n + \delta_0(x),$$

where $\deg(\delta_0(x)) \le n - 1$ and $\deg(\delta_1(x)) \le k - 1$. We then compute as before that y is equivalent to

$$\delta_0 \oplus \delta_1 \oplus (\delta_1 \ll k).$$

This latter polynomial will have degree $\max(n - 1, 2k - 1)$, so if we choose in our trinomial

$$k \le n/2,$$

then the following algorithm will perform our division by remainder step. Let g denote the polynomial of degree $2n - 2$ that we wish to reduce modulo f, where we assume a bit representation for these polynomials.

```
g1=g>>n;
g0=g[n-1..0];
g=g0^g1^(g1<<k);
g1=g>>n;
g0=g[n-1..0];
g=g0^g1^(g1<<k);
```

So to complete our description of how to multiply elements in $\mathbb{F}_{2^n}$ we need to explain how to perform the multiplication of two binary polynomials of large degree $n - 1$.

Again one can use a naive multiplication algorithm. Often however one uses a look-up table for polynomial multiplication of polynomials of degree less than eight, i.e. for operands which fit into one byte. Then multiplication of larger degree polynomials is reduced to multiplication of polynomials of degree less than eight by using a variant of the standard long multiplication algorithm from school. This algorithm will have complexity $O(n^2)$, where n is the degree of the polynomials involved.

Suppose we have a routine which uses a look-up table to multiply two binary polynomials of degree less than eight, returning a binary polynomial of degree less than sixteen. This function we denote by Mult_Tab(a,b) where a and b are 8-bit integers representing the input polynomials.

To perform a multiplication of two n-bit polynomials represented by two n-bit integers x and y we perform the following code, where y>>8 represents shifting to the right by 8 bits.

```
z=0;   i=0;
while (x!=0)
  { u=y;   j=0;
    while (u!=0)
      { w=Mult_Tab(x&255,u&255);
        w=w<<(8*(i+j));
        ans=ans^w;
        u=u>>8;   j=j+1;
      }
    x=x>>8; i=i+1;
  }
```

Just as with integer multiplication one can use a divide and conquer technique based on Karatsuba multiplication, which again will have a complexity of $O(n^{1.58})$. Suppose the two polynomials we wish to multiply are given by

$$a = a_0 + x^{n/2}a_1,$$
$$b = b_0 + x^{n/2}b_2,$$

where a_0, a_1, b_0, b_1 are polynomials of degree less than $n/2$. We then multiply a and b by computing

$$A = a_0 \cdot b_0,$$
$$B = (a_0 + a_1) \cdot (b_0 + b_1),$$
$$C = a_1 \cdot b_1.$$

The product $a \cdot b$ is then given by

$$Cx^n + (B - A - C)x^{n/2} + A = a_1 b_1 x^n + (a_1 b_0 + a_0 b_1)x^{n/2} + a_0 b_0$$
$$= (a_0 + x^{n/2} a_1) \cdot (b_0 + x^{n/2} b_2)$$
$$= a \cdot b.$$

Again to multiply a_0 and b_0 etc. we use the Karatsuba multiplication method recursively. Once we reduce to the case of multiplying two polynomials of degree less than eight we resort to using our look-up table to perform the polynomial multiplication. Unlike the integer case we now find that Karatsuba multiplication is more efficient than the school-book method even for polynomials of quite small degree, say $n \approx 100$.

One should note that squaring polynomials in characteristic two is particularly easy. Suppose we have a polynomial

$$a = a_0 + a_1 x + a_2 x^2 + a_3 x^3,$$

where $a_i = 0$ or 1. Then to square a we simply 'thin out' the coefficients as follows:

$$a^2 = a_0 + a_1 x^2 + a_2 x^4 + a_3 x^6.$$

This means that squaring an element in a finite field of characteristic two is very fast compared with a multiplication operation.

Chapter Summary

- Modular exponentiation, or exponentiation in any group, can be computed using the binary exponentiation method. Often it is more efficient to use a window based method, or to use a signed exponentiation method in the case of elliptic curves.

- For RSA special optimizations are performed. In the case of the public exponent we choose one which is both small and has very low Hamming weight. For the exponentiation by the private exponent we use knowledge of the prime factorization of the modulus and the Chinese Remainder Theorem.

- For DSA verification there is a method based on simultaneous exponentiation which is often more efficient than performing two single exponentiations and then combining the result.

- Modular arithmetic is usually implemented using the technique of Montgomery representation. This allows us to avoid costly division operations by replacing the division with simple shift operations. This however is at the expense of using a non-standard representation for the numbers.

- Finite fields in characteristic two can also be implemented efficiently. But now the modular reduction operation can be made simple by choosing a special polynomial $f(x)$. Inversion is also particular simple using a variant of the binary Euclidean algorithm, although often inversion is still 3–10 times slower than multiplication.

Further Reading

The standard reference work for the type of algorithms considered in this chapter is Volume 2 of Knuth. A more gentle introduction can be found in the book by Bach and Shallit, whilst for more algorithms one should consult the book by Cohen. The first chapter of Cohen gives a number of lessons learnt in the development of the PARI/GP calculator which can be useful, whilst Bach and Shallit provides an extensive bibliography and associated commentary.

E. Bach and S. Shallit. *Algorithmic Number Theory, Volume 1: Efficient Algorithms.* MIT Press, 1996.

H. Cohen. *A Course in Computational Algebraic Number Theory.* Springer-Verlag, 1993.

D. Knuth. *The Art of Computing Programming, Volume 2 : Seminumerical Algorithms.* Addison-Wesley, 1975.

Review Exercises

11.1.1   What is the maximum and average number of multiplications in the basic binary exponentiation algorithm?

11.1.2   Why is the smallest possible Hamming weight of an RSA public exponent equal to two?

11.1.3   What stops one using signed exponentiation techniques in an RSA implementation?

11.1.4   Why is Karatsuba multiplication rarely used in an RSA implementation?

11.1.5   What is meant by Montgomery representation and why does it offer advantages in systems implementing algorithms such as RSA?

11.1.6   In algorithms for finite fields of characteristic two, why does one use an analogue of Karatsuba multiplication and not an analogue of Montgomery multiplication?

Programming Exercises

11.2.1   (Assumes knowledge of C/Java) Compare the binary exponentiation algorithm in the text with the one below:

```
y=1;
while (d<>0)
  { if ((d&1)!=0)
      { y=(y*x)%n; }
    d>>=1;
    x=(x*x)%n;
  }
```

Why is the above version more efficient? Can you find any other ways of making it more efficient?

11.2.2 Implement functions to perform addition, multiplication and division in finite fields of characteristic two. Your algorithm should work on fields of degree up to 500 over $\mathbb{F}_2$.

11.2.3 Implement functions to perform an elliptic curve point multiplication operation using a curve defined over a characteristic two field of around 190 bits and a prime field of around 190 bits. Example curves and fields can be found in one of the many cryptographic standards which are available on the Internet

Standard Exercises

11.3.1 Assume modular multiplication of a k-bit number requires k^2 operations. How much faster is two 512-bit modular exponentiations by 512-bit exponents, compared to a single 1024-bit modular exponentiation by a 1024-bit exponent? Conclude that the CRT method for RSA decryption and signing is more efficient.

11.3.2 Suppose a device uses the Chinese Remainder Theorem to speed up RSA decryption or signatures, i.e. it computes

$$m_p = c^{d \ (\text{mod} \ p-1)} \ (\text{mod} \ p),$$
$$m_q = c^{d \ (\text{mod} \ q-1)} \ (\text{mod} \ q),$$

and then computes m from m_p and m_q via the Chinese Remainder Theorem. However an attacker manages to get the device to compute m_p incorrectly. Show that if m_q is still computed correctly then the attacker can use this broken device to recover the private key.

11.3.3 Prove that the two versions of pseudo-code for Montgomery reduction given in the text actually produce the result we claim that they do. Show that the interleaved Montgomery multiplication routine is also correct.

11.3.4 Show that the RSA encryption and decryption algorithms can be implemented in $O(n^3)$-bit operations, where n is the bit length of the modulus N.

11.3.5 Show that ElGamal encryption requires about $2\log p$ multiplications modulo p. Hence deduce its bit complexity is $O((\log p)^3)$.

11.3.6   By solving the recurrence relation given in the text show that Karatsuba multiplication does indeed have complexity $O(n^{1.58})$.

11.3.7   Karatsuba multiplication of polynomials works by splitting each polynomial into two halves. Give a variant of Karatsuba multiplication which splits each polynomial into thirds.

Table 11.1   Trinomials and pentanomials

n	$k/k_1, k_2, k_3$	n	$k/k_1, k_2, k_3$	n	$k/k_1, k_2, k_3$
2	1	3	1	4	1
5	2	6	1	7	1
8	7,3,2	9	1	10	3
11	2	12	3	13	4,3,1
14	5	15	1	16	5,3,1
17	3	18	3	19	5,2,1
20	3	21	2	22	1
23	5	24	8,3,2	25	3
26	4,3,1	27	5,2,1	28	1
29	2	30	1	31	3
32	7,3,2	33	10	34	7
35	2	36	9	37	6,4,1
38	6,5,1	39	4	40	5,4,3
41	3	42	7	43	6,4,3
44	5	45	4,3,1	46	1
47	5	48	11,5,1	49	9
50	4,3,2	51	6,3,1	52	3
53	6,2,1	54	9	55	7
56	7,4,2	57	4	58	19
59	7,4,2	60	1	61	5,2,1
62	29	63	1	64	11,2,1
65	32	66	3	67	5,2,1
68	33	69	6,5,2	70	37,34,33
71	35	72	36,35,33	73	42
74	35	75	35,34,32	76	38,33,32
77	38,33,32	78	41,37,32	79	40,36,32
80	45,39,32	81	35	82	43,35,32
83	39,33,32	84	35	85	35,34,32
86	49,39,32	87	46,34,32	88	45,35,32
89	38	90	35,34,32	91	41,33,32
92	37,33,32	93	35,34,32	94	43,33,32
95	41,33,32	96	57,38,32	97	33
98	63,35,32	99	42,33,32	100	37
101	40,34,32	102	37	103	72
104	43,33,32	105	37	106	73,33,32
107	54,33,32	108	33	109	34,33,32
110	33	111	49	112	73,51,32
113	37,33,32	114	69,33,32	115	53,33,32
116	48,33,32	117	78,33,32	118	33

119	38	120	41,35,32	121	35,34,32
122	39,34,32	123	42,33,32	124	37
125	79,33,32	126	49	127	63
128	55,33,32	129	46	130	61,33,32
131	43,33,32	132	44,33,32	133	46,33,32
134	57	135	39,33,32	136	35,33,32
137	35	138	57,33,32	139	38,33,32
140	45	141	85,35,32	142	71,33,32
143	36,33,32	144	59,33,32	145	52
146	71	147	49	148	61,33,32
149	64,34,32	150	53	151	39
152	35,33,32	153	71,33,32	154	109,33,32
155	62	156	57	157	47,33,32
158	76,33,32	159	34	160	79,33,32
161	39	162	63	163	48,34,32
164	42,33,32	165	35,33,32	166	37
167	35	168	134,33,32	169	34
170	105,35,32	171	125,34,32	172	81
173	71,33,32	174	57	175	57
176	79,37,32	177	88	178	87
179	80,33,32	180	33	181	46,33,32
182	81	183	56	184	121,39,32
185	41	186	79	187	37,33,32
188	46,33,32	189	37,34,32	190	47,33,32
191	51	192	147,33,32	193	73
194	87	195	50,34,32	196	33
197	38,33,32	198	65	199	34
200	57,35,32	201	59	202	55
203	68,33,32	204	99	205	94,33,32
206	37,33,32	207	43	208	119,34,32
209	45	210	49,35,32	211	175,33,32
212	105	213	75,33,32	214	73
215	51	216	115,34,32	217	45
218	71	219	54,33,32	220	33
221	63,33,32	222	102,33,32	223	33
224	39,33,32	225	32	226	59,34,32
227	81,33,32	228	113	229	64,35,32
230	50,33,32	231	34	232	191,33,32
233	74	234	103	235	34,33,32
236	50,33,32	237	80,34,32	238	73
239	36	240	177,35,32	241	70
242	95	243	143,34,32	244	111
245	87,33,32	246	62,33,32	247	82

248	155,33,32	249	35	250	103
251	130,33,32	252	33	253	46
254	85,33,32	255	52	256	91,33,32
257	41	258	71	259	113,33,32
260	35	261	89,34,32	262	86,33,32
263	93	264	179,33,32	265	42
266	47	267	42,33,32	268	61
269	207,33,32	270	53	271	58
272	165,35,32	273	53	274	67
275	81,33,32	276	63	277	91,33,32
278	70,33,32	279	38	280	242,33,32
281	93	282	35	283	53,33,32
284	53	285	50,33,32	286	69
287	71	288	111,33,32	289	36
290	81,33,32	291	168,33,32	292	37
293	94,33,32	294	33	295	48
296	87,33,32	297	83	298	61,33,32
299	147,33,32	300	45	301	83,33,32
302	41	303	36,33,32	304	203,33,32
305	102	306	66,33,32	307	46,33,32
308	40,33,32	309	107,33,32	310	93
311	78,33,32	312	87,33,32	313	79
314	79,33,32	315	132,33,32	316	63
317	36,34,32	318	45	319	36
320	135,34,32	321	41	322	67
323	56,33,32	324	51	325	46,33,32
326	65,33,32	327	34	328	195,37,32
329	50	330	99	331	172,33,32
332	89	333	43,34,32	334	43,33,32
335	113,33,32	336	267,33,32	337	55
338	86,35,32	339	72,33,32	340	45
341	126,33,32	342	125	343	75
344	135,34,32	345	37	346	63
347	56,33,32	348	103	349	182,34,32
350	53	351	34	352	147,34,32
353	69	354	99	355	43,33,32
356	112,33,32	357	76,34,32	358	57
359	68	360	323,33,32	361	56,33,32
362	63	363	74,33,32	364	67
365	303,33,32	366	38,33,32	367	171
368	283,34,32	369	91	370	139
371	116,33,32	372	111	373	299,33,32
374	42,33,32	375	64	376	227,33,32

377	41	378	43	379	44,33,32
380	47	381	107,34,32	382	81
383	90	384	295,34,32	385	51
386	83	387	162,33,32	388	159
389	275,33,32	390	49	391	37,33,32
392	71,33,32	393	62	394	135
395	301,33,32	396	51	397	161,34,32
398	122,33,32	399	49	400	191,33,32
401	152	402	171	403	79,33,32
404	65	405	182,33,32	406	141
407	71	408	267,33,32	409	87
410	87,33,32	411	122,33,32	412	147
413	199,33,32	414	53	415	102
416	287,38,32	417	107	418	199
419	200,33,32	420	45	421	191,33,32
422	149	423	104,33,32	424	213,34,32
425	42	426	63	427	62,33,32
428	105	429	83,33,32	430	62,33,32
431	120	432	287,34,32	433	33
434	55,33,32	435	236,33,32	436	165
437	40,34,32	438	65	439	49
440	63,33,32	441	35	442	119,33,32
443	221,33,32	444	81	445	146,33,32
446	105	447	73	448	83,33,32
449	134	450	47	451	406,33,32
452	97,33,32	453	87,33,32	454	128,33,32
455	38	456	67,34,32	457	61
458	203	459	68,33,32	460	61
461	194,35,32	462	73	463	93
464	143,33,32	465	59	466	143,33,32
467	156,33,32	468	33	469	116,34,32
470	149	471	119	472	47,33,32
473	200	474	191	475	134,33,32
476	129	477	150,33,32	478	121
479	104	480	169,35,32	481	138
482	48,35,32	483	288,33,32	484	105
485	267,33,32	486	81	487	94
488	79,33,32	489	83	490	219
491	61,33,32	492	50,33,32	493	266,33,32
494	137	495	76	496	43,33,32
497	78	498	155	499	40,33,32
500	75				

CHAPTER 12

Obtaining Authentic Public Keys

Chapter Goals

- To describe the notion of digital certificates.
- To explain the notion of a PKI.
- To examine different approaches such as X509, PGP and SPKI.
- To show how an implicit certificate scheme can operate.
- To explain how identity based cryptographic schemes operate.

12.1 GENERALITIES ON DIGITAL SIGNATURES

Digital signatures have a number of uses which go beyond the uses of handwritten signatures. For example we can use digital signatures to

- control access to data,
- allow users to authenticate themselves to a system,
- allow users to authenticate data,
- sign 'real' documents.

Each application has a different type of data being bound, a different length of the lifetime of the data to be signed, different types of principals performing the signing and verifying and different awareness of the data being bound.

For example an interbank payment need only contain the two account numbers and the amount. It needs to be signed by the payee and verified only by the computer which will carry out the transfer. The lifetime of the signature is only until the accounts are reconciled, for example when the account statements are sent to the customers and a suitable period has elapsed to allow the customers to complain of any error.

As another example consider a challenge response authentication mechanism. Here the user, to authenticate itself to the device, signs a challenge provided by the device. The lifetime of the signature may only be a few seconds. The user of course assumes that the challenge is random and is not a hash of an interbank payment. Hence, it is probably prudent that we use different keys for our authentication tokens and our banking applications.

As a final example consider a digital will or a mortgage contract. The length of time that this signature must remain valid may (hopefully in the case of a will) be many years. Hence, the security requirements for long-term legal documents will be very different from those of an authentication token.

You need to remember however that digital signatures are unlike handwritten signatures in that they are

- NOT necessarily on a document: Any piece of digital stuff can be signed.

- NOT transferable to other documents: Unlike a handwritten signature, a digital signature is different on each document.

- NOT modifiable after they are made: One cannot alter the document and still have the digital signature remaining valid.

- NOT produced by a person: A digital signature is never produced by a person, unless the signature scheme is very simple (and weak) or the person is a mathematical genius.

All they do is bind knowledge of an unrevealed private key to a particular piece of data.

12.2 DIGITAL CERTIFICATES AND PKI

When using a symmetric key system we assume we do not have to worry about which key belongs to which principle. It is tacitly assumed, see for example the chapter dealing with symmetric key agreement protocols and the BAN logic, that if Alice holds a long-term secret key K_{ab} which she thinks is shared with Bob, then Bob really does have a copy of the same key. This assurance is often achieved using a trusted physical means of long-term key distribution, using for example armed couriers.

In a public key system the issues are different. Alice may have a public key which she thinks is associated with Bob, but we usually do not assume that Alice is 100 percent certain that it really belongs to Bob. This is because we do not, in the public key model, assume a physically secure key distribution system. After all, that was the point of public key cryptography in the first place: to make key management easier. Alice may have obtained the public key she thinks belongs to Bob from Bob's web page, but how does she know the web page has not been spoofed?

The process of linking a public key to an entity or principal, be it a person, machine or process, is called binding. One way of binding, common in many applications where the principal really does need to be present, is by using a physical token such as a smart card. Possession of the token, and knowledge of any PIN/password needed to unlock the token, is assumed to be equivalent to being the designated entity. This solution has a number of problems associated with it, since cards can be lost or stolen, which is why we protect them using a PIN (or in more important applications by using biometrics). The major problem is that most entities are non-human, they are computers and computers do not carry cards. In addition many public key protocols are performed over networks where physical presence of the principal (if it is human) is not something one can test.

Hence, some form of binding is needed which can be used in a variety of very different applications. The main binding tool in use today is the digital certificate. In this a special trusted third party, or TTP, called a certificate authority, or CA, is used to vouch for the validity of the public keys.

A CA based system works as follows:

- All users have a trusted copy of the public key of the CA. For example these come embedded in your browser when you buy your computer, and you 'of course' trust the vendor of the computer and the manufacturer of the software on your computer.

- The CA's job is to digitally sign data strings containing the following information

  (Alice, Alice's public key).

  This data string, and the associated signature is called a digital certificate. The CA will only sign this data if it truly believes that the public key really does belong to Alice.

- When Alice now sends you her public key, contained in a digital certificate, you now trust that the purported key really is that of Alice, since you trust the CA to do its job correctly.

This use of a digital certificate binds the name 'Alice' with the 'Key', it is therefore often called an identity certificate. Other bindings are possible, we shall see some of these later related to authorizations.

Public key certificates will typically (although not always) be stored in repositories and accessed as required. For example, most browsers keep a list of the certificates that they have come across. The digital certificates do not need to be stored securely since they cannot be tampered with as they are digitally signed.

To see the advantage of certificates and CAs in more detail consider the following example of a world without a CA. In the following discussion we break with our colour convention for a moment and now use red to signal public keys which must be obtained in an authentic manner and blue to signal public keys which do not need to be obtained in an authentic manner.

In a world without a CA you obtain many individual public keys from each individual in some authentic fashion. For example

6A5DEF....A21	Jim Bean's public key,
7F341A....BFF	Jane Doe's public key,
B5F34A....E6D	Microsoft's update key.

Hence, each key needs to be obtained in an authentic manner, as does every new key you obtain.

Now consider the world with a CA. You obtain a single public key in an authentic manner, namely the CA's public key. We shall call our CA Ted since he is trustworthy. You then obtain many individual public keys, signed by the CA, in possibly an unauthentic manner. For example they could be attached at the bottom of an email, or picked up whilst browsing the web.

A45EFB....C45   Ted's totally trustworthy key,
6A5DEF....A21   Ted says 'This is Jim Bean's public key',
7F341A....BFF   Ted says 'This is Jane Doe's public key',
B5F34A....E6D   Ted says 'This is Microsoft's update key'.

If you trust Ted's key and you trust Ted to do his job correctly then you trust all the public keys you hold to be authentic.

In general a digital certificate is not just a signature on the single pair

(Alice, Alice's public key),

one can place all sorts of other, possibly application specific, information into the certificate. For example it is usual for the certificate to contain the following information.

- user's name,

- user's public key,

- is this an encryption or signing key?

- name of the CA,

- serial number of the certificate,

- expiry date of the certificate,

- ....

Commercial certificate authorities exist who will produce a digital certificate for your public key, often after payment of a fee and some checks on whether you are who you say you are. The certificates produced by commercial CAs are often made public, so one can call them public 'public key certificates', in that there use is mainly over open public networks.

CAs are also used in proprietary systems, for example in debit/credit card systems or by large corporations. In such situations it may be the case that the end users do not want their public key certificates to be made public, in which case one can call them private 'public key certificates'. But one should bear in mind that whether the digital certificate is public or private should not effect the security of the private key associated to the public key contained in the certificate. The decision to make one's certificates private is often one of business rather than security.

It is common for more than one CA to exist. A quick examination of the properties of your web browser will reveal a large number of certificate authorities which your browser assumes you 'trust' to perform the function of a CA. As there are more than one CA it is common for one CA to sign a digital certificate containing the public key of another CA, and vice versa, a process which is known as cross-certification.

Cross-certification is needed if more than one CA exists, since a user may not have a trusted copy of the CA's public key needed to verify another user's digital certificate. This is solved by cross-certificates, i.e. one CA's public key is signed by another CA. The user first verifies the appropriate cross-certificate, and then verifies the user certificate itself.

With many CAs one can get quite long certificate chains, as Fig. 12.1 illustrates. Suppose Alice trusts the Root CA's public key and she obtains Bob's public key which is signed by the private key of CA2. She then obtains CA2's public key, either along with Bob's digital certificate or by some other means. CA2's public key comes in a certificate which is signed by the private key of the Root CA. Hence, by verifying all the signatures she ends up trusting Bob's public key.

Fig. 12.1 Example certification hierarchy

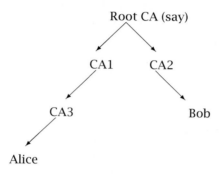

Often the function of a CA is split into two parts. One part deals with verifying the user's identity and one part actually signs the public keys. The signing is performed by the CA, whilst the identity of the user is parcelled out to a registration authority, or RA. This can be a good practice, with the CA implemented in a more secure environment to protect the long-term private key.

The main problem with a CA system arises when a user's public key is compromised or becomes untrusted for some reason. For example

- a third party has gained knowledge of the private key,

- an employee leaves the company.

As the public key is no longer to be trusted all the associated digital certificates are now invalid and need to be revoked. But these certificates can be distributed over a large number of users, each one of which needs to be told to no longer trust this certificate. The CA must somehow inform all users that the certificate(s) containing this public key is/are no longer valid, in a process called certificate revocation.

One way to accomplish this is via a Certificate Revocation List, or CRL, which is a signed statement by the CA containing the serial numbers of all certificates which have been revoked by that CA and whose validity period has not expired. One clearly need not include in this the serial numbers of certificates which have passed their expiry date. Users must then ensure they have the latest CRL. This can be achieved by issuing CRLs at regular intervals even if the list has not changed. Such a system can work well in a corporate environment when overnight background jobs are often used to make sure each desktop computer in the company is up to date with the latest software etc.

For other situations it is hard to see how the CRLs can be distributed, especially if there are a large number of CAs trusted by each user.

In summary, with secret key cryptography the main problems were ones of

- key management,

- key distribution.

These problems resulted in keys needing to be distributed via secure channels. In public key systems we replace these problems with those of

- key authentication,

in other words which key belongs to who. Hence, keys needed to be distributed via authentic channels. The use of digital certificates provides the authentic channels needed to distribute the public keys.

The whole system of CAs and certificates is often called the Public Key Infrastructure or PKI. This essentially allows a distribution of trust; the need to trust the authenticity of each individual public key in your possession is replaced by the need to trust a body, the CA, to do its job correctly.

In ensuring the CA does its job correctly you can either depend on the legal system, with maybe a state sponsored CA, or you can trust the business system in that it would not be in the CA's business interests to not act properly. For example, if it did sign a key in your name by mistake then you could apply publicly for exemplary restitution.

We end this section by noting that we have now completely solved the key distribution problem: For two users to agree on a shared secret key, they first obtain authentic public keys from a CA. Then secure session keys are obtained using, for example, signed Diffie–Hellman,

$$
\begin{array}{cc}
\text{Alice} & \text{Bob} \\
(g^a, \text{Sign}_{\text{Alice}}(g^a)) \quad \longrightarrow & \\
\longleftarrow \quad & (g^b, \text{Sign}_{\text{Bob}}(g^b))
\end{array}
$$

12.3   EXAMPLE APPLICATIONS OF PKI

In this section we shall look at some real systems which distribute trust via digital certificates. The examples will be

- PGP,

- SSL,

- X509 (or PKIX),

- SPKI.

12.3.1 PGP

The email encryption program Pretty Good Privacy, or PGP, takes a bottom-up approach to the distribution of trust. The design goals of PGP were to give a low-cost encryption/signature system for all users, hence the use of an expensive top-down global PKI would not fit this model. Instead the system makes use of what it calls a 'Web of Trust'.

The public key management is done from the bottom up by the users themselves. Each user acts as their own CA and signs other user's public keys. So Alice can sign Bob's public key and then Bob can give this signed 'certificate' to Charlie, in which case Alice is acting as a CA for Bob. If Charlie trusts Alice's judgement with respect to signing people's keys then she will trust that Bob's key really does belong to Bob. It is really up to Charlie to make this decision. As users keep doing this cross-certification of each other's keys, a web of trusted keys grows from the bottom up.

PGP itself as a program uses RSA public key encryption for low-volume data such as session keys. The block cipher used for bulk transmission is called IDEA. This block cipher has a 64-bit block size and a 128-bit key size and is used in CFB mode. Digital signatures in PGP can be produced either with the RSA or the DSA algorithm, after a message digest is taken using either MD5 or SHA-1.

The keys that an individual trusts are held in a so-called key ring. This means users have control over their own local public key store. This does not rule out a centralized public key store, but means one is not necessarily needed.

Key revocation is still a problem with PGP as with all such systems. The ad-hoc method adopted by PGP is that if your key is compromised then you should tell all your friends, who have a copy of your key, to delete the key from their key ring. All your friends should then tell all their friends and so on.

12.3.2 Secure Socket Layer

Whilst the design of PGP was driven by altruistic ideals, namely to provide encryption for the masses, the Secure Socket Layer, or SSL, was driven by commercial requirements, namely to provide a secure means for web based shopping and sales. Essentially SSL adds security to the TCP level of the IP stack. It provides security of data and not parties but allows various protocols to be transparently layered on top, for example HTTP, FTP, TELNET, etc.

The primary objective was to provide channel security, to enable the encrypted transmission of credit card details or passwords. After an initial handshake all subsequent traffic is encrypted. The server side of the communication, namely the website or the host computer in a Telnet session, is always authenticated for the benefit of the client. Optionally the client may be authenticated to the user, but this is rarely done in practice for web based transactions.

As in PGP, bulk encryption is performed using a block or stream cipher (usually either DES or an algorithm from the RC family). The choice of precise cipher is chosen between the client and server during the initial handshake. The session key to be used is derived using standard protocols such as the Diffie–Hellman protocol, or RSA based key transport.

The server is authenticated since it provides the client with an X509 public key certificate. This, for web shopping transactions, is signed by some global CA whose public key comes embedded into the user's web browser. For secure Telnet sessions (often named SSH after the program which runs them) the server side certificate is usually a self-signed certificate from the host computer.

The following is a simplified overview of how SSL can operate.

- The client establishes connection with the server on a special port number so as to signal this will be a secure session.

- The server sends a certified public key to the client.

- The client verifies the certificate and decides whether it trusts this public key.

- The client chooses a random secret.

- The client encodes this with the server's public key and sends this back to the server.

- The client and server now securely share the secret.

- The server now authenticates itself to the client by responding using the shared secret.

The determination of session keys can be a costly operation for both the server and the client, especially when the data may come in bursts, as when one is engaged in shopping transactions, or performing some remote access to a computer. Hence, there is some optimization made to enable reuse of session keys. The client is allowed to quote a previous session key, the server can either accept it or ask for a new one to be created. So as to avoid any problems this ability is limited by two rules. Firstly a session key should have a very limited lifetime and secondly any fatal error in any part of the protocols will immediately invalidate the session key and require a new one to be determined. In SSL the initial handshake is also used for the client and the server to agree on which bulk encryption algorithm to use, this is usually chosen from the list of RC4, RC5, DES or Triple DES.

12.3.3   X509 Certificates

When discussing SSL we mentioned that the server uses an X509 public key certificate. X509 is a standard which defines a structure for public key certificates, currently it is the most widely deployed certificate standard. A CA assigns a unique name to each user and issues a signed certificate. The name is often the URL or email address. This can cause problems since, for example, many users may have different versions of the same email address. If you send a signed email containing your certificate for your email 'address'

$$N.P.Smart@some.where.com$$

but your email program sends this from the 'address'

$$Nigel.Smart@some.where.com$$

then, even though you consider both addresses to be equivalent, the email client of the recipient will often complain saying that the signature is not to be trusted.

The CAs are connected in a tree structure, with each CA issuing a digital certificate for the one beneath it. In addition cross-certification between the branches is allowed.

The X509 certificates themselves are defined in standards using a language called ASN.1, or Abstract Syntax Notation. This can be rather complicated at first sight and the processing of all the possible options often ends up with incredible 'code bloat'.

The basic X509 certificate structure is very simple, but can end up being very complex in any reasonable application. This is because some advanced applications may want to add additional information into the certificates which enable authorization and other capabilities. However, the following records are always in a certificate.

- The version number of the X509 standard which this certificate conforms to.

- The certificate serial number.

- The CA's signing algorithm identifier. This should specify the algorithm and the domain parameters used, if the CA has multiple possible algorithms or domain parameters.

- The issuer's name, i.e. the name of the issuing CA.

- The validity period in the form of a not-before and not-after date.

- The subject's name, i.e. whose public key is being signed. This could be an email address or a domain name.

- The subject's public key. This contains the algorithm name and any associated domain parameters plus the actual value of the public key

- The issuer's signature on the subject's public key and all data that is to be bound to the subject's public key, such as the subject's name.

12.3.4   SPKI

In response to some of the problems associated with X509, another type of certificate format has been proposed called SPKI, or Simple Public Key Infrastructure. This system aims to bind authorizations as well as identities, and also tries to deal with the issue of delegation of authorizations and trust. Thus it may be suitable for business to business e-commerce transactions. For example, when managers go on holiday they can delegate their authorizations for certain tasks to their subordinates.

SPKI does not assume the global CA hierarchy which X509 does. It assumes a more ground-up approach like PGP. However, it is currently not used much commercially since PKI vendors have a lot of investment in X509 and are probably not willing to switch over to a new system (and the desktop applications such as your web browser would also need significant alterations).

Instead of using ASN.1 to describe certificates, SPKI uses S-expressions. These are LISP-like structures which are very simple to use and describe. In addition S-expressions can be made very simple even for humans to understand, as opposed to the machine-only readable formats of X509 certificates. S-expressions can even come with display hints to enable greater readability. The current draft standard specifies these display hints as simple MIME-types.

Each SPKI certificate has an issuer and a subject both of which are public keys (or a hash of a public key), and not names. This is because SPKI's authors claim that it is a key which does something and not a name. After all it is a key which is used to sign a document etc. Focusing on the keys also means we can concentrate more on the functionality. There are two types of SPKI certificates: ones for binding identities to keys and ones for binding authorizations to keys. Internally these are represented as tuples of 4 and 5 objects, which we shall now explain.

12.3.4.1 SPKI 4-Tuples To give an identity certificate and bind a name with a key, like X509 does, SPKI uses a 4-tuple structure. This is an internal abstraction of what the certificate represents and is given by:

(Issuer, Name, Subject, Validity).

In real life this would consist of the following five fields:

- issuer's public key,

- name of the subject,

- subject's public key,

- validity period,

- signature of the issuer on the triple (Name, Subject, Validity).

Anyone is able to issue such a certificate, and hence become a CA.

12.3.4.2 SPKI 5-Tuples 5-tuples are used to bind keys to authorizations. Again this is an internal abstraction of what the certificate represents and is given by

(Issuer, Subject, Delegation, Authorization, Validity).

In real life this would consist of the following six fields:

- issuer's public key.

- subject's public key.

- delegation. A 'Yes' or 'No' flag, saying whether the subject can delegate the permission or not.

- authorization. What the subject is being given permission to do

- validity. How long the authorization is for.

- signature of the issuer on the quadruple (S,D,A,V).

One can combine an authorization certificate and an identity certificate to obtain an audit trail. This is needed since the authorization certificate only allows a key to perform an action. It does not say who owns the key. To find out who owns a key you need to use an identity certificate.

When certificate chains are eventually checked to enable some authorization, a 5-tuple reduction procedure is carried out. This can be represented by the following rule

$$(I_1, S_1, D_1, A_1, V_1) + (I_2, S_2, D_2, A_2, V_2)$$
$$= (I_1, S_2, D_2, A_1 \cap A_2, V_1 \cap V_2).$$

This equality holds only if

- $S_1 = I_2$

- $D_1 = \mathsf{True}.$

This means the first two certificates together can be interpreted as the third. This third 5-tuple is not really a certificate, it is the meaning of the first two when they are presented together.

As an example we will show how combining two 5-tuples is equivalent to delegating authority. Suppose our first 5-tuple is given by:

- I_1 = Alice

- S_1 = Bob

- D_1 = True

- A_1 = Spend up to £100 on Alice's account

- V_1 = forever.

So Alice allows Bob to spend up to £100 on her account and allows Bob to delegate this authority to anyone he chooses.

Now consider the second 5-tuple given by

- I_2 = Bob

- S_2 = Charlie

- D_2 = False

- A_2 = Spend between £50 and £200 on Alice's account

- V_2 = before tomorrow morning.

So Bob is saying Charlie can spend between £50 and £200 of Alice's money, as long as it happens before tomorrow morning.

We combine these two 5-tuples, using the 5-tuple reduction rule, to form the new 5-tuple

- I_3 = Alice

- S_3 = Charlie

- D_3 = False

- A_3 = Spend between £50 and £100 on Alice's account

- V_3 = before tomorrow morning.

Since Alice has allowed Bob to delegate she has in effect allowed Charlie to spend between £50 and £100 on her account before tomorrow morning.

12.4   OTHER APPLICATIONS OF TRUSTED THIRD PARTIES

In some applications it is necessary for signatures to remain valid for a long time. Revocation of a public key, even long after the legitimate creation of the signature, potentially invalidates all digital signatures made using that key, even those in the past. This is a major problem if digital signatures are to be used for documents of long-term value such as wills, life insurance and mortgage contracts. We essentially need methods to prove that a digital signature was made prior to the revocation of the key and not after it. This brings us to the concept of time stamping.

A time stamping service is a means whereby a trusted entity will take a signed message, add a date/timestamp and sign the result using its own private key. This proves when a signature was made (like a notary service in standard life insurance). However, there is the requirement that the public key of the time stamping service must never be revoked. An alternative to the use of a time stamping service is the use of a secure archive for signed messages.

As another application of a trusted third-party consider the problem associated with keeping truly secret keys for encryption purposes.

- What if someone loses or forgets a key? They could lose all your encrypted data.

- What if the holder of the key resigns from the company or is killed? The company may now want access to the encrypted data.

- What if the user is a criminal? Here the government may want access to the encrypted data.

One solution is to deposit a copy of your key with someone else in case you lose yours, or something untoward happens. On the other hand, simply divulging the key to anybody, even the government, is very insecure.

A proposed solution is key escrow implemented via a secret sharing scheme. Here the private key is broken into pieces, each of which can be verified to be correct. Each piece is then given to some authority. At some later point if the key needs to be recovered then a subset of the authorities can come together and reconstruct it from their shares. The authorities implementing this escrow facility are another example of a Trusted Third Party, since you really have to trust them. In fact the trust required is so high that this solution has been a source of major debate within the cryptographic and governmental communities in the past. The splitting of the key between the various escrow authorities can be accomplished using the trick of a secret sharing scheme which we discussed in Chapter 6.

12.5   IMPLICIT CERTIFICATES

One issue with digital certificates is that they can be rather large. Each certificate needs to at least contain both the public key of the user and the signature of the certificate authority on that key. This can lead to quite large certificate sizes, as the following table demonstrates:

	RSA	DSA	EC-DSA
User's key	1024	1024	160
CA sig	1024	320	320

This assumes for RSA keys one uses a 1024-bit modulus, for DSA one uses a 1024-bit prime p and a 160-bit prime q and for EC-DSA one uses a 160-bit curve. Hence, for example, if the CA is using 1024-bit RSA and they are signing the public key of a user using 1024-bit DSA then the total certificate size must be at least 2048 bits. An interesting question is whether this can be made smaller.

Implicit certificates enable this. An implicit certificate looks like

$$X|Y$$

where

- X is the data being bound to the public key,

- Y is the implicit certificate on X.

From Y we need to be able to recover the public key being bound to X and implicit assurance that the certificate was issued by the CA. In the system we describe below, based on a DSA or EC-DSA, the size of Y will be 1024 or 160 bits respectively. Hence, the size of the certificate is reduced to the size of the public key being certified.

12.5.1 System Setup

The CA chooses a public group G of known order n and an element $P \in G$. The CA then chooses a long-term private key c and computes the public key

$$Q = P^c.$$

This public key should be known to all users.

12.5.2 Certificate Request

Suppose Alice wishes to request a certificate and the public key associated to the information ID, which could be her name. Alice computes an ephemeral secret key t and an ephemeral public key

$$R = P^t.$$

Alice sends R and ID to the CA.

12.5.3 Processing of the request

The CA checks that he wants to link ID with Alice. The CA picks another random number k and computes

$$g = P^k R = P^k P^t = P^{k+t}.$$

Then the CA computes

$$s = cH(ID\|g) + k \pmod{n}.$$

Then the CA sends back to Alice the pair

$$(g, s).$$

The implicit certificate is the pair

$$(ID, g).$$

We now have to convince you that

- Alice can recover a valid public/private key pair,

- any other user can recover Alice's public key from this implicit certificate

12.5.4 Alice's Key Discovery

Alice knows the following information

$$t, s, R = P^t.$$

From this she can recover her private key

$$a = t + s \ (\text{mod } n).$$

Note, Alice's private key is known only to Alice and not to the CA. In addition Alice has contributed some randomness t to her private key, as has the CA who contributed k. Her public key is then

$$P^a = P^{t+s} = P^t P^s = R \cdot P^s.$$

12.5.5 User's Key Discovery

Since s and R are public, a user, say Bob, can recover Alice's public key from the above message flows via

$$R \cdot P^s.$$

But this says nothing about the linkage between the CA, Alice's public key and the ID information. Instead Bob recovers the public key from the implicit certificate

$$(ID, g)$$

and the CA's public key

$$Q$$

via the equation

$$P^a = Q^{H(ID\|g)} g.$$

As soon as Bob sees Alice's key used in action, say he verifies a signature purported to have been made by Alice, he knows implicitly that it must have been issued by the CA, since otherwise Alice's signature would not verify correctly.

There are a number of problems with the above system which mean that implicit certificates are not used much in real life. For example,

1. What do you do if the CA's key is compromised? Usually you pick a new CA key and re-certify the user's keys. But you cannot do this since the user's public key is chosen interactively during the certification process.

2. Implicit certificates require the CA and users to work at the same security level. This is not considered good practice, as usually one expects the CA to work at a higher security level (say 2048-bit DSA) than the user (say 1024-bit DSA).

However for devices with restricted bandwidth they can offer a suitable alternative where traditional certificates are not available.

12.6 IDENTITY BASED CRYPTOGRAPHY

Another way of providing authentic public keys, without the need for certificates, is to use a system whereby the user's key is given by their identity. Such a system is called an identity based encryption scheme or an identity based signature scheme. Such systems do not remove the need for a trusted third-party to perform the original authentication of the user, but they do however remove the need for storage and transmission of certificates.

The first scheme of this type was a signature scheme invented by Shamir in 1984. It was not until 2001 however that an identity based encryption scheme was given by Boneh and Franklin. We shall only describe the original identity based signature scheme of Shamir, which is based on the RSA problem.

A trusted third-party first calculates an RSA modulus N, keeping the two factors secret. The TTP also publishes a public exponent e, keeping the corresponding private exponent d to themselves. In addition there is decided a mapping

$$I : \{0, 1\}^* \longrightarrow (\mathbb{Z}/N\mathbb{Z})^*$$

which takes bit strings to elements of $(\mathbb{Z}/N\mathbb{Z})^*$. Such a mapping could be implemented by a hash function.

Now suppose Alice wishes to obtain the private key g corresponding to her name 'Alice'. This is calculated for her by the TTP using the equation

$$g = I(\text{Alice})^d \pmod{N}.$$

To sign a message m, Alice generates the pair (t, s) via the equations

$$t = r^e \pmod{N},$$
$$s = g \cdot r^{H(m \| t)} \pmod{N},$$

where r is a random integer and H is a hash function.

To verify the signature (t, s) on the message m another user can do this, simply by knowing the TTP's public data and the identity of Alice, by checking that the following equation holds modulo N,

$$I(\text{Alice}) \cdot t^{H(m \| t)} = g^e \cdot r^{e \cdot H(m \| t)}$$
$$= \left(g \cdot r^{H(m \| t)} \right)^e$$
$$= s^e.$$

Chapter Summary

- Digital certificates allow us to bind a public key to some other information, such as an identity.

- This binding of key with identity allows us to solve the problem of how to distribute authentic public keys.

- Various PKI systems have been proposed, all of which have problems and benefits associated with them.

- PGP and SPKI work from the bottom up, whilst X509 works in a top-down manner.

- SPKI contains the ability to delegate authorizations from one key to another.

- Other types of trusted third-party applications exist such as time stamping and key escrow.

- Implicit certificates aim to reduce the bandwidth requirements of standard certificates, however they come with a number of drawbacks.

- Identity based cryptography helps authenticate a user's public key by using their identity as the public key, but it does not remove the need for trusted third parties.

Further Reading

A good overview of the issues related to PKI can be found in the book by Adams and Lloyd. For further information on PGP and SSL look at the books by Garfinkel and Rescorla.

C. Adams and S. Lloyd. *Understanding Public-Key Infrastructure: Concepts, Standards and Deployment Considerations.* New Riders Publishing, 1999.

S. Garfinkel. *PGP: Pretty Good Privacy.* O'Reilly & Associates, 1994.

E. Rescorla. *SSL and TLS: Design and Building Secure Systems.* Addison-Wesley, 2000.

Review Exercises

12.1.1   What service does a certificate authority offer?

12.1.2   Why does a certificate usually contain an expiry date?

12.1.3   What is cross-certification and why is it needed?

12.1.4   Explain the main differences between PGP, X509 and SPKI.

12.1.5   Does SSL usually use key transport or key agreement?

CHAPTER 13

Protocols

Chapter Goals

- To introduce commitment schemes.

- To introduce zero-knowledge proofs.

- To explain how these can be used in a voting protocol.

13.1 INTRODUCTION

In this chapter we shall examine a number of cryptographic protocols which enable higher level services to be created. We shall particularly focus on protocols for

- commitment schemes,

- zero-knowledge proofs.

Whilst there is a large body of literature on these protocols, we shall keep our feet on the ground and focus on protocols which can be used in real life to achieve practical higher level services. To illustrate these protocols in action we shall end the chapter with a description of an electronic voting system.

13.2 COMMITMENT SCHEMES

Suppose Alice wishes to play 'paper-scissors-stone' over the telephone with Bob. The idea of this game is that Alice and Bob both choose simultaneously one of the set {paper,scissors,stone}. Then the outcome of the game is determined by the rules

- Paper wraps stone. Hence if Alice chooses paper and Bob chooses stone then Alice wins.

- Stone blunts scissors. Hence if Alice chooses stone and Bob chooses scissors then Alice wins.

- Scissors cut paper. Hence if Alice chooses scissors and Bob chooses paper then Alice wins.

If both Alice and Bob choose the same item then the game is declared a draw. When conducted over the telephone we have the problem that whoever goes first is going to lose the game.

One way around this is for the party who goes first to 'commit' to their choice, in such a way that the other party cannot determine what was committed to. Then the two parties can reveal their choices, with the idea that the other party can then verify that the revealing party has not altered its choice between the commitment and the revealing stage. Such a system is called a commitment scheme. An easy way to do this is to use a cryptographic hash function as follows:

$$A \longrightarrow B : h_A = H(R_A \| \text{paper}),$$
$$B \longrightarrow A : \text{scissors},$$
$$A \longrightarrow B : R_A, \text{paper}.$$

Bob needs to verify that the h_A sent by Alice is equal to $H(R_A \| \text{paper})$, if so he knows that Alice has not cheated. The result of this protocol is that Alice loses the game since scissors cut paper.

Let us look at the above from Alice's perspective. She first commits to the value paper by sending Bob the hash value h_A. This means that Bob will not be able to determine that Alice has committed to the value paper since Bob does not know the random value of R_A used and is unable to invert the hash function. This property of the commitment scheme that Bob cannot determine what value was committed to is called concealing.

Bob now sends the value scissors to Alice. Alice now knows she has lost but is unable to cheat, since to cheat she would need to come up with a different value of R_A, say R_A', which satisfied

$$H(R_A \| \text{paper}) = H(R_A' \| \text{stone}).$$

But this would mean that Alice could find collisions in the hash function, which for a suitable chosen hash function is believed to be impossible. Actually we require that the hash function is second-preimage resistant in this case. This property of the commitment scheme, that Alice cannot change her mind after the commitment procedure, is called binding.

Let us now study these properties of concealing and binding in more detail. Recall that we said that an encryption function has information theoretic security if an adversary with infinite computing power could not break the scheme, whilst an encryption function is called computationally secure if it is only secure when faced with an adversary with polynomially bounded computing power. A similar division can be made with commitment schemes, but now we have two security properties, namely concealing and binding.

Definition 13.1 *A commitment scheme is said to be:*

- *Information theoretically binding if a sender is unable to change the value committed to after the commitment stage, no matter how much computing power is available.*

- *Computationally binding if a sender can change the value committed to, but only after a huge amount of computation.*

- *Information theoretically concealing if the receiver is unable to determine the value of the commitment before the revealing stage, no matter how much computing power is available.*

- *Computationally concealing if the receiver, after expending a large but finite amount of computing resources, is able to determine the value committed to, before it is revealed.*

With these definitions it is then clear that

Lemma 13.2 *Using the commitment scheme defined as*

$$H(R\|C),$$

for a random value R, the committed value C and some cryptographic hash function H, is at best

- *computationally binding,*

- *computationally concealing.*

Proof
All cryptographic hash functions we have met are only computationally secure against preimage resistance and second-preimage resistance.

The binding property of the above scheme is only guaranteed by the second-preimage resistance of the underlying hash function. Hence, the binding property is only computationally secure.

The concealing property of the above scheme is only guaranteed by the preimage resistance of the underlying hash function. Hence, the concealing property is also only computationally secure.

Q.E.D.

One could therefore ask is it possible to obtain a commitment scheme which is both information theoretically binding and information theoretically concealing? It seems hard, if not impossible, to come up with such a scheme, however one can invent two quite elegant and simple schemes which are either information theoretically binding or information theoretically concealing.

Let G denote a finite abelian group of prime order q which is generated by g. We let $h \in \langle g \rangle$, where the discrete logarithm of h to the base g is unknown by any user in the system. This latter property is quite easy to ensure, for example for a finite field $\mathbb{F}_p^*$, with q dividing $p - 1$ we create g as follows (with a similar procedure being used to determine h):

- Pick a random $r \in \mathbb{Z}$.

- Compute $f = H(r) \in \mathbb{F}_p^*$ for some cryptographic hash function H.

- Set $g = f^{(p-1)/q} \pmod p$. If $g = 1$ then return to the first stage, else output (r, g).

This generates a random element of the subgroup of $\mathbb{F}_p^*$ of order q, with the property that it is generated verifiably at random since one outputs the seed r used to generate the random element.

Given g, h we define two commitment schemes, $B(x)$ and $B_a(x)$, to commit to an integer x modulo q,

$$B(x) = g^x,$$
$$B_a(x) = h^x g^a,$$

where a is a random integer modulo q. The value a is called the blinding number, since it blinds the value of the commitment x even to a computationally unbounded adversary. To reveal the commitments the user publishes the value x in the first scheme and the pair (a, x) in the second scheme.

Lemma 13.3 *The commitment scheme $B(x)$ is at most information theoretically binding and computationally concealing.*

Proof
Suppose Alice having published
$$c = B(x) = g^x$$
wished to change her mind as to which element of $\mathbb{Z}/q\mathbb{Z}$ she wants to commit to. Alas, for Alice no matter how much computing power she has there is mathematically only one element in $\mathbb{Z}/q\mathbb{Z}$, namely x, which is the discrete logarithm of the commitment c to the base g. Hence, the scheme is clearly information theoretically binding.

Now suppose the recipient of the commitment wanted to determine the concealed element. All they need do is compute the discrete logarithm of the commitment c to the base g. Hence, the scheme is only computationally concealing.

Q.E.D.

Lemma 13.4 *The commitment scheme $B_a(x)$ is at most computationally binding and information theoretically concealing. That it is computationally binding only holds if the committer does not know the discrete logarithm of h to the base g.*

Proof
Now suppose Alice, after having committed to
$$b = B_a(x) = h^x g^a$$
wishes to change her mind, so as to commit to y instead. All that Alice need do is to compute
$$f = \frac{b}{h^y}.$$

Alice then computes the discrete logarithm a' of f to the base g. When Alice is now asked to reveal her commitment she outputs (a', y) instead of (a, x). Hence the scheme is at most computationally binding.

Now suppose the recipient wishes to determine which is the committed value, before the revealing stage is carried out. Since, for a given value of b and every value of x, there is a value of a which makes a valid commitment, even a computationally un-bounded adversary could determine no information. Hence, the scheme is information theoretically concealing.

Q.E.D.

We end this section by noticing that the two discrete logarithm based commitment schemes we have given possess the homomorphic property:

$$B(x_1) \cdot B(x_2) = g^{x_1} \cdot g^{x_2}$$
$$= g^{x_1 + x_2}$$
$$= B(x_1 + x_2),$$
$$B_{a_1}(x_1) \cdot B_{a_2}(x_2) = h^{x_1} \cdot g^{a_1} \cdot h^{x_2} \cdot g^{a_2}$$
$$= h^{x_1 + x_2} \cdot g^{a_1 + a_2}$$
$$= B_{a_1 + a_2}(x_1 + x_2).$$

We shall use this homomorphic property when we discuss our voting protocol at the end of the chapter.

13.3 ZERO-KNOWLEDGE PROOFS

Suppose Alice wants to convince Bob that she knows something without Bob finding out exactly what Alice knows. This apparently contradictory state of affairs is dealt with using zero-knowledge proofs. In the literature of zero-knowledge proofs the role of Alice is called the prover, since she wishes to prove something, whilst the role of Bob is called the verifier, since he wishes to verify that the prover actually knows something. Often, and we shall also follow this convention, the prover is called Peggy and the verifier is called Victor.

The classic example of zero-knowledge proofs is based on the graph isomorphism problem. Given two graphs G_1 and G_2, with the same number of vertices, we say that the two graphs are isomorphic if there is a relabelling of the vertices of one graph which produces the second graph. This relabelling ϕ is called the graph isomorphism which is denoted by

$$\phi : G_1 \longrightarrow G_2.$$

It is a hard computational problem to determine a graph isomorphism between two graphs.

Suppose Peggy knows the graph isomorphism ϕ between two public graphs G_1 and G_2. We call ϕ the prover's private input, whilst the groups G_1 and G_2 are the public or common input. Peggy wishes to convince Victor that she knows the graph isomorphism, without revealing to Victor the precise nature of the graph isomorphism. This is done using the following zero-knowledge proof.

Peggy takes the graph G_2 and applies a secret random permutation ψ to the vertices of G_2 to produce another isomorphic graph H. Peggy now publishes H as a **commitment**, she of course knows the following secret graph isomorphisms

$$\phi : G_1 \longrightarrow G_2,$$
$$\psi : G_2 \longrightarrow H,$$
$$\psi \circ \phi : G_1 \longrightarrow H.$$

Victor now gives Peggy a **challenge**, he selects $b \in \{1,2\}$ and asks for the graph isomorphism between H and G_b. Peggy now gives her **response** by returning either $\chi = \psi$ or $\chi = \psi \circ \phi$. The transcript of the protocol then looks like

$$P \longrightarrow V : H,$$
$$V \longrightarrow P : b,$$
$$P \longrightarrow V : \chi.$$

Let us first examine how Peggy can cheat. If Peggy does not know the graph isomorphism ϕ then she will need to know, before Victor gives his challenge, the graph G_b which Victor is going to pick. Hence, if Peggy is cheating she will only be able to respond to Victor correctly 50 percent of the time. So, repeating the above protocol a number of times, a non-cheating Peggy will be able to convince Victor that she really does know the graph isomorphism, with a small probability of error of Victor being convinced incorrectly.

Now we need to determine whether Victor learns anything from running the protocol, i.e. is Peggy's proof really zero-knowledge? We first notice that Peggy needs to produce a different value of H on every run of the protocol, otherwise Victor can trivially cheat. We assume therefore that this does not happen.

One way to see whether Victor has learnt something after running the protocol is to look at the transcript of the protocol and ask after having seen the transcript whether Victor has gained any knowledge, or for that matter whether anyone looking at the protocol but not interacting learns anything. One way to see that Victor has not learnt anything is to see that Victor could have written down a valid protocol transcript without interacting with Peggy at all. Hence, Victor cannot use the protocol transcript to convince someone else that he knows Peggy's secret isomorphism. He cannot even use the protocol transcript to convince another party that Peggy knows the secret graph isomorphism.

Victor can produce a valid protocol transcript using the following simulation:

- Choose $b \in \{1, 2\}$.

- Generate a random isomorphism χ of the graph G_b to produce the graph H.

- Output the transcript

$$P \longrightarrow V : H,$$
$$V \longrightarrow P : b,$$
$$P \longrightarrow V : \chi.$$

Hence, the interactive nature of the protocol means that it is a zero-knowledge proof. We remark that the three-pass system of

$$\text{commitment} \longrightarrow \text{challenge} \longrightarrow \text{response}$$

is the usual characteristic of such protocols.

Just as with commitment schemes we can divide zero-knowledge protocols into categories depending on whether they are secure with respect to computationally bounded or unbounded adversaries. Clearly two basic properties of an interactive proof system are

- **Completeness:** If Peggy really knows the thing being proved, then Victor should accept her proof with probability one.

- **Soundness:** If Peggy does not know the thing being proved, then Victor should only have a small probability of actually accepting the proof.

We usually assume that Victor is a polynomially bounded party, whilst Peggy is unbounded.

The zero-knowledge property we have already noted is related to the concept of a simulation. Suppose the set of valid transcripts (produced by true protocol runs) is denoted by $\mathcal{V}$ and let the set of possible simulations be denoted by S. The security is therefore related to how much like the set $\mathcal{V}$ is the set S.

A zero-knowledge proof is said to have perfect zero-knowledge if the two sets $\mathcal{V}$ and S cannot be distinguished from each other by a computationally unbounded adversary. However, if the two sets are only indistinguishable by a computationally bounded adversary we say that the zero-knowledge proof has computational zero-knowledge.

One can use a zero-knowledge proof of possession of some secret as an identification scheme. The trouble with the above protocol for graph isomorphisms is that it is not very practical. The data structures required are very large, and the protocol needs to be repeated a large number of times before Victor is convinced that Peggy really knows the secret.

Luckily we have already seen a protocol which has better bandwidth and error properties when we discussed Schnorr signatures in Chapter 10. Suppose Peggy's secret is now the discrete logarithm x of y with respect to g in some finite abelian group G of prime order q.

The protocol for proof of knowledge now goes as follows

$$P \longrightarrow V : r = g^k \text{ for a random } k,$$
$$V \longrightarrow P : e,$$
$$P \longrightarrow V : s = k + xe \pmod{q}.$$

Victor now verifies that Peggy knows the secret discrete logarithm x by verifying that

$$r = g^s y^{-e}.$$

Let us examine this protocol in more detail; if Peggy does not know the discrete logarithm x then she will only be able to cheat with probability $1/q$, which is much better than the $1/2$ from the earlier graph isomorphism based protocol.

But does Victor learn anything from the protocol? The answer to this is no, since Victor could simulate the whole transcript in the following way:

- Generate a random value of e modulo q.

- Compute $r = g^s y^{-e}$.

- Output the transcript

$$P \longrightarrow V : r,$$
$$V \longrightarrow P : e,$$
$$P \longrightarrow V : s.$$

The above simulation will be important when we study the security of Schnorr signatures in Chapter 17.

One problem with the above zero-knowledge proofs is that they are interactive in nature:

$$P \longrightarrow V : \text{Co},$$
$$V \longrightarrow P : \text{Ch},$$
$$P \longrightarrow V : \text{Re},$$

where Co is the commitment, Ch is the challenge and Re is the response. They can easily be made non-interactive by replacing the challenge with the evaluation of a cryptographic hash function applied to the commitment,

$$\text{Ch} = H(\text{Co}).$$

The idea here is that the prover cannot fix the challenge before coming up with the commitment, since that would imply they could invert the hash function. The non-interactive protocol no longer has the zero-knowledge property, since it is not simulatable. In addition a computationally unbounded Peggy could invert the hash function, hence we need to restrict the prover to be computationally bounded. In such a situation, where we restrict to a computationally bounded prover, we say we have a zero-knowledge argument as opposed to a zero-knowledge proof.

One could also add some other data into the value which is hashed, for example a message. In this way we turn an interactive proof of knowledge into a digital signature scheme,

$$\text{Ch} = H(\text{Co}\|\text{Message}).$$

You should now be able to see how Schnorr signatures are exactly what one obtains when one uses the hash of the commitment and a message as the challenge, in the above proof of knowledge of discrete logarithms.

We end this section by giving a protocol, which is a zero-knowledge argument, which will be required when we discuss voting schemes. Consider the earlier commitment scheme given by

$$B_a(x) = h^x g^a,$$

where $G = \langle g \rangle$ is a finite abelian group of prime order q, h is an element of G whose discrete logarithm with respect to g is unknown, x is the value being committed and a is a random nonce. We are interested in the case where the value committed is restricted to be either plus or minus one, i.e. $x \in \{-1, 1\}$. It will be important in our application for the person committing to prove that their commitment is from the set $\{-1, 1\}$ without revealing what the actual value of the commitment is.

To do this we execute the following protocol.

- As well as publishing the commitment $B_a(x)$, Peggy also chooses random numbers d, r and w modulo q and then publishes α_1 and α_2 where

$$\alpha_1 = \begin{cases} g^r \, (B_a(x)h)^{-d} & \text{if } x = 1 \\ g^w & \text{if } x = -1, \end{cases}$$

$$\alpha_2 = \begin{cases} g^w & \text{if } x = 1 \\ g^r \, (B_a(x)h^{-1})^{-d} & \text{if } x = -1. \end{cases}$$

- Victor now sends a random challenge c to Peggy.

- Peggy responds by setting

$$d' = c - d,$$
$$r' = w + ad'.$$

Then Peggy returns the values

$$(d_1, d_2, r_1, r_2) = \begin{cases} (d, d', r, r') & \text{if } x = 1 \\ (d', d, r', r) & \text{if } x = -1. \end{cases}$$

- Victor then verifies that the following three equations hold

$$c = d_1 + d_2,$$
$$g^{r_1} = \alpha_1 (B_a(x)h)^{d_1},$$
$$g^{r_2} = \alpha_2 (B_a(x)h^{-1})^{d_2}.$$

To show that the above protocol works we need to show that

1. If Peggy responds honestly then Victor will verify that the above three equations hold.

2. If Peggy has not committed to plus or minus one then she will find it hard to produce a response to Victor's challenge which is correct.

3. The protocol reveals no information to any party as to the exact value of Peggy's commitment, bar that it come from the set $\{-1, 1\}$.

We leave the verification of these three points to the reader. Note that the above protocol can clearly be conducted in a non-interactive manner by defining

$$c = H\left(\alpha_1 \| \alpha_2 \| B_a(x)\right).$$

13.4 AN ELECTRONIC VOTING SYSTEM

In this section we describe an electronic voting system which utilizes some of the primitives we have been discussing in this chapter and in earlier chapters. The purpose is to show how basic cryptographic primitives can be combined into a complicated application giving real value. Our voting system will assume that we have m voters, and that there are n centres which perform the tallying. The use of a multitude of tallying centres is to allow voter anonymity and stop a few centres colluding to fix the vote. We shall assume that voters are only given a choice of one of two candidates, for example Democrat or Republican.

The voting system we shall describe will have the following seven properties.

1. Only authorized voters will be able to vote.

2. No one will be able to vote more than once.

3. No stakeholder will be able to determine how someone else has voted.

4. No one can duplicate someone else's vote.

5. The final result will be correctly computed.

6. All stakeholders will be able to verify that the result was computed correctly.

7. The protocol will work even in the presence of some bad parties.

13.4.1 System Setup

Each of the n tally centres has a public key encryption function E_i. We assume a finite abelian group G is fixed, of prime order q, and two elements $g, h \in G$ are selected for which no party (including the tally centres) know the discrete logarithm

$$h = g^x.$$

Each voter has a public key signature algorithm.

13.4.2 Vote Casting

Each of the m voters picks a vote v_j from the set $\{-1, 1\}$. The voter picks a random blinding value $a_j \in \mathbb{Z}/q\mathbb{Z}$ and publishes their vote

$$B_j = B_{a_j}(v_j),$$

using the bit commitment scheme given earlier. This vote is public to all participating parties, both tally centres and other voters. Along with the vote B_j the voter also publishes a non-interactive version of the earlier protocol to show that the vote was chosen from the set $\{-1, 1\}$. The vote and its proof are then digitally signed using the signing algorithm of the voter.

13.4.3   Vote Distribution

We now need to distribute the votes cast around the tally centres so that the final tally can be computed. Each voter employs Shamir's secret sharing scheme as follows, to share the a_j and v_j around the tallying centres: Each voter picks two random polynomials modulo q of degree $t < n$.

$$R_j(X) = v_j + r_{1,j}X + \cdots + r_{t,j}X^t,$$
$$S_j(X) = a_j + s_{1,j}X + \cdots + s_{t,j}X^t.$$

The voter computes

$$(u_{i,j}, w_{i,j}) = (R_j(i), S_j(i)) \text{ for } 1 \le i \le n.$$

The voter encrypts the pair $(u_{i,j}, w_{i,j})$ using the ith tally centre's encryption algorithm E_i. This encrypted share is sent to the relevant tally centre. The voter then publishes it commitments to the polynomial $R_j(X)$ by publicly posting

$$B_{l,j} = B_{s_{l,j}}(r_{l,j}) \text{ for } 1 \le l \le t,$$

again using the earlier commitment scheme.

13.4.4   Consistency Check

Each centre i needs to check that the values of

$$(u_{i,j}, w_{i,j})$$

it has received from voter j are consistent with the commitments made by the voter. This is done by verifying the following equation

$$B_j \prod_{l=1}^{t} B_{l,j}{}^{i^l} = B_{a_j}(v_j) \prod_{l=1}^{t} B_{s_{l,j}}(r_{l,j})^{i^l}$$

$$= h^{v_j}g^{a_j} \prod_{l=1}^{t} \left(h^{r_{l,j}}g^{s_{l,j}}\right)^{i^l}$$

$$= h^{\left(v_j + \Sigma_{l=1}^{t} r_{l,j}i^l\right)}g^{\left(a_j + \Sigma_{l=1}^{t} s_{l,j}i^l\right)}$$

$$= h^{u_{i,j}}g^{w_{i,j}}.$$

13.4.5   Tally Counting

Each of the n tally centres now computes and publicly posts its sum of the shares of the votes cast

$$T_i = \sum_{j=1}^{m} u_{i,j}$$

plus it posts its sum of shares of the blinding factors

$$A_i = \sum_{j=1}^{m} w_{i,j}.$$

Every other party, both other centres and voters can check that this has been done correctly by verifying that

$$\prod_{j=1}^{m} \left(B_j \prod_{l=1}^{t} B_{l,j}{}^{j^l} \right) = \prod_{j=1}^{m} h^{u_{i,j}} g^{w_{i,j}}$$
$$= h^{T_i} g^{A_i}.$$

Any party can compute the final tally by taking t of the values T_i and interpolating them to reveal the final tally. This is because T_i is the evaluation at i of a polynomial which shares out the sum of the votes. To see this we have

$$T_i = \sum_{j=1}^{m} u_{i,j}$$
$$= \sum_{j=1}^{m} R_j(i)$$
$$= \left(\sum_{j=1}^{m} v_j \right) + \left(\sum_{j=1}^{m} r_{1,j} \right) i + \cdots + \left(\sum_{j=1}^{m} r_{t,j} \right) i^t.$$

If the final tally is negative then the majority of people voted -1, whilst if the final tally is positive then the majority of people voted $+1$. You should now convince yourself that the above protocol has the seven properties we said it would at the beginning.

Chapter Summary

- A commitment scheme allows one party to bind themselves to a value, and then reveal it later.

- A commitment scheme needs to be both binding and concealing. Efficient schemes exist which are either information theoretically binding or information theoretically concealing, but not both.

- An interactive proof of knowledge leaks no information if the transcript could be simulated without the need of the secret information.

- Interactive proofs of knowledge can be turned into digital signature algorithms by replacing the challenge by the hash of the commitment concatenated with the message.

- Quite complicated protocols can then be built on top of our basic primitives of encryption, signatures, commitment and zero-knowledge proofs. As an example we gave an electronic voting protocol.

Further Reading

The book by Goldreich has more details on zero-knowledge proofs, whilst a good overview of this area is given in Stinson's book. The voting scheme we describe is given in the paper of Cramer et al. from EuroCrypt.

R. Cramer, M. Franklin, B. Schoenmakers and M. Yung. *Multi-authority secret-ballot elections with linear work.* In Advances in Cryptology – EuroCrypt '96, Springer-Verlag LNCS 1070, 72–83, 1996.

O. Goldreich. *Modern Cryptography, Probabilistic Proofs and Pseudo-randomness.* Springer-Verlag, 1999.

D. Stinson. *Cryptography: Theory and Practice.* CRC Press, 1995.

Review Exercises

13.1.1   What is a commitment scheme?

13.1.2   What does it mean for a commitment scheme to be binding or concealing?

13.1.3   How can a zero-knowledge protocol for proof of knowledge be used as an identification scheme?

13.1.4   In the protocol for graph isomorphism, show that if Peggy produces the same graph H in two different runs of the protocol, then Victor can determine the secret graph isomorphism.

13.1.5   How do you turn an interactive zero-knowledge identification scheme into a digital signature scheme?

Standard Exercises

13.2.1   Given a group G and four elements g_1, g_2, h_1, h_2, suppose Peggy knows that

$$\log_{g_1}(h_1) = \log_{g_2}(h_2) = x$$

and that Peggy knows x. Give a protocol for Peggy to convince Victor that not only she knows the discrete logarithm but that the two discrete logarithms are equal.

13.2.2   Show that the zero-knowledge proof of validity for the commitment $B_a(x)$ given in the text for when $x \in \{-1, 1\}$ satisfies the three requirements.

13.2.3   Show that the voting protocol has the seven desired properties. Determine how many dishonest tallying centres the protocol can cope with before our properties no longer hold.

Security Issues

Having developed the basic public key cryptographic primitives we require, we now show that this is not enough. Often weaknesses occur because the designers of a primitive do not envisage how the primitive is actually going to be used in real life. We first outline a number of attacks, and then we try and define what it means to be secure; this leads us to deduce that the primitives we have given earlier are not really secure enough.

This then leads us to look at two approaches to build secure systems. One based on pure complexity theory ends up being doomed to failure, since pure complexity theory is about worst case rather than average case hardness of problems. The second approach of provable security ends up being more suitable and has in fact turned out to be highly influential on modern cryptography. This second approach also derives from complexity theory, but is based on the relative average case hardness of problems, rather than the absolute hardness of the worst case instance.

Attacks on Public Key Schemes

Chapter Goals

- To explain Wiener's attack based on continued fractions.

- To describe lattice basis reduction algorithms and give some examples of how they are used to break cryptographic systems.

- To explain the technique of Coppersmith for finding small roots of modular polynomial equations and describe some of the cryptographic applications.

- To introduce the notions of partial key exposure and fault analysis.

14.1 INTRODUCTION

In this chapter we explain a number of attacks against naive implementations of schemes such as RSA and DSA. We shall pay particular attention to the techniques of Coppersmith, based on lattice basis reduction. What this chapter aims to do is show you that even though a cryptographic primitive such as the RSA function

$$x \longrightarrow x^e \ (\text{mod } N)$$

is a trapdoor one-way permutation, this on its own is not enough to build secure encryption systems. It all depends on how you use the RSA function. In later chapters we go on to show how one can build secure systems out of the RSA function and the other public key primitives we have met.

14.2 WIENER'S ATTACK ON RSA

We have mentioned in earlier chapters that often one uses a small public RSA exponent e so as to speed up the public key operations in RSA. Sometimes we have applications where it is more important to have a fast private key operation. Hence, one could be tempted to choose a small value of the private exponent d. Clearly this will lead to a large value of the encryption exponent e and we cannot choose too small a value for d, otherwise an attacker could find d using exhaustive search. However, it turns out that d needs to be at least the size of $\frac{1}{3}N^{1/4}$ due to an ingenious attack by Wiener which uses continued fractions.

Let $\alpha \in \mathbb{R}$, we define the following sequences, starting with $\alpha_0 = \alpha$, $p_0 = q_0 = 1$, $p_1 = a_0 a_1 + 1$ and $q_1 = a_1$,

$$a_i = \lfloor \alpha_i \rfloor,$$
$$\alpha_{i+1} = \frac{1}{\alpha_i - a_i},$$
$$p_i = a_i p_{i-1} + p_{i-2} \text{ for } i \geq 2,$$
$$q_i = a_i q_{i-1} + q_{i-2} \text{ for } i \geq 2.$$

The integers $a_0, a_1, a_2, \ldots$ are called the continued fraction expansion of α and the fractions

$$\frac{p_i}{q_i}$$

are called the convergents. The denominators of these convergents grow at an exponential rate and the convergent above is a fraction in its lowest terms since one can show

$$\gcd(p_i, q_i) = 1$$

for all values of i.

The important result is that if p and q are two integers with

$$\left| \alpha - \frac{p}{q} \right| \leq \frac{1}{2q^2}$$

then $\frac{p}{q}$ is a convergent in the continued fraction expansion of α.

Wiener's attack uses continued fractions as follows. We assume we have an RSA modulus $N = pq$ with $q < p < 2q$. In addition assume that the attacker knows that we have a small encryption exponent $d < \frac{1}{3}N^{1/4}$. The encryption exponent e is given to the attacker, where this exponent satisfies

$$ed = 1 \pmod{\Phi},$$

with

$$\Phi = \phi(N) = (p-1)(q-1).$$

We also assume $e < \Phi$, since this holds in most systems. First notice that this means there is an integer k such that

$$ed - k\Phi = 1.$$

Hence, we have

$$\left| \frac{e}{\Phi} - \frac{k}{d} \right| = \frac{1}{d\Phi}.$$

Now, $\Phi \approx N$, since

$$|N - \Phi| = |p + q - 1| < 3\sqrt{N}.$$

So we should have that $\frac{e}{N}$ is a close approximation to $\frac{k}{d}$.

$$\left| \frac{e}{N} - \frac{k}{d} \right| = \left| \frac{ed - Nk}{dN} \right|$$

$$= \left| \frac{ed - k\Phi - Nk + k\Phi}{dN} \right|$$

$$= \left| \frac{1 - k(N - \Phi))}{dN} \right|$$

$$\leq \left| \frac{3k\sqrt{N}}{dN} \right|$$

$$= \frac{3k}{d\sqrt{N}}.$$

Since $e < \Phi$, it is clear that we have $k < d$, which is itself less than $\frac{1}{3}N^{1/4}$ by assumption. Hence,

$$\left| \frac{e}{N} - \frac{k}{d} \right| < \frac{1}{2d^2}.$$

Since $\gcd(k, d) = 1$ we see that $\frac{k}{d}$ will be a fraction in its lowest terms. Hence, the fraction

$$\frac{k}{d}$$

must arise as one of the convergents of the continued fraction expansion of

$$\frac{e}{N}.$$

The correct one can be detected by simply testing which one gives a d which satisfies

$$(m^e)^d = m \pmod{N}$$

for some random value of m. The total number of convergents we will need to take is of order $O(\log N)$, hence the above gives a linear time algorithm to determine the private exponent when it is less than $\frac{1}{3}N^{1/4}$.

As an example suppose we have the RSA modulus

$$N = 9\,449\,868\,410\,449$$

with the public key

$$e = 6\,792\,605\,526\,025.$$

We are told that the decryption exponent satisfies $d < \frac{1}{3}N^{1/4} \approx 584$. To apply Wiener's attack we compute the continued fraction expansion of the number

$$\alpha = \frac{e}{N},$$

and check each denominator of a convergent to see whether it is equal to the private key d. The convergents of the continued fraction expansion of α are given by

$$1, \frac{2}{3}, \frac{3}{4}, \frac{5}{7}, \frac{18}{25}, \frac{23}{32}, \frac{409}{569}, \frac{1659}{2308}, \cdots$$

Checking each denominator in turn we see that the decryption exponent is given by

$$d = 569,$$

which is the denominator of the 7th convergent.

14.3 LATTICES AND LATTICE REDUCTION

We shall see later in this chapter that lattice basis reduction provides a crucial tool in various attacks on a number of public key systems. So we spend this section giving an overview of this important area. We first need to recap on some basic linear algebra.

Suppose $x = (x_1, x_2, \ldots, x_n)$ is an n-dimension real vector, i.e. for all i we have $x_i \in \mathbb{R}$. The set of all such vectors is denoted $\mathbb{R}^n$. On two such vectors we can define an *inner product*

$$\langle x, y \rangle = x_1 y_1 + x_2 y_2 + \cdots + x_n y_n,$$

which is a function from pairs of n-dimensional vectors to the real numbers. You probably learnt at school that two vectors x and y are orthogonal, or meet at right angles, if and only if we have

$$\langle x, y \rangle = 0.$$

Given the inner product we can then define the size, or length, of a vector by

$$\|x\| = \sqrt{\langle x, x \rangle} = \sqrt{x_1^2 + x_2^2 + \cdots + x_n^2}.$$

This length corresponds to the intuitive notion of length of vectors which we have, in particular the length satisfies a number of properties.

- $\|x\| \geq 0$, with equality if and only if x is the zero vector.

- Triangle inequality: For two n-dimensional vectors x and y

$$\|x + y\| \leq \|x\| + \|y\|.$$

- Scaling: For a vector x and a real number a

$$\|ax\| = |a| \cdot \|x\|.$$

A set of vectors $\{b_1, \ldots, b_m\}$ in $\mathbb{R}^n$ is called linearly independent if the equation

$$a_1 b_1 + \cdots + a_m b_m = 0,$$

for real numbers a_i, implies that all a_i are equal to zero. If the set is linearly independent then we must have $m \leq n$.

Suppose we have a set of m linearly independent vectors, $\{b_1, \ldots, b_m\}$. We can look at the set of all real linear combinations of these vectors,

$$V = \left\{ \sum_{i=1}^{m} a_i b_i : a_i \in \mathbb{R} \right\}.$$

This is a vector subspace of $\mathbb{R}^n$ of dimension m and the set $\{b_1, \ldots, b_m\}$ is called a basis of this subspace. If we form the matrix B consisting of the ith column of B being equal to b_i then we have

$$V = \{Ba : a \in \mathbb{R}^m\}.$$

The matrix B is called the basis matrix.

Every subspace V has a large number of possible basis matrices. Given one such basis it is often required to produce a basis with certain prescribed nice properties. Often in applications throughout science and engineering one requires a basis which is pairwise orthogonal, i.e.

$$\langle b_i, b_j \rangle = 0$$

for all $i \neq j$. Luckily there is a well-known method which takes one basis, $\{b_1, \ldots, b_m\}$ and produces a basis $\{b_1^*, \ldots, b_m^*\}$ which is pairwise orthogonal. This method is called the Gram–Schmidt process and the basis $\{b_1^*, \ldots, b_m^*\}$ produced from $\{b_1, \ldots, b_m\}$ via this process is called the Gram–Schmidt basis corresponding to $\{b_1, \ldots, b_m\}$. One computes the b_i^* from the b_i via the equations

$$\mu_{i,j} = \frac{\langle b_i, b_j^* \rangle}{\langle b_j^*, b_j^* \rangle}, \text{ for } 1 \leq j < i \leq n,$$

$$b_i^* = b_i - \sum_{j=1}^{i-1} \mu_{i,j} b_j^*.$$

For example if we have

$$b_1 = \begin{pmatrix} 2 \\ 0 \end{pmatrix} \text{ and } b_2 = \begin{pmatrix} 1 \\ 1 \end{pmatrix}$$

then we compute

$$b_1^* = b_1 = \begin{pmatrix} 2 \\ 0 \end{pmatrix},$$

$$b_2^* = b_2 - \mu_{2,1} b_1^* = \begin{pmatrix} 1 \\ 1 \end{pmatrix} - \frac{1}{2} \begin{pmatrix} 2 \\ 0 \end{pmatrix} = \begin{pmatrix} 0 \\ 1 \end{pmatrix},$$

since

$$\mu_{2,1} = \frac{\langle b_2, b_1^* \rangle}{\langle b_1^*, b_1^* \rangle} = \frac{2}{4} = \frac{1}{2}.$$

Notice how we have $\langle b_1^*, b_2^* \rangle = 0$, so the new Gram–Schmidt basis is orthogonal.

A *lattice* is like the vector subspace V above, but given a set of basis vectors $\{b_1, \ldots, b_m\}$ instead of taking the real linear combinations of the b_i we are only allowed to take the *integer* linear combinations of the b_i,

$$L = \left\{ \sum_{i=1}^{m} a_i b_i : a_i \in \mathbb{Z} \right\} = \{ Ba : a \in \mathbb{Z}^m \}.$$

The set $\{b_1, \ldots, b_m\}$ is still called the set of basis vectors and the matrix B is still called the basis matrix. To see why lattices are called lattices, consider the lattice L generated by the two vectors

$$b_1 = \begin{pmatrix} 2 \\ 0 \end{pmatrix} \text{ and } b_2 = \begin{pmatrix} 1 \\ 1 \end{pmatrix}.$$

This is the set of all vectors of the form

$$\begin{pmatrix} 2x + y \\ y \end{pmatrix},$$

where $x, y \in \mathbb{Z}$. If one plots these points in the plane then one sees that these points form a 2-dimensional lattice.

A lattice is a discrete version of a vector subspace. Since it is discrete there is a well-defined smallest element, bar the trivially small element of the zero vector of course. Many hard tasks in computing, and especially cryptography, can be reduced to trying to determine the smallest non-zero vector in a lattice. We shall see some of these applications later, but before continuing with our discussion on lattices in general we pause to note that it is generally considered to be a hard problem to determine the smallest non-zero vector in an arbitrary lattice. Later we shall see that whilst this problem is hard in general it is in fact easy in low dimension, a situation which we shall use to our advantage later on.

Let us now return to considering lattices in general. Just as with vector subspaces, given a lattice basis one could ask is there a nicer basis? Suppose B is a basis matrix for a lattice L. To obtain another basis matrix B' the only operation we are allowed to do is post-multiply B by a uni-modular integer matrix. This means we must have

$$B' = BU$$

for some integer matrix U with $\det(U) = \pm 1$. This means that the absolute value of the determinant of a basis matrix of a lattice is an invariant of the lattice, i.e. it does not depend on the choice of basis. Given a basis matrix B we call

$$\Delta = |\det(B^t B)|^{1/2}$$

the *discriminant* of the lattice. If L is a lattice of full rank, i.e. B is a square matrix, then we have

$$\Delta = |\det(B)|.$$

One could ask, given a lattice L does there exist an orthogonal basis? In general the answer to this last question is no. If one looks at the Gram–Schmidt process in more detail one sees that, even if one starts out with integer vectors, the coefficients $\mu_{i,j}$ almost always end up not being integers. Hence, whilst the Gram–Schmidt basis vectors span the same vector subspace as the original basis they do not span the same lattice as the original basis. This is because we are not allowed to make a change of basis which consists of non-integer coefficients. However, we could try and make a change of basis so that the new basis is 'close' to being orthogonal in that

$$|\mu_{i,j}| \le \frac{1}{2} \text{ for } 1 \le j < i \le n.$$

These considerations led Lenstra, Lenstra and Lovász to define the following notion of reduced basis, called an LLL reduced basis after its inventors:

Definition 14.1 *A basis* $\{b_1, \ldots, b_m\}$ *is called LLL reduced if the associated Gram–Schmidt basis* $\{b_1^*, \ldots, b_m^*\}$ *satisfies*

$$|\mu_{i,j}| \le \frac{1}{2} \text{ for } 1 \le j < i \le m, \tag{14.1}$$

$$\|b_i^*\|^2 \ge \left(\frac{3}{4} - \mu_{i,i-1}^2 \right) \|b_{i-1}^*\|^2 \text{ for } 1 < i \le m. \tag{14.2}$$

What is truly amazing about an LLL reduced basis is

- An LLL reduced basis can be computed in polynomial time, see below for the method.

- The first vector in the reduced basis is very short, in fact it is close to the shortest non-zero vector in that for all non-zero $x \in L$ we have

$$\|b_1\| \leq 2^{(m-1)/2}\|x\|.$$

- $\|b_1\| \leq 2^{m/4}\Delta^{1/m}$.

The constant $2^{(m-1)/2}$ in the second bullet point above is a worst case constant. In practice for many lattices of reasonable dimension after one applies the LLL algorithm to obtain an LLL reduced basis, the first vector in the LLL reduced basis is in fact equal to the smallest vector in the lattice.

The LLL algorithm works as follows: We keep track of a copy of the current lattice basis B and the associated Gram–Schmidt basis B^*. At any point in time we are examining a fixed column k, where we start with $k = 2$.

- If condition (14.1) does not hold for $\mu_{k,j}$ with $1 \leq j < k$ then we alter the basis B so that it does.

- If condition (14.2) does not hold for column k and column $k - 1$ we swap columns k and $k - 1$ around and decrease the value of k by one (unless k is already equal to two). If condition (14.2) holds then we increase k by one.

At some point we will obtain $k = m$ and the algorithm terminates. In fact one can show that the number of iterations where one decreases k is bounded and so one is guaranteed for the algorithm to terminate. When the algorithm terminates it clearly will produce an LLL reduced basis.

As an example we take the above example basis of a two-dimensional lattice in $\mathbb{R}^2$, we take the lattice basis

$$b_1 = \begin{pmatrix} 2 \\ 0 \end{pmatrix}, \ b_2 = \begin{pmatrix} 1 \\ 1 \end{pmatrix}.$$

The associated Gram–Schmidt basis is given by

$$b_1^* = \begin{pmatrix} 2 \\ 0 \end{pmatrix}, \ b_2^* = \begin{pmatrix} 0 \\ 1 \end{pmatrix}.$$

But this is not a basis of the associated lattice since one cannot pass from $\{b_1, b_2\}$ to $\{b_1^*, b_2^*\}$ via a unimodular transformation.

We now apply the LLL algorithm with $k = 2$ and find that the first condition (14.1) is satisfied since $\mu_{2,1} = \frac{1}{2}$. However, the second condition (14.2) is not satisfied because

$$1 = \|b_2^*\|^2 \leq \left(\frac{3}{4} - \mu_{2,1}^2\right)\|b_1^*\|^2 = \frac{1}{2} \cdot 4 = 2.$$

Hence, we need to swap the two basis vectors around and compute the corresponding Gram–Schmidt vectors. We then obtain the new lattice basis vectors

$$b_1 = \begin{pmatrix} 1 \\ 1 \end{pmatrix}, \ b_2 = \begin{pmatrix} 2 \\ 0 \end{pmatrix},$$

with the associated Gram–Schmidt basis vectors

$$b_1^* = \begin{pmatrix} 1 \\ 1 \end{pmatrix}, \ b_2^* = \begin{pmatrix} 1 \\ -1 \end{pmatrix}.$$

We now go back to the first condition again. This time we see that we have $\mu_{2,1} = 1$ which violates the first condition. To correct this we subtract one lot of b_1 from the vector b_2 so as to obtain $\mu_{2,1} = 0$. We now find the lattice basis is given by

$$b_1 = \begin{pmatrix} 1 \\ 1 \end{pmatrix}, \ b_2 = \begin{pmatrix} 1 \\ -1 \end{pmatrix}$$

and the Gram–Schmidt basis is then identical to this lattice basis, in that

$$b_1^* = \begin{pmatrix} 1 \\ 1 \end{pmatrix}, \ b_2^* = \begin{pmatrix} 1 \\ -1 \end{pmatrix}.$$

Now we are left to check the second condition again, we find

$$2 = \|b_2^*\|^2 \geq \left(\frac{3}{4} - \mu_{2,1}^2 \right) \|b_1^*\|^2 = \frac{3}{4} \cdot 2 = \frac{3}{2}.$$

Hence, both conditions are satisfied and we conclude that

$$b_1 = \begin{pmatrix} 1 \\ 1 \end{pmatrix}, \ b_2 = \begin{pmatrix} 1 \\ -1 \end{pmatrix}$$

is a reduced basis for the lattice L.

We end this introduction to lattices by noticing that there is a link between continued fractions and lattice reduction. Applying the continued fraction algorithm to a real number α is used to find values of p and q, with q not too large, so that

$$|q\alpha - p|$$

is small. A similar effect can be achieved using lattices by applying the LLL algorithm to the lattice generated by the columns of the matrix

$$\begin{pmatrix} 1 & 0 \\ C\alpha & -C \end{pmatrix},$$

for some constant C. This is because the lattice L contains the 'short' vector

$$\begin{pmatrix} q \\ C(q\alpha - p) \end{pmatrix} = \begin{pmatrix} 1 & 0 \\ C\alpha & -C \end{pmatrix} \cdot \begin{pmatrix} q \\ p \end{pmatrix}.$$

In some sense we therefore can consider the LLL algorithm to be a multi-dimensional generalization of the continued fraction algorithm.

14.4 LATTICE BASED ATTACKS ON RSA

In this section we examine how lattices can be used to attack certain systems, when some other side information is known. This is analogous to Wiener's attack above where one could break RSA given the side information that the decryption exponent was exceedingly short. Much of the work in this area is derived from initial work of Coppersmith, which was later simplified by Howgrave-Graham.

The basic technique is a method to solve the following problem: Given a polynomial

$$f(x) = f_0 + f_1 x + \cdots + f_{d-1} x^{d-1} + x^d$$

over the integers of degree d and the side information that there exists a root x_0 modulo N which is small, say $|x_0| < N^{1/d}$, can one efficiently find the small root x_0? The answer is surprisingly yes, and this leads to a number of interesting cryptographic consequences.

The basic idea is to find a polynomial $h(x) \in \mathbb{Z}[x]$ which has the same root modulo N as the target polynomial $f(x)$ does. This new polynomial $h(x)$ should be small in the sense that the norm of its coefficients,

$$\|h\|^2 = \sum_{i=0}^{\deg(h)} h_i^2$$

should be small. If such an $h(x)$ can be found then we can appeal to the following lemma.

Lemma 14.2 *Let $h(x) \in \mathbb{Z}[x]$ denote a polynomial of degree at most n and let X and N be a positive integers. Suppose*

$$\|h(xX)\| < N/\sqrt{n}$$

then if $|x_0| < X$ satisfies

$$h(x_0) = 0 \pmod{N}$$

then $h(x_0) = 0$ over the integers and not just modulo N.

Now we return to our original polynomial $f(x)$ of degree d and notice that if

$$f(x_0) = 0 \pmod{N}$$

then we also have

$$f(x_0)^k = 0 \pmod{N^k}.$$

Moreover, if we set, for some given value of m,

$$g_{u,v}(x) = N^{m-v} x^u f(x)^v$$

then

$$g_{u,v}(x_0) = 0 \pmod{N^m}$$

for all $0 \le u < d$ and $0 \le v \le m$. We then fix m and try to find $a_{u,v} \in \mathbb{Z}$ so that

$$h(x) = \sum_{u \ge 0} \sum_{v=0}^{m} a_{u,v} g_{u,v}(x)$$

satisfies the conditions of the above lemma.

In other words we wish to find integer values of $a_{u,v}$ so that the resulting polynomial h satisfies

$$\|h(xX)\| \leq N^m/\sqrt{d(m+1)},$$

with

$$h(xX) = \sum_{u \geq 0} \sum_{v=0}^{m} a_{u,v} g_{u,v}(xX).$$

This is a minimization problem which can be solved using lattice basis reduction, as we shall now show in a simple example.

Suppose our polynomial $f(x)$ is given by

$$f(x) = x^2 + ax + b$$

and we wish to find an x_0 such that

$$f(x_0) = 0 \pmod{N}.$$

We set $m = 2$ in the above construction and compute

$$g_{0,0}(xX) = N^2,$$
$$g_{1,0}(xX) = XN^2x,$$
$$g_{0,1}(xX) = bN + aXNx + NX^2x^2,$$
$$g_{1,1}(xX) = bNXx + aNX^2x^2 + NX^3x^3,$$
$$g_{0,2}(xX) = b^2 + 2baXx + (a^2 + 2b)X^2x^2 + 2aX^3x^3 + X^4x^4,$$
$$g_{1,2}(xX) = b^2Xx + 2baX^2x^2 + (a^2 + 2b)X^3x^3 + 2aX^4x^4 + X^5x^5.$$

We are asking for a linear combination of the above six polynomials such that the resulting polynomial has small coefficients. Hence we are led to look for small vectors in the lattice generated by the columns of the following matrix, where each column represents one of the polynomials above and each row represents a power of x,

$$A = \begin{pmatrix} N^2 & 0 & bN & 0 & b^2 & 0 \\ 0 & XN^2 & aXN & bNX & 2abX & Xb^2 \\ 0 & 0 & NX^2 & aNX^2 & (a^2+2b)X^2 & 2abX^2 \\ 0 & 0 & 0 & NX^3 & 2aX^3 & (a^2+2b)X^3 \\ 0 & 0 & 0 & 0 & X^4 & 2aX^4 \\ 0 & 0 & 0 & 0 & 0 & X^5 \end{pmatrix}.$$

This matrix has determinant equal to

$$\det(A) = N^6X^{15},$$

and so applying the LLL algorithm to this matrix we obtain a new lattice basis B. The first vector b_1 in B will satisfy

$$\|b_1\| \leq 2^{6/4}\det(A)^{1/6} = 2^{3/2}NX^{5/2}.$$

So if we form the polynomial

$$h(x) = b_1^{(1)} g_{0,0}(x) + b_1^{(2)} g_{1,0}(x) + \cdots + b_1^{(6)} g_{1,2}(x)$$

then we will have

$$\|h(xX)\| \leq 2^{3/2} N X^{5/2}.$$

To apply Lemma 14.2 we will require that

$$2^{3/2} N X^{5/2} < N^2/\sqrt{6}.$$

Hence by determining an integer root of $h(x)$ we will determine the small root x_0 of $f(x)$ modulo N assuming that

$$|x_0| \leq X = \frac{N^{2/5}}{48^{1/5}}.$$

In particular this will work when $|x_0| \leq N^{0.39}$.

A similar technique can be applied to any polynomial of degree d so as to obtain

Theorem 14.3 (Coppersmith) *Let $f \in \mathbb{Z}[x]$ be a monic polynomial of degree d and N an integer. If there is some root x_0 of f modulo N such that $|x_0| \leq X = N^{1/d-\epsilon}$ then one can find x_0 in time a polynomial in $\log N$ and $1/\epsilon$, for fixed values of d.*

Similar considerations apply to polynomials in two variables, the analogue of Lemma 14.2 becomes:

Lemma 14.4 *Let $h(x,y) \in \mathbb{Z}[x,y]$ denote a sum of at most w monomials and suppose*

- *$h(x_0, y_0) = 0 \pmod{N^e}$ for some positive integers N and e where the integers x_0 and y_0 satisfy $|x_0| < X$ and $|y_0| < Y$,*

- *$\|h(xX, yY)\| < N^e/\sqrt{w}$.*

Then $h(x_0, y_0) = 0$ holds over the integers.

However, the analogue of Theorem 14.3 then becomes only a heuristic result.

We now use Theorem 14.3 and its generalizations to describe a number of attacks against RSA.

14.4.1   Hastad's Attack

In Chapter 7 we saw the following attack on the RSA system: Given three public keys (N_i, e_i) all with the same encryption exponent $e_i = 3$, if a user sent the same message to all three public keys then an adversary could recover the plaintext using the Chinese Remainder Theorem.

Now suppose that we protect against this attack by insisting that before encrypting a message m we first pad with some user-specific data. For example the ciphertext becomes, for user i,

$$c_i = (i \cdot 2^h + m)^3 \pmod{N_i}.$$

However, one can still break this system using an attack due to Hastad. Hastad's attack is related to Coppersmith's Theorem since we can interpret the attack scenario, generalized to k users and public encryption exponent e, as being given k polynomials of degree e

$$g_i(x) = (i \cdot 2^h + x)^e - c_i, \ 1 \le i \le k.$$

Then given that there is an m such that

$$g_i(m) = 0 \ (\text{mod } N_i),$$

the goal is to recover m. We can assume that m is smaller than any one of the moduli N_i. Setting

$$N = N_1 N_2 \cdots N_k$$

and using the Chinese Remainder Theorem we can find t_i so that

$$g(x) = \sum_{i=1}^{k} t_i g_i(x)$$

and

$$g(m) = 0 \ (\text{mod } N).$$

Then, since g has degree e and is monic, using Theorem 14.3 we can recover m in polynomial time, as long as we have at least as many ciphertexts as the encryption exponent i.e. $k > e$, since

$$m < \min_i N_i < N^{1/k} < N^{1/e}.$$

14.4.2 Franklin–Reiter Attack and Coppersmith's Generalization

Now suppose we have one RSA public key (N, e) owned by Alice. The Franklin–Reiter attack applies to the following situation: Bob wishes to send two related messages m_1 and m_2 to Alice, where the relation is given by the public polynomial

$$m_2 = f(m_1) \ (\text{mod } N).$$

Given c_1 and c_2 an attacker has a good chance of determining m_1 and m_2 for any small encryption exponent e. The attack is particularly simple when

$$f = ax + b \text{ and } e = 3,$$

with a and b fixed and given to the attacker. The attacker knows that m_2 is a root, modulo N, of the two polynomials

$$g_1(x) = x^3 - c_2,$$
$$g_2(x) = f(x)^3 - c_1.$$

So the linear factor $x - m_2$ divides both $g_1(x)$ and $g_2(x)$.

We now form the greatest common divisor of $g_1(x)$ and $g_2(x)$. Strictly speaking this is not possible in general since $\mathbb{Z}/N\mathbb{Z}[x]$ is not a Euclidean ring, but if the Euclidean algorithm breaks down then we would find a factor of N and so be able to find Alice's private key in any case. One can show that when

$$f = ax + b \text{ and } e = 3,$$

the resulting gcd, when it exists, must always be the linear factor $x - m_2$, and so the attacker can always find m_2 and then m_1.

Coppersmith extended the attack of Franklin and Reiter, in a way which also extends the padding result from Hastad's attack. Suppose before sending a message m we pad it with some random data. So for example if N is an n-bit RSA modulus and m is a k-bit message then we could append $n - k$ random bits to either the top or bottom of the message. Say

$$m' = 2^{n-k}m + r$$

where r is some, per message, random number of length $n - k$. Coppersmith showed that this padding is insecure.

Suppose Bob sends the same message to Alice twice, i.e. we have ciphertexts c_1 and c_2 corresponding to the messages

$$m_1 = 2^{n-k}m + r_1,$$
$$m_2 = 2^{n-k}m + r_2,$$

where r_1, r_2 are two different random $(n-k)$-bit numbers. The attacker sets $y_0 = r_2 - r_1$ and is led to solve the simultaneous equations

$$g_1(x, y) = x^e - c_1,$$
$$g_2(x, y) = (x + y)^e - c_2.$$

The attacker forms the resultant $h(y)$ of $g_1(x, y)$ and $g_2(x, y)$ with respect to x. Now $y_0 = r_2 - r_1$ is a small root of the polynomial $h(y)$, which has degree e^2. Using Coppersmith's Theorem 14.3 the attacker recovers $r_2 - r_1$ and then recovers m_2 using the method of the Franklin–Reiter attack.

Whilst the above trivial padding scheme is therefore insecure, one can find secure padding schemes for the RSA encryption algorithm. We shall return to padding schemes for RSA in Chapter 17.

14.4.3 Extension to Wiener's Attack

Recall that Wiener's attack on RSA applied when it was known that the private decryption exponent d was small, in the sense that

$$d \leq \frac{1}{3}N^{1/4}.$$

Boneh and Durfee, using an analogue of the bivariate case of Coppersmith's Theorem 14.3, extended Wiener's attack to the case where

$$d \leq N^{0.292},$$

using a heuristic algorithm. We do not go into the details but show how Boneh and Durfee proceed to a problem known as the small inverse problem.

Suppose we have an RSA modulus N, with encryption exponent e and decryption exponent d. By definition there is an integer k such that

$$ed + \frac{k\Phi}{2} = 1,$$

where $\Phi = \phi(N)$. Expanding the definition of Φ we find

$$ed + k\left(\frac{N+1}{2} - \frac{p+q}{2}\right) = 1.$$

We set

$$s = -\frac{p+q}{2},$$
$$A = \frac{N+1}{2}.$$

Then finding d, where d is small say $d < N^\delta$, is equivalent to finding the two small solutions k and s to the following congruence

$$f(k,s) = k(A+s) = 1 \pmod{e}.$$

To see that k and s are small relative to the modulus e for the above equation, notice that $e \approx N$ since d is small, and so

$$|s| < 2N^{0.5} \approx e^{0.5} \text{ and } |k| < \frac{2de}{\Phi} \le \frac{3de}{N} \approx e^\delta.$$

We can interpret this problem as finding an integer which is close to A whose inverse is small modulo e. This is called the small inverse problem. Boneh and Durfee show that this problem has a solution when $\delta \le 0.292$, hence extending the result of Wiener's attack. This is done by applying the multivariate analogue of Coppersmith's method to the polynomial $f(k,s)$.

14.5 PARTIAL KEY EXPOSURE ATTACKS

Partial key exposure is related to the following question: Suppose in some crypto-graphic scheme the attacker recovers a certain set of bits of the private key, can the attacker use this to recover the whole private key? In other words, does partial exposure of the key result in a total break of the system? We shall present a number of RSA examples, however these are not the only ones. There are a number of results related to partial key exposure which relate to other schemes such as DSA or symmetric key based systems.

14.5.1 Partial Exposure of the MSBs of the RSA Decryption Exponent

Somewhat surprisingly for RSA, in the more common case of using a small public exponent e, one can trivially recover half of the most significant bits of the private key d as follows. Recall there is a value of k such that $0 < k < e$ with

$$ed - k(N - (p+q) + 1) = 1.$$

Now suppose for each possible value of i, $0 < i \le e$, the attacker computes

$$d_i = \lfloor (iN+1)/e \rfloor.$$

Then we have

$$|d_k - d| \le k(p + q)/e \le 3k\sqrt{N}/e < 3\sqrt{N}.$$

Hence, d_k is a good approximation for the actual value of d.

Now it is clear that k must be even so when $e = 3$ we must have $k = 2$ and so d_2 reveals half of the most significant bits of d. Unluckily for the attack, and luckily for the user, there is no known way to recover the rest of d given only the most significant bits.

14.5.2   Partial Exposure of some bits of the RSA Prime Factors

Suppose our n-bit RSA modulus N is given by $p \cdot q$, with $p \approx q$ and that the attacker has found the $n/4$ least significant bits of p. Recall that p is only around $n/2$-bits long in any case, so this means the attacker is given the lower half of all the bits making up p. We write

$$p = x_0 2^{n/4} + p_0.$$

We then have, writing $q = y_0 2^{n/4} + q_0$,

$$N = p_0 q_0 \pmod{2^{n/4}}.$$

Hence, we can determine the value of q_0. We now write down the polynomial

$$\begin{aligned}
p(x, y) &= (p_0 + 2^{n/4}x)(q_0 + 2^{n/4}y) \\
&= p_0 q_0 + 2^{n/4}(p_0 y + q_0 x) + 2^{n/2} xy.
\end{aligned}$$

Now $p(x, y)$ is a bivariate polynomial of degree two which has known small solution modulo N, namely (x_0, y_0) where $0 < x_0, y_0 \le 2^{n/4} \approx N^{1/4}$. Hence, using the heuristic bivariate extension of Coppersmith's Theorem 14.3, we can recover x_0 and y_0 in polynomial time and so factor the modulo N.

A similar attack applies when the attacker knows the $n/4$ most significant bits of p.

14.5.3   Partial Exposure of the LSBs of the RSA Decryption Exponent

We now suppose we are given, for small public exponent e, a quarter of the least significant bits of the private exponent d. That is we have d_0 where

$$d = d_0 + 2^{n/4} x_0$$

where $0 \le x_0 \le 2^{3n/4}$. Recall there is an even value of k with $0 < k < e$ such that

$$ed - k(N - (p + q) + 1) = 1.$$

We then have, since $N = pq$,

$$edp - kp(N - p + 1) + kN = p.$$

If we set $p_0 = p \pmod{2^{n/4}}$ then we have the equation

$$ed_0 p_0 - kp_0(N - p_0 + 1) + kN - p_0 = 0 \pmod{2^{n/4}}. \tag{14.3}$$

This gives us the following algorithm to recover the whole of d. For each even value of k less than e we solve Equation (14.3) modulo $2^{n/4}$ for p_0. Each value of k will result in $O(\frac{n}{4})$ possible values for p_0. Using each of these values of p_0 in turn, we apply the previous technique for factoring N from Section 14.5.2. One such value of p_0 will be the correct value of $p \pmod{2^{n/4}}$ and so the above factorization algorithm will work and we can recover the value of d.

14.6 FAULT ANALYSIS

An interesting class of attacks results from trying to induce faults within a cryptographic system. We shall describe this area in relation to the RSA signature algorithm but similar attacks can be mounted on other cryptographic algorithms, both public and secret key.

Imagine we have a hardware implementation of RSA, in a smart card say. On input of some message m the chip will sign the message for us, using some internal RSA private key. The attacker wishes to determine the private key hidden within the smart card. To do this the attacker can try to make the card perform some of the calculation incorrectly, by either altering the card's environment by heating or cooling it or by damaging the circuitry of the card in some way.

An interesting case is when the card uses the Chinese Remainder Theorem to perform the signing operation, to increase efficiency, as explained in Chapter 11. The card first computes the hash of the message

$$h = H(m).$$

Then the card computes

$$s_p = h^{d_p} \pmod{p},$$
$$s_q = h^{d_q} \pmod{q},$$

where $d_p = d \pmod{p-1}$ and $d_q = d \pmod{q-1}$. The final signature is produced by the card from s_p and s_q via the Chinese Remainder Theorem using

- $u = (s_q - s_p)T \pmod{q}$,

- $s = s_p + up$,

where $T = p^{-1} \pmod{q}$.

Now suppose that the attacker can introduce a fault into the computation so that s_p is computed incorrectly. The attacker will then obtain a value of s such that

$$s^e \neq h \pmod{p},$$
$$s^e = h \pmod{q}.$$

Hence, by computing

$$q = \gcd(s^e - h, N)$$

we can factor the modulus.

Chapter Summary

- Using a small private decryption exponent in RSA is not a good idea due to Wiener's attack.

- Lattices are discrete analogues of vector spaces, as such they have a shortest non-zero vector.

- Lattice basis reduction often allows us to find the shortest non-zero vector in a given lattice.

- Coppersmith's Theorem allows us to solve a modular polynomial equation when the solution is known to be small. The method works by building a lattice depending on the polynomial and then applying lattice basis reduction to obtain short vectors within this lattice.

- The Hastad and Franklin–Reiter attacks imply that one needs to be careful when designing padding schemes for RSA.

- Using Coppersmith's Theorem one can show that the revealing of a proportion of the bits of either p, q or d in RSA can lead to a complete break of the system.

Further Reading

The main paper on Coppersmith's lattice based attacks on RSA is by Coppersmith himself. Coppersmith's approach has itself been simplified somewhat in the paper of Howgrave-Graham. Our treatment of attacks on RSA in this chapter has closely followed the survey article by Boneh. A complete survey of lattice based methods in cryptography is given in the survey article by Nguyen and Stern.

D. Boneh. *Twenty years of attacks on the RSA cryptosystem.* Notices of the American Mathematical Society (AMS), **46**, 203–213, 1999.

D. Coppersmith. *Small solutions to polynomial equations, and low exponent RSA vulnerabilities.* J. Cryptology, **10**, 233–260, 1997.

N. Howgrave-Graham. *Finding small solutions of univariate modular equations revisited.* In Cryptography and Coding, Springer-Verlag LNCS 1355, 131–142, 1997.

P. Nguyen and J. Stern. *The two faces of lattices in cryptology.* In CALC '01, Springer-Verlag LNCS 2146, 146–180, 2001.

Review Exercises

14.1.1   How does one compute the continued fraction expansion of a real number α?

14.1.2   In Wiener's attack on small private exponent RSA, what number does one compute the continued fraction expansion of?

14.1.3   What is a lattice?

14.1.4   What do you think is the most important property of an LLL reduced lattice basis, from the point of view of a cryptographer?

14.1.5   Suppose I have the equation $f(x_0) = 0 \pmod N$ where f is a polynomial of degree d. How small must x_0 be before Coppersmith's method will find it in polynomial time?

14.1.6   Explain what is meant by Hastad's attack against RSA.

Programming Exercises

14.2.1   Implement the various attacks in this chapter, such as Wiener's attack and the attacks which make use of LLL. Are there any situations where the heuristic arguments in the text break down or situations where the attacks are more successful than our theoretical analysis would lead you to believe?

Standard Exercises

14.3.1   Show that for an LLL reduced basis of an n-dimensional lattice L, if x is a non-zero vector in L then

$$\|b_1\| \le 2^{(n-1)/2}\|x\|.$$

14.3.2   Formally show that the LLL algorithm described in the text actually terminates in polynomial time for a lattice whose basis vectors consist entirely of integers.

14.3.3   Prove Lemma 14.2.

14.3.4   Show in the Franklin–Reiter attack that if $f = ax + b$ and $e = 3$ the resulting gcd, when it exists, is always linear.

14.3.5   Show how to factor an RSA modulus when you are given the bits of the most significant half of one of the prime factors.

CHAPTER 15

Definitions of Security

Chapter Goals

- To explain the various notions of security of encryption schemes, especially semantic security and indistinguishability of encryptions.

- To explain the various attack notions, in particular the adaptive chosen ciphertext attack.

- To show how the concept of non-malleability and adaptive chosen ciphertext attacks are related.

- To examine the RSA and ElGamal encryption schemes in terms of these definitions of security and attacks.

- To explain notions related to the security of signature schemes.

- To show that naive (unhashed) RSA signatures are not secure due to the homo-morphic property.

15.1 SECURITY OF ENCRYPTION

Up to now we have not looked much at how cryptographic primitives are turned into real protocols and systems. In designing cryptographic systems we need to understand exactly what security properties are guaranteed by the primitives and how the schemes can be made secure against all possible attacks.

Essentially, a cryptographic primitive is something like the raw RSA function or the modular exponentiation operation. Both are one-way functions, the RSA function being a trap-door one-way function and modular exponentiation being a one-way function. One needs to be careful how one uses these primitives in a real scheme. For example the raw RSA function is completely deterministic and so if used naively will always result in identical ciphertexts if you encrypt the same plaintext twice under the same key. This is a bad idea as we saw in Chapters 7 and 14. But there is a more fundamental reason to avoid deterministic public key encryption algorithms; to see why you need to consider what it means for an encryption scheme to be secure.

There are three things we need to define

- the goal of the adversary,
- the types of attack allowed,
- the computational model.

Our discussion will be in the context of public key encryption, but similar notions hold for symmetric ciphers.

15.1.1 Notions of Security

There are essentially three notions of security which we need to understand,

- perfect security,
- semantic security,
- polynomial security.

We shall discuss each of these notions in turn. These notions are far stronger than the simple notion of either recovering the private key or determining the plaintext which we have considered previously.

15.1.1.1 Perfect Security: Recall that a scheme is said to have perfect security, or to have information theoretic security, if an adversary with infinite computing power can learn nothing about the plaintext given the ciphertext. Shannon's Theorem, Theorem 4.4, essentially states that this means that the key is as long as the message, and the same key is never used twice.

The problem is that such systems cannot exist in the public key model, since the encryption key is assumed to be used for many messages and is usually assumed to be very short.

15.1.1.2 Semantic Security: Semantic security is like perfect security but we only allow an adversary with polynomially bounded computing power. Formally, for all probability distributions on the message space whatever an adversary can compute in polynomial time about the plaintext given the ciphertext, they should also be able to compute without the ciphertext. In other words, having the ciphertext does not help finding anything about the message.

The following is a simplified formal definition: Suppose that the information we wish to compute on the message space is a single bit, i.e. there is some function

$$g : M \longrightarrow \{0, 1\}.$$

We assume that over the whole message space we have

$$\Pr\left(g(m) = 1\right) = \Pr\left(g(m) = 0\right) = \frac{1}{2},$$

and that the plaintexts and ciphertexts are all of the same length (so for example the length of the ciphertext reveals nothing about the underlying plaintext).

The adversary we shall model as an algorithm S which on input of a public key y and a ciphertext c, encrypted under the private key x corresponding to y, will attempt to produce an evaluation of the function g on the plaintext for which c is the associated ciphertext. The output of S will therefore be a single bit corresponding to the value of g.

The adversary is deemed to be successful if the probability of it being correct is greater than one half. Clearly the adversary could always just guess the bit without seeing this ciphertext, hence we are saying a successful adversary is one which can do better after seeing the ciphertext. We therefore define the advantage of the adversary S as

$$\text{Adv}_S = \left| \Pr\left(S(c, y) = g(d_x(c))\right) - \frac{1}{2} \right|,$$

where d_x denotes decryption under the private key x associated to the public key y. A scheme is then said to be semantically secure if we have

$$\text{Adv}_S \leq \frac{1}{p(k)},$$

for all adversaries S, all functions g and all polynomial functions $p(k)$ when the security parameter k is sufficiently large.

15.1.1.3 Polynomial Security:
The trouble with the definition of semantic security is that it is hard to show that a given encryption scheme has this property. Polynomial security, sometimes called indistinguishability of encryptions, is a much easier property to show that a given system has. Luckily, we will show that if a system has polynomial security then it has semantic security. Hence, to show a system is semantically secure all we need do is show that it is polynomially secure.

A system is said to have indistinguishable encryptions, or to have polynomial security, if no adversary can win the following game with probability greater than one half. The adversary A is given a public key encryption function f_y corresponding to some public key y. The adversary now runs in two stages:

- **Find**: In the find stage the adversary produces two plaintext messages m_0 and m_1.

- **Guess**: The adversary is now given the encryption c_b of one of the plaintexts m_b for some secret hidden bit b. The goal of the adversary is to now guess the value of b with probability greater than one half.

Note, this means that an encryption function which is polynomially secure must be probabilistic in nature, otherwise in the guess stage the adversary can compute

$$c_1 = f_y(m_1)$$

and test whether this is equal to c_b or not. The advantage of an adversary A is therefore defined to be

$$\text{Adv}_A = \left| \Pr\left(A(\textbf{guess}, c_b, y, m_0, m_1) = b\right) - \frac{1}{2} \right|,$$

since the adversary A could always simply guess the hidden bit b. A scheme is then said to be polynomially secure if we have

$$\text{Adv}_A \leq \frac{1}{p(k)},$$

for all adversaries A and all polynomials p and sufficiently large k.

15.1.2   Notions of Attacks

At this stage we need to introduce various attack models. There are three basic attack models:

- passive attack, sometimes called a chosen plaintext attack, often denoted CPA,

- chosen ciphertext attack, often denoted CCA1,

- adaptive chosen ciphertext attack, often denoted CCA2.

15.1.2.1   Passive Attack: A passive attack is a very weak form of attack.   The adversary Eve is allowed to look at various encrypted messages. She also has access to a (black) box which performs encryption but not decryption. Hence this models a simple attack on a public key system, since in a public key system everyone, including the attacker, has access to the encryption function.

15.1.2.2   Chosen Ciphertext Attack: A chosen ciphertext attack (CCA1) is often called a lunch-time attack and represents a slightly stronger form of attack. Eve is now given access to a black box which performs decryptions. Eve can ask the box to decrypt a polynomial number of ciphertexts of her choosing, at lunch-time whilst the real user of the box is away at lunch. After this, at some point in the afternoon, she is given a target ciphertext and asked to decrypt this, or find information about the underlying plaintext, on her own, without using the box.

In the context of our game of polynomial security given above, this means that the adversary can query the decryption box during the **find** stage of the algorithm but not the **guess** stage.

15.1.2.3   Adaptive Chosen Ciphertext Attack: An adaptive chosen ciphertext attack (CCA2) is a very strong form of attack. Eve is now allowed to ask the decryption box to decrypt any ciphertext of her choosing, bar the target ciphertext. It is widely regarded that any new proposed public key encryption algorithm should meet the requirements of polynomial security under an adaptive chosen ciphertext attack.

Hence, in our game of polynomial security, the adversary can in both the **find** and **guess** stages ask the decryption box to decrypt any ciphertext, except they are not allowed to ask the box to decrypt the challenge c_b, since otherwise the game would be far too easy.

The following definition is the accepted definition of what it means for a public encryption scheme to be secure, a similar notion applies to symmetric key systems.

Definition 15.1 *A public key encryption algorithm is said to be secure if it is* semantically secure *against an adaptive chosen ciphertext attack.*

However, usually it is easier to show security under the following definition.

Definition 15.2 *A public key encryption algorithm is said to be secure if it is* polynomially secure *against an adaptive chosen ciphertext attack.*

These two notions are however related. For example, we shall now show the following important result:

Theorem 15.3 *For a passive adversary, a system which is polynomially secure must necessarily be semantically secure.*

Proof
We proceed by contradiction. Assume that there is an encryption algorithm which is not semantically secure, i.e. there is an algorithm S with

$$\text{Adv}_S > \frac{1}{p(k)}$$

for a polynomial $p(k)$ and all sufficiently large values of k. We shall show that it is then not polynomial secure either. To do this we construct an adversary A against the polynomial security of the scheme, which uses the adversary S against the semantic security as an oracle.

The **find** stage of adversary A outputs two messages m_0 and m_1 such that

$$g(m_0) \neq g(m_1).$$

Such messages will be easy to find given our earlier simplified formal definition of semantic security, since the output of g is equiprobable over the whole message space.

The adversary A is then given an encryption c_b of one of these and is asked to determine b. In the **guess** stage the adversary passes the ciphertext c_b to the oracle S. The oracle S returns with its best guess as to the value of

$$g(m_b).$$

The adversary A can now compare this value with that of $g(m_0)$ and $g(m_1)$ and hence output a guess as to what the value of b is.

Clearly if S is successful in breaking the semantic security of the scheme, then A will be successful in breaking the polynomial security. So

$$\Pr\left(A(\textbf{guess}, c_b, y, m_0, m_1) = b\right) = \Pr\left(S(c, y) = g(d_x(c))\right).$$

So

$$\text{Adv}_A = \text{Adv}_S > \frac{1}{p(k)}.$$

Hence, polynomial security must imply semantic security.

$$\text{Q.E.D.}$$

Note, with a more complicated definition of semantic security it can be shown that for passive adversaries the notions of semantic and polynomial security are equivalent.

15.1.3   Other Security Concepts

15.1.3.1   Non-Malleability: An encryption scheme is said to be non-malleable if given a plaintext/ciphertext pair

$$(M, C)$$

it is impossible to determine a valid ciphertext C' on a 'related' message M', without knowing M. Note, that 'related' is defined vaguely here on purpose. Non-malleability is important due to the following result, for which we only give an informal proof based on our vague definition of non-malleability. A formal proof can however be given, with an associated formal definition of non-malleability.

Lemma 15.4 *A malleable encryption scheme is not secure against an adaptive chosen ciphertext attack.*

Proof
Suppose the scheme is malleable, then given the target ciphertext c_b we alter it to a related one, namely c_b'. The relation should be such that there is also a known relationship between m_b' and m_b. Then the adversary can ask the decryption oracle to decrypt c_b' to reveal m_b', an oracle query which is allowed in our prior game. Then from m_b' the adversary can recover m_b.

Q.E.D.

Later we shall show that almost all the public key schemes we have seen so far are malleable. However, it is known that a scheme which is non-malleable against a CCA2 attack is also polynomially secure against a CCA2 attack and viceversa. Hence, a non-malleable encryption scheme will meet our previous definition of security of a public key encryption scheme.

15.1.3.2 Plaintext Aware: If a scheme is plaintext aware then we have a very strong notion of security. A scheme is called plaintext aware if it is computationally difficult to construct a valid ciphertext without being given the corresponding plaintext to start with. Hence, plaintext awareness implies one cannot mount a CCA attack. Since to write down a ciphertext requires you to know the plaintext, so why would you ask the decryption oracle to decrypt the ciphertext?

Plaintext awareness has only been defined within the context of the *random oracle model* of computation. In this model one assumes that idealized hash functions exist; these are one-way functions which:

- take polynomial time to evaluate,

- to an observer cannot be distinguished from random functions.

The random oracle model occurs in a number of proofs of security. These proofs tell us nothing about the real-world security of the scheme under consideration. But they do show that any real-world attack must make use of the actual definition of the hash function deployed. The usual state of affairs is that we prove a protocol secure in the random oracle model and then make a real-life protocol by replacing the random oracle with a hash function like SHA-1 or MD5.

15.2 SECURITY OF ACTUAL ENCRYPTION ALGORITHMS

In this section we show that neither the RSA or ElGamal public key encryption algorithms meet our stringent goals of semantic security against an adaptive chosen ciphertext attack. This should surprise you since we have claimed that RSA is one of the most used and important algorithms around. But we have not shown you how RSA is actually used in practice. So far we have only given the simple mathematical description of the algorithms. As we progress onwards the mathematics of public key encryption gets left behind and becomes replaced by cryptographic engineering.

To make the discussion easier we will use the fact that semantic security and indistinguishability of encryptions (polynomial security) are equivalent.

15.2.1 RSA

Lemma 15.5 *RSA is not polynomially secure.*

Proof
Suppose the attacker knows that the user only encrypts one of two messages

$$m_1 \text{ or } m_2.$$

These could be buy or sell, yes or no etc. The attacker is assumed to know the user's public key, namely N and e. On receiving the ciphertext c the attacker wants to determine whether the corresponding plaintext m was equal to m_1 or m_2. All the adversary need do is compute

$$c' = m_1^e \pmod{N}.$$

Then

- if $c' = c$ then the attacker knows that $m = m_1$,

- if $c' \neq c$ then the attacker knows that $m = m_2$.

Q.E.D.

The problem is that the attacker has access to the encryption function, it is a public key scheme after all.

Now suppose that decryption was not injective, that each plaintext could correspond to a large number of ciphertexts. The exact ciphertext produced being determined by the encryption function at runtime. In other words the encryption algorithm should be probabilistic in nature and not just deterministic. Later we shall see a variant of RSA which has this property and so the attack described in the above proof does not apply. But using a deterministic encryption function is not the only problem with RSA.

Essentially RSA is malleable due to the homomorphic property.

Definition 15.6 (Homomorphic Property) *Given the encryption of m_1 and m_2 we can determine the encryption of $m_1 \cdot m_2$, without knowing m_1 or m_2.*

That RSA has the homomorphic property follows from the equation

$$(m_1 \cdot m_2)^e \pmod{N} = ((m_1{}^e \pmod{N}) \cdot (m_2{}^e \pmod{N})) \pmod{N}.$$

One can use the homomorphic property to show that RSA is insecure under an adaptively chosen ciphertext attack.

Lemma 15.7 *RSA is not CCA2 secure.*

Proof

Suppose the message Eve wants to break is

$$c = m^e \ (\text{mod } N).$$

Eve creates the 'related' ciphertext $c' = 2^e c$ and asks her oracle to decrypt c' to give m'. Eve can then compute

$$\frac{m'}{2} = \frac{c'^d}{2} = \frac{(2^e c)^d}{2}$$

$$= \frac{2^{ed} c^d}{2} = \frac{2m}{2} = m.$$

Q.E.D.

15.2.2   ElGamal

Recall the decision Diffie–Hellman (known as DDH) assumption for a group $G = \langle g \rangle$ is, given g^x, g^y and g^z, determine whether

$$x \cdot y = z \ (\text{mod } \#G).$$

Lemma 15.8 *If DDH is hard in the group G then ElGamal is polynomially secure against a passive adversary.*

Proof

To show that ElGamal is polynomially secure assuming that DDH holds we first assume that we have a polynomial-time algorithm A which breaks the polynomial security of ElGamal. Then using this algorithm A as a subroutine we give an algorithm to solve the DDH problem. This is similar to the technique used in an earlier chapter where we showed that an algorithm which could break ElGamal, in the sense of decrypting a ciphertext to reveal a plaintext, could be used to solve the computational Diffie–Hellman problem. Now with our stronger definition of security, namely polynomial security, we can only relate breaking the system to the solution of a (supposedly) easier problem.

Recall A should run in two stages:

- A **find** stage which outputs two messages and some state information and which takes a public key as input.

- A **guess** stage which takes as input a ciphertext, a public key, two messages and some state information and guesses which plaintext the ciphertext corresponds to.

In addition, recall the ElGamal ciphertext is of the form

$$(g^k, m \cdot h^k)$$

where

- k is an ephemeral per message secret,

- h is the public key.

Our algorithm for solving DDH now proceeds as follows:

1. As input we have g^x, g^y and g^z.

2. Set $h = g^x$.

3. $(m_0, m_1, s) = A(\textbf{find}, h)$.

4. Put $c_1 = g^y$.

5. Choose b randomly from $\{0, 1\}$.

6. Put $c_2 = m_b \cdot g^z$.

7. $b' = A(\textbf{guess}, (c_1, c_2), h, m_0, m_1, s)$.

8. If $b = b'$ then output TRUE.

9. Else output FALSE.

To see why this algorithm solves the DDH problem consider the following argument.

- In the case when $z = x \cdot y$ then the encryption input into the guess stage of algorithm A will be a valid encryption of m_b. Hence, if algorithm A can really break the semantic security of ElGamal then the output b' will be correct and the above algorithm will return TRUE.

- Now suppose that $z \neq x \cdot y$ then the encryption input into the guess stage is almost definitely invalid, i.e. not an encryption of m_1 or m_2. Hence, the output b' of the guess stage will be independent of the value of b. Therefore we expect the above algorithm to return TRUE or FALSE with equal probability.

If we repeat the above algorithm a few times, then we obtain a probabilistic polynomial-time algorithm to solve the DDH problem. But we have assumed that no such algorithm exists, so this implies that our algorithm A cannot exist either. So the DDH assumption implies that no adversary against the polynomial security of ElGamal under chosen plaintext attacks can exist.

Q.E.D.

However although it is semantically secure against chosen plaintext attacks, ElGamal is trivially malleable.

Lemma 15.9 *ElGamal is malleable.*

Proof
Suppose Eve sees the ciphertext

$$(c_1, c_2) = (g^k, m \cdot h^k).$$

She can then create a valid ciphertext of the message $2 \cdot m$ without ever knowing m, nor the ephemeral key k nor the private key x. The ciphertext she can produce is given by

$$(c_1, 2 \cdot c_2) = (g^k, 2 \cdot m \cdot h^k).$$

Q.E.D.

One can use this malleability property, just as we did with RSA, to show that ElGamal is insecure under an adaptively chosen ciphertext attack.

Lemma 15.10 *ElGamal is not CCA2 secure.*

Proof
Suppose the message Eve wants to break is

$$c = (c_1, c_2) = (g^k, m \cdot h^k).$$

Eve creates the related message

$$c' = (c_1, 2c_2)$$

and asks her decryption oracle to decrypt c' to give m'. Then Eve computes

$$\frac{m'}{2} = \frac{2c_2 c_1^{-x}}{2} = \frac{2mh^k g^{-xk}}{2}$$
$$= \frac{2mg^{xk}g^{-xk}}{2} = \frac{2m}{2} = m.$$

Q.E.D.

15.3 A SEMANTICALLY SECURE SYSTEM

We have seen that RSA is not semantically secure even against a passive attack; it would be nice to give a system which is semantically secure and is based on some factoring-like assumption. Historically the first system to meet these goals was one by Goldwasser and Micali, although this is not used in real-life applications. This scheme's security is based on the hardness of the QUADRES problem, namely given a composite integer N it is hard to test whether a is a quadratic residue or not without knowledge of the factors of N.

Let us recap that the set of squares in $(\mathbb{Z}/N\mathbb{Z})^*$ is denoted by

$$Q_N = \{x^2 \pmod{N} : x \in (\mathbb{Z}/N\mathbb{Z})^*\},$$

and J_N denotes the set of elements with Jacobi symbol equal to plus one, i.e.

$$J_N = \left\{x \in (\mathbb{Z}/N\mathbb{Z})^* : \left(\frac{a}{N}\right) = 1\right\}.$$

The set of pseudo-squares is the difference $J_N \setminus Q_N$. For an RSA-like modulus $N = p \cdot q$ the number of elements in J_N is equal to $(p-1)(q-1)/2$, whilst the number of elements in Q_N is $(p-1)(q-1)/4$. The QUADRES problem is that given an element x of J_N, it is hard to tell whether $x \in Q_N$, whilst it is easy to tell if $x \in J_N$ or not.

We can now explain the Goldwasser–Micali encryption system.

15.3.0.1 Key Generation: As a private key we take two large prime number p and q and then compute the public modulus

$$N = p \cdot q.$$

The public key also contains an integer

$$y \in J_N \setminus Q_N.$$

The value of y is computed by the public key owner by first computing elements $y_p \in \mathbb{F}_p^*$ and $y_q \in \mathbb{F}_q^*$ such that

$$\left(\frac{y_p}{p} \right) = \left(\frac{y_q}{q} \right) = -1.$$

Then the value of y is computed from y_p and y_q via the Chinese Remainder Theorem. A value of y computed in this way clearly does not lie in Q_N, but it does lie in J_N since

$$\left(\frac{y}{N} \right) = \left(\frac{y}{p} \right) \cdot \left(\frac{y}{q} \right) = \left(\frac{y_p}{p} \right) \cdot \left(\frac{y_q}{q} \right) = (-1) \cdot (-1) = 1.$$

15.3.0.2 Encryption: The Goldwasser–Micali encryption system encrypts one bit of information at a time. To encrypt the bit b,

- pick $x \in (\mathbb{Z}/N\mathbb{Z})^*$ at random,
- compute $c = y^b x^2 \pmod{N}$.

The ciphertext is then the value of c. Notice that this is very inefficient since a single bit of plaintext requires $\log_2 N$ bits of ciphertext to transmit it.

15.3.0.3 Decryption: Notice that the ciphertext c will always be an element of J_N. However, if the message bit b is zero then the value of c will be a quadratic residue, otherwise it will be a quadratic non-residue. So all the decryptor has to do to recover the message is determine whether c is a quadratic residue or not modulo N. But the decryptor is assumed to know the factors of N and so can compute the Legendre symbol

$$\left(\frac{c}{p} \right).$$

If this Legendre symbol is equal to plus one then c is a quadratic residue and so the message bit is zero. If however the Legendre symbol is equal to minus one then c is not a quadratic residue and so the message bit is one.

15.3.0.4 Proof of Security: We wish to show that the Goldwasser–Micali encryption system is secure against passive adversaries assuming that the QUADRES problem is hard for the modulus N.

Lemma 15.11 *If the QUADRES problem is hard for the modulus N then the above encryption system is polynomially secure against passive adversaries.*

Proof

To do this we assume we have such an adversary A against the above encryption scheme of Goldwasser and Micali. We will now show how to use this adversary to solve a QUADRES problem.

Suppose we are given $j \in J_N$ and we are asked to determine whether $j \in Q_N$. Since our system only encrypts bits the **find** stage of the adversary A, on input of the public key (y, N), will simply output the two messages

$$m_0 = 0 \text{ and } m_1 = 1.$$

We now form the ciphertext

$$c = j.$$

Note that if j is a quadratic residue then this value of c will be a valid encryption of the message m_0, however if j is not a quadratic residue then this value of c will be a valid encryption of the message m_1. We therefore ask our adversary A to **guess** which message is c a valid encryption of. Hence, from the output of A we can decide whether the value of j is an element of Q_N or not.

Q.E.D.

15.3.0.5   Adaptive Adversaries: Note the above argument says nothing about whether the Goldwasser–Micali encryption scheme is secure against adaptive adversaries. In fact one can show it is not secure against such adversaries.

Lemma 15.12 *The Goldwasser–Micali encryption scheme is insecure against an adaptive chosen ciphertext attack.*

Proof
Suppose c is the target ciphertext and we want to determine what bit b is, that c is a valid encryption of. Recall

$$c = y^b x^2 \pmod{N}.$$

Now the rules of the game do not allow us to ask our decryption oracle to decrypt c, but we can ask our oracle to decrypt any other ciphertext.

We therefore produce the ciphertext

$$c' = c \cdot z^2 \pmod{N},$$

for some random value of $z \neq 0$. It is easy to see that c' is an encryption of the same bit b. Hence, by asking our oracle to decrypt c' we will obtain the decryption of c.

Q.E.D.

15.4   SECURITY OF SIGNATURES

There are a number of possible security notions for signature schemes. Just as with standard handwritten signatures we are interested in trying to stop the adversary forging a signature on a given message. The three main types of forgery are:

Total Break: The forger can produce signatures just as if he were the valid key holder. This is akin to recovering the private key and corresponds to the similar type of break of an encryption algorithm.

Selective Forgery: In this case the adversary is able to forge a signature on a single message of her choosing. This is similar to the ability of an adversary of an encryption algorithm being able to decrypt a message but not recover the private key.

Existential Forgery: In this case the adversary is able to forge a signature on a single message, which could just be a random bit string. You should think of this as being analogous to semantic security of encryption schemes.

In practice we usually want our schemes to be secure against an attempt to produce a selective forgery. But we do not know how the signature scheme is to be used in real life, for example it may be used in a challenge/response protocol where random bit strings are signed by various parties. Hence, it is prudent to insist that any signature scheme should be secure against an existential forgery.

Along with types of forgery we also have types of attack. The weakest attack is that of a passive attacker, who is simply given the public key and is then asked to produce a forgery, be it selective or existential. The strongest form of attacker is an adaptive active attacker, such an attacker is given access to a signing oracle which will produce valid signatures for the public key. The goal of an active attacker is to produce a signature on a message which they have not yet asked their signing oracle. This leads to the following definition:

Definition 15.13 *A signature scheme is deemed to be secure if it is infeasible for an adaptive adversary to produce an existential forgery.*

We have already remarked that the use of hash functions is crucial in a signature algorithm. One can see this again by considering a raw RSA signature algorithm defined by

$$s = m^d \pmod{N}.$$

It is trivial to produce an existential forgery with such a scheme via a passive attack. The attacker picks s at random and then computes

$$m = s^e \pmod{N}.$$

The attacker then has the signature s on the message m.

With such a scheme it is also very easy for an active attacker to produce a selective forgery: Suppose the attacker wishes to produce a signature s on the message m. They first generate a random $m_1 \in (\mathbb{Z}/N\mathbb{Z})^*$ and compute

$$m_2 = \frac{m}{m_1}.$$

Then the attacker asks her oracle to sign the messages m_1 and m_2. This results in two signatures s_1 and s_2 such that

$$s_i = m_i{}^d \pmod{N}.$$

The attacker can then compute the signature on the message m by computing

$$s = s_1 \cdot s_2 \pmod{N}$$

since

$$s = s_1 \cdot s_2 \;(\text{mod } N)$$
$$= m_1{}^d \cdot m_2{}^d \;(\text{mod } N)$$
$$= (m_1 \cdot m_2)^d \;(\text{mod } N)$$
$$= m^d \;(\text{mod } N).$$

Chapter Summary

- The definition of what it means for a scheme to be secure can be different from one's initial naive view.

- Today the notion of semantic security is the de facto standard definition for encryption schemes.

- Semantic security is hard to prove but it is closely related to the simpler notion of polynomial security, often called indistinguishability of encryptions.

- We also need to worry about the capabilities of the adversary. For encryption this is divided into three categories: chosen plaintext attacks, chosen ciphertext attacks and adaptive chosen ciphertext attacks.

- Some schemes, such as ElGamal and the Goldwasser–Micali system, are polynomially secure against passive adversaries, but not against active adaptive adversaries. Others, such as RSA, are not even polynomially secure against passive adversaries.

- Security against adaptive adversaries and the notion of non-malleability are closely related.

- Similar considerations apply to the security of signature schemes, where we are now interested in the notion of existential forgery under an active attack.

Further Reading

A good introduction to the definitional work in cryptography based on provable security and its extensions and foundations in the idea of zero-knowledge proofs can be found in the book by Goldreich. A survey of the initial work in this field, up to around 1990, can be found in the article by Goldwasser.

O. Goldreich. *Modern Cryptography, Probabilistic Proofs and Pseudo-randomness.* Springer-Verlag, 1999.

S. Goldwasser. *The Search for Provable Secure Cryptosystems.* In *Cryptology and Computational Number Theory*, Proc. Symposia in Applied Maths, Volume 42, 1990.

Review Exercises

15.1.1   What is meant by the term semantic security, and how does this relate to the concept of perfect security?

15.1.2   Give the definition of polynomial security.

15.1.3   What restriction is put on the decryption oracle in an adaptive chosen ciphertext attack?

15.1.4   Give two problems with the RSA encryption algorithm as described in earlier chapters.

15.1.5   In the Goldwasser–Micali encryption scheme, show that if c is a valid encryption of a bit b then so is

$$c' = c \cdot z^2 \ (\text{mod } N),$$

for any value of $z \neq 0$.

15.1.6   What are the three main goals an adversary can have against a digital signature scheme?

16

Complexity Theoretic
Approaches

Chapter Goals

- To introduce the concepts of complexity theory needed to study cryptography.

- To understand why complexity theory on its own cannot lead to secure crypto-graphic systems.

- To explain the Merkle–Hellman system and why it is weak.

- To introduce the concept of bit security.

- To introduce the idea of random self-reductions.

16.1 POLYNOMIAL COMPLEXITY CLASSES

A common mistake in building new cryptographic schemes is to pick hard problems which are only hard on certain problem instances and are not hard for an average instance. To elaborate on this in more detail we need to recap some basic ideas from complexity theory.

Recall a decision problem $\mathcal{DP}$ is a problem with a yes/no answer, which has inputs (called instances) I coded in some way (for example as a binary string of some given size n). Often one has a certain subset S of instances in mind and one is asking 'Is $I \in S$?'. For example one could have

- I is the set of all integers, S is the subset of primes. Hence the decision problem is: Given an integer say whether it is prime or not.

- I is the set of all graphs, S is the subset of all graphs which are colourable using k colours only. Hence the decision problem is: Given a graph tell me whether it is colourable using only k colours. Recall a graph consisting of vertices V and edges E is colourable by k colours if one can assign k colours (or labels) to each vertex so that no two vertices connected by an edge share the same colour.

Whilst we have restricted ourselves to decision problems, one can often turn a standard computational problem into a decision problem. As an example of this consider the cryptographically important knapsack problem.

Definition 16.1 (Decision Knapsack Problem) *Given a pile of n items, each with differ-ent weights w_i, is it possible to put items into a knapsack to make a specific weight S? In other words, do there exist $b_i \in \{0,1\}$ such that*

$$S = b_1 w_1 + b_2 w_2 + \cdots + b_n w_n?$$

Note, the time taken to solve this seems to grow in the worst case as an exponential function in terms of the number of weights.

As stated above the knapsack problem is a decision problem but we could ask for an algorithm to actually find the values b_i.

Definition 16.2 (Knapsack Problem) *Given a pile of n items, each with different weights w_i, is it possible to put items into a knapsack to make a specific weight S? If so can one find the $b_i \in \{0,1\}$ such that*

$$S = b_1 w_1 + b_2 w_2 + \cdots + b_n w_n?$$

We assume only one such assignment of weights is possible.

We can turn an oracle for the decision knapsack problem into one for the knapsack problem proper. To see this consider the following algorithm which assumes an oracle O(w[1],..., w[n],S) for the decision knapsack problem.

```
if (O(w[1],..., w[n],S)== False)
   { Output False; }
T=S;
b[1] = b[2] = ... = b[n] = 0.
for (i=1; i<=n; i++)
  { if (T==0)
       { Output (b[1], ..., b[n]). }
    if O(w[i+1],... , w[n],T-w[i])==True)
       { T=T-w[i];
         b[i]=1;
       }
  }
```

A decision problem $\mathcal{DP}$ is said to lie in complexity class $\mathcal{P}$ if there is an algorithm which takes any instance I, for which the answer is *yes*, and delivers the answer, namely *yes*, in polynomial time. We measure time in terms of bit operations and polynomial time means the number of bit operations is bounded by some polynomial function of the input size of the instance I. If the answer to the instance is *no* then the algorithm is not even required to answer in polynomial time, but if it does answer then it should return the correct answer.

By replacing *yes* by *no* in the above paragraph we obtain the class co $- \mathcal{P}$. This is the set of problems for which there exists an algorithm which on input of an instance I, for which the answer is *no*, will output *no* in polynomial time.

Lemma 16.3

$$\mathcal{P} = \text{co} - \mathcal{P}.$$

Proof

Suppose A is the algorithm which for a problem instance I outputs *yes* if the answer is *yes* in time n^c for some constant c.

We turn A into a polynomial-time algorithm to answer *no* if the answer is *no* in time $n^c + 1$. We simply run A; if it takes more than n^c steps then we terminate A and output *no*.

Q.E.D.

The problems which lie in complexity class $\mathcal{P}$ are those for which we have an efficient solution algorithm. In other words these are the things which are easy to compute. For example

- Given integers x, y and z do we have $z = x \cdot y$, i.e. is multiplication easy?

- Given a ciphertext c, a key k and a plaintext m, is c the encryption of m under your favourite encryption algorithm?

Of course in the last example I have assumed your favourite encryption algorithm has an encryption/decryption algorithm which runs in polynomial time. If your favourite encryption algorithm is not of this form, then one must really ask how have you read so far in this book?

A decision problem lies in complexity class $\mathcal{NP}$, called non-deterministic polynomial time, if for every instance for which the answer is *yes*, there exists a witness for this which can be checked in polynomial time. If the answer is *no* we again do not assume the algorithm terminates, but if it does it must do so by answering *no*. One should think of the witness as a proof that the instance I lies in the subset S.

Examples include

- The problem 'Is N composite?' lies in $\mathcal{NP}$ as one can give a non-trivial prime factor as a witness. This witness can be checked in polynomial time since division can be performed in polynomial time.

- The problem 'Is G k-colourable?' lies in $\mathcal{NP}$ since as a witness one can give the colouring.

- The problem 'Does this knapsack problem have a solution?' lies in $\mathcal{NP}$ since as a witness we can give the values b_i.

Note, in none of these examples have we assumed the witness itself can be computed in polynomial time, only that the witness can be checked in polynomial time. Note that we trivially have

$$\mathcal{P} \subset \mathcal{NP}.$$

The main open problem in theoretical computer science is the question does $P = \mathcal{NP}$? Most people believe in the conjecture

Conjecture 16.4

$$P \neq \mathcal{NP}.$$

The set $\text{co} - \mathcal{NP}$ is defined in the same way that the class $\text{co} - \mathcal{P}$ was derived from $\mathcal{P}$. The class $\text{co} - \mathcal{NP}$ is the set of problems for which a witness exists for every instance with a *no* response which can be checked in polynomial time. Unlike the case of $\text{co} - \mathcal{P}$ and $\mathcal{P}$ we have

$$\text{If } \mathcal{P} \neq \mathcal{NP} \text{ then } \mathcal{NP} \neq \text{co} - \mathcal{NP}.$$

Hence, one should assume that $\mathcal{NP} \neq \text{co} - \mathcal{NP}$.

One can consider trying to see how small a witness for being in class $\mathcal{NP}$ can be found. For example consider the problem *COMPOSITES*. Namely given $N \in \mathbb{Z}$ determine whether N is composite. As we remarked earlier this clearly lies in class $\mathcal{NP}$. But a number N can be proved composite in the following ways:

- Giving a factor. In this case the size of the witness is

$$O(\log n).$$

- Giving a Miller–Rabin witness a. Now, assuming the Generalized Riemann Hypothesis (GRH) the size of the witness is

$$O(\log \log n)$$

   since we have

$$a \leq O((\log n)^2).$$

A decision problem $\mathcal{DP}$ is said to be $\mathcal{NP}$-complete if every other problem in class $\mathcal{NP}$ can be reduced to this problem in polynomial time. In other words we have

$$\mathcal{DP} \in \mathcal{P} \text{ implies } \mathcal{P} = \mathcal{NP}.$$

In some sense the $\mathcal{NP}$-complete problems are the hardest problems for which it is feasible to ask for a solution. There are a huge number of $\mathcal{NP}$-complete problems of which the two which will interest us are

- the k-colouring problem,

- the knapsack problem.

We know factoring (or *COMPOSITES*) lies in $\mathcal{NP}$ but it is unknown whether it is $\mathcal{NP}$-complete. In fact it is a widely held view that all the hard problems on which cryptography is based, e.g. factoring, discrete logarithms etc., are not related to an $\mathcal{NP}$-complete problem even though they lie in class $\mathcal{NP}$.

From this we can conclude that factoring is not a very difficult problem at all, not at least compared with the knapsack problem or the k-colouring problem. So why do we not use $\mathcal{NP}$-complete problems on which to base our cryptographic schemes? These are after all a well-studied set of problems for which we do not expect there ever to be an efficient solution.

However, this approach has had a bad track record, as we shall show later when we consider the knapsack based system of Merkle and Hellman. For now we simply mention that complexity theory, and so the theory of $\mathcal{NP}$-completeness, is about worst case complexity. But for cryptography we want a problem which, for suitably chosen parameters, is hard on average. It turns out that the knapsack problems that have in the past been proposed for use in cryptography are always 'average' and efficient algorithms can always be found to solve them.

We end this section by illustrating this difference between hard and average problems using the k-colouring problem, when $k = 3$. Although determining whether a graph is 3-colourable is in general (in the worst case) $\mathcal{NP}$-complete, it is very easy on average. This is because the average graph, no matter how large it is, will not be 3-colourable. In fact, for almost all input graphs the following algorithm will terminate saying that the graph is not 3-colourable in a constant number of iterations.

- Take a graph G and order the vertices in any order $v_1, \ldots, v_t$.

- Call the colours $\{1, 2, 3\}$.

- Now traverse the graph in the order of the vertices just decided.

- On visiting a new vertex use the smallest possible colour (i.e. one from the set $\{1, 2, 3\}$ which does not appear as the colour of an adjacent vertex).

- If you get stuck traverse back up the graph to the most recently coloured vertex and use the next colour available, then continue again.

- If at any point you run out of colours for the first vertex then terminate and say the graph is *not* 3-colourable.

- If you are able to colour the last vertex then terminate and output that the graph *is* 3-colourable.

The interesting thing about the above algorithm is that it can be shown that for a *random* graph of t vertices the average number of vertices travelled in the algorithm is less than 197 regardless of the number of vertices t in the graph.

16.2 KNAPSACK-BASED CRYPTOSYSTEMS

One of the earliest public key cryptosystems was based on the knapsack, or subset sum, problem which was believed to be very hard in general to solve. In fact it is $\mathcal{NP}$-complete, however it turns out that this knapsack-based scheme, and almost all others, can be shown to be insecure.

The idea is to create two problem instances. A public one which is hard, which is believed to be a general knapsack problem, and a private problem which is easy. In addition there should be some private trapdoor information which transforms the hard problem into the easy one.

This is rather like the use of the RSA assumption. It is hard to extract eth roots modulo a composite number, but easy to extract eth roots modulo a prime number. Knowing the trapdoor information, namely the factorization of the RSA modulus, allows us to transform the hard problem into the easy problem. However, the crucial difference is that whilst factoring (for suitably chosen moduli) is hard on average, it is difficult to produce knapsack problems which are hard on average. This is even though the general knapsack problem is considered harder than the general factorization problem.

Whilst the general knapsack problem is hard there is a particularly easy set of problems based on super-increasing knapsacks. A super-increasing knapsack problem is one where the weights are such that each one is greater than the sum of the preceding ones, i.e.

$$w_i \geq \sum_{i=1}^{i-1} w_i.$$

As an example one could take the set

$$\{2,3,6,13,27,52\}$$

or one could take
$$\{1,2,4,8,16,32,64,\ldots\}.$$

Given a super-increasing knapsack problem, namely an ordered set of such super-increasing weights $\{w_1,\ldots,w_n\}$ and a target weight S, determining which weights to put in the sack is a linear operation.

```
for (i=n; i>=1; i--)
   { if (S>=w[i])
       { b[i]=1;
         S=S-w[i];
       }
     else
       { b[i]=0; }
   }
if (S==0) then
     Output (b[1],b[2],...,b[n])
else
     Output ''No Solution''
```

The Merkle–Hellman cryptosystem takes as a private key a super-increasing knapsack problem and from this creates (using a private transform) a so-called 'hard knapsack' problem. This hard problem is then the public key.

This transform is achieved by choosing two private integers N and M, such that

$$\gcd(N,M) = 1$$

and multiplying all values of the super-increasing sequence by N (mod M). For example if we take as the private key

- the super-increasing knapsack $\{2,3,6,13,27,52\}$,

- $N = 31$ and $M = 105$.

Then the associated public key is given by the 'hard' knapsack

$$\{62,93,81,88,102,37\}.$$

We then publish the hard knapsack as our public key, with the idea that only someone who knows N and M can transform back to the easy super-increasing knapsack.

For Bob to encrypt a message to us, he first breaks the plaintext into blocks the size of the weight set. The ciphertext is then the sum of the weights where a bit is set. So for example if the message is given by

$$\text{Message} = 011000\ 110101\ 101110$$

Bob obtains, since our public knapsack is $\{62, 93, 81, 88, 102, 37\}$, that the ciphertext is

$$174, 280, 333,$$

since

- 011000 corresponds to $93 + 81 = 174$,

- 110101 corresponds to $62 + 93 + 88 + 37 = 280$,

- 101110 corresponds to $62 + 81 + 88 + 102 = 333$.

The legitimate recipient knows the private key N, M and $\{2, 3, 6, 13, 27, 52\}$. Hence, by multiplying each ciphertext block by N^{-1} (mod M) the hard knapsack is transformed into the easy knapsack problem.

In our case $N^{-1} = 61$ (mod M), and so the decryptor performs the operations

- $174 \cdot 61 = 9 = 3 + 6 = 011000$,

- $280 \cdot 61 = 70 = 2 + 3 + 13 + 52 = 110101$,

- $333 \cdot 61 = 48 = 2 + 6 + 13 + 27 = 101110$.

The final decoding is done using the simple easy knapsack,

$$\{2, 3, 6, 13, 27, 52\},$$

and our earlier linear time algorithm for super-increasing knapsack problems.

Our example knapsack problem of six items is too small; typically one would have at least 250 items. The values of N and M should also be around 400 bits. But, even with parameters as large as these, the above Merkle–Hellman scheme has been broken using lattice based techniques, using a method which we will now explain.

If $\{w_1, \ldots, w_n\}$ are a set of knapsack weights then we define the density of the knapsack to be

$$d = \frac{n}{\max\{\log_2 w_i : 1 \le i \le n\}}.$$

One can show, using the following method, that a knapsack with low density will be easy to solve using lattice basis reduction. Why this allows us to break the Merkle–Hellman scheme is that the Merkle–Hellman construction will always produce a low-density public knapsack.

Suppose we wish to solve the knapsack problem given by the weights $\{w_1, \ldots, w_n\}$ and the target S. Consider the lattice L of dimension $n + 1$ generated by columns of the following matrix:

$$A = \begin{pmatrix} 1 & 0 & 0 & \cdots & 0 & \frac{1}{2} \\ 0 & 1 & 0 & \cdots & 0 & \frac{1}{2} \\ 0 & 0 & 1 & \cdots & 0 & \frac{1}{2} \\ \vdots & \vdots & \vdots & \ddots & \vdots & \vdots \\ 0 & 0 & 0 & \cdots & 1 & \frac{1}{2} \\ w_1 & w_2 & w_3 & \cdots & w_n & S \end{pmatrix}.$$

Now, since we are assuming there is a solution to our knapsack problem, given by the bit vector $(b_1, \ldots, b_n)$, we know that the vector

$$y = A \cdot x,$$

is in our lattice, where $x = (b_1, \ldots, b_n, -1)$. But the components of y are given by

$$y_i = \begin{cases} b_i - \frac{1}{2} & 1 \le i \le n \\ 0 & i = n + 1. \end{cases}$$

Hence, the vector y is very short since it has length bounded by

$$\|y\| = \sqrt{y_1{}^2 + \cdots + y_{n+1}{}^2} = \frac{\sqrt{n}}{2}.$$

But a low-density knapsack will usually result in a lattice with relatively large discriminant, hence the vector y is exceptionally short in the lattice. If we now apply the LLL algorithm to the matrix A we obtain a new basis matrix A'. The first basis vector a'_1 of this LLL reduced basis is then likely to be the smallest vector in the lattice and so we are likely to have

$$a'_1 = y.$$

But given y we can then solve for x and recover the solution to the original knapsack problem.

As an example we take out earlier knapsack problem of

$$b_1 62 + b_2 93 + b_3 81 + b_4 88 + b_5 102 + b_6 37 = 174.$$

We form the matrix

$$A = \begin{pmatrix} 1 & 0 & 0 & 0 & 0 & 0 & \frac{1}{2} \\ 0 & 1 & 0 & 0 & 0 & 0 & \frac{1}{2} \\ 0 & 0 & 1 & 0 & 0 & 0 & \frac{1}{2} \\ 0 & 0 & 0 & 1 & 0 & 0 & \frac{1}{2} \\ 0 & 0 & 0 & 0 & 1 & 0 & \frac{1}{2} \\ 0 & 0 & 0 & 0 & 0 & 1 & \frac{1}{2} \\ 62 & 93 & 81 & 88 & 102 & 37 & 174 \end{pmatrix}.$$

We apply the LLL algorithm to this matrix so as to obtain the new lattice basis,

$$A' = \frac{1}{2} \begin{pmatrix} 1 & -1 & -2 & 2 & 3 & 2 & 0 \\ -1 & -3 & 0 & -2 & -1 & -2 & 0 \\ -1 & -1 & -2 & 2 & -1 & 2 & 0 \\ 1 & -1 & -2 & 0 & -1 & -2 & -2 \\ 1 & -1 & 0 & 2 & -3 & 0 & 4 \\ 1 & 1 & 0 & -2 & 1 & 2 & 0 \\ 0 & 0 & -2 & 0 & 0 & -2 & 2 \end{pmatrix}.$$

We write

$$y = \frac{1}{2} \begin{pmatrix} 1 \\ -1 \\ -1 \\ 1 \\ 1 \\ 1 \\ 0 \end{pmatrix},$$

and compute

$$x = A^{-1} \cdot y = \begin{pmatrix} 0 \\ -1 \\ -1 \\ 0 \\ 0 \\ 0 \\ 1 \end{pmatrix}.$$

So we see that we take

$$(b_1, b_2, b_3, b_4, b_5, b_6) = (0, 1, 1, 0, 0, 0),$$

as a solution to our knapsack problem.

16.3   BIT SECURITY

Earlier we looked at decision problems, i.e. those problems which output a single bit, and showed that certain other non-decision problems, such as the knapsack problem, could be reduced to looking at decision problems only. A similar situation arises in cryptography where we wish to know whether computing a single bit of information is as hard as computing all of the information.

For example suppose one is using the RSA function

$$x \longmapsto y = x^e \pmod{N}.$$

It may be that in a certain system the attacker only cares about computing $b = x \pmod 2$ and not the whole of x. We would like it to be true that computing even this single bit of information about x is as hard as computing all of x. In other words we wish to study the so-called bit security of the RSA function.

We can immediately see that bit security is related to semantic security. For example if an attacker could determine the parity of an underlying plaintext given only the ciphertext they could easily break the semantic security of the encryption algorithm.

First we define some notation:

Definition 16.5 *Let* $f : S \rightarrow T$ *be a one-way function where S and T are finite sets and let* $B : S \rightarrow \{0, 1\}$ *denote a binary function (called a predicate). A hard predicate* $B(x)$ *for f is one which is easy to compute given* $x \in S$ *and for which it is hard to compute* $B(x)$ *given only* $f(x)$.

The way one proves a predicate is a hard predicate, assuming f is a one-way function, is to assume we are given an oracle which computes $B(x)$ given $f(x)$, and then show that this oracle can be used to easily invert f.

A k-bit predicate and hard k-bit predicate are defined in an analogous way but now assuming the codomain of B is the set of bit strings of length k rather than just single bits. We would like to show that various predicates, for given cryptographically useful functions f, are in fact hard predicates.

16.3.1 Hard Predicates for Discrete Logarithms

Let G denote a finite abelian group of prime order q and let g be a generator. Consider the predicate

$$B_2 : x \longmapsto x \ (\text{mod} \ 2)$$

we can show

Theorem 16.6 *The predicate* B_2 *is a hard predicate for the function*

$$x \longmapsto g^x.$$

Proof
Let $\mathcal{O}(h, g)$ denote an oracle which returns the least significant bit of the discrete logarithm of h to the base g, i.e. it computes $B_2(x)$ for $x = \log_g h$. We need to show how to use $\mathcal{O}$ to solve a discrete logarithm problem.

Suppose we are given $h = g^x$, we perform the following steps. First we let $t = \frac{1}{2} \ (\text{mod} \ q)$, then we set $y = 0$, $z = 1$ and compute until $h = 1$ the following steps:

- $b = \mathcal{O}(h, g)$.

- If $b = 1$ then $y = y + z$ and $h = h/g$.

- Set $h = h^t$ and $z = 2 \cdot z$.

We then output y as the discrete logarithm of h with respect to g.

Q.E.D.

To see this work consider the field $\mathbb{F}_{607}$ and the element $g = 64$ of order $q = 101$. We wish to find the discrete logarithm of $h = 56$ with respect to g. Using the algorithm in the above proof we compute

h	$\mathcal{O}(h,g)$	z	y
56	0	1	0
451	1	2	2
201	1	4	6
288	0	8	6
100	1	16	22
454	0	32	22
64	1	64	86

One can indeed check that

$$g^{86} = h \ (\mathrm{mod}\ p).$$

16.3.2 Hard Predicates for the RSA Problem

The RSA problem, namely given $c = m^e$ (mod N) has the following three hard predicates:

- $B_1(m) = m$ (mod 2).

- $B_h(m) = 0$ if $m < N/2$ otherwise $B_h(m) = 1$.

- $B_k(m) = m$ (mod 2^k) where $k = O(\log \log N)$.

We denote the corresponding oracles by $\mathcal{O}_1(c,N)$, $\mathcal{O}_h(c,N)$ and $\mathcal{O}_k(c,N)$. We do not deal with the last of these but we note that the first two are related since,

$$\mathcal{O}_h(c,N) = \mathcal{O}_1(c \cdot 2^e \ (\mathrm{mod}\ N), N),$$
$$\mathcal{O}_1(c,N) = \mathcal{O}_h(c \cdot 2^{-e} \ (\mathrm{mod}\ N), N).$$

We then have, given an oracle for $\mathcal{O}_h$ or $\mathcal{O}_1$, that we can invert the RSA function using the following algorithm, which is based on the standard binary search algorithm. We let $y = c$, $l = 0$ and $h = N$, then while $h - l \geq 1$ we perform

- $b = \mathcal{O}_h(y,N)$,

- $y = y \cdot 2^e$ (mod N),

- $m = (h + l)/2$,

- If $b = 1$ then set $l = m$, otherwise set $h = m$.

On exiting the above loop the value of $\lfloor h \rfloor$ should be the preimage of c under the RSA function.

As an example suppose we have

$$N = 10\,403 \text{ and } e = 7$$

as the public information and we wish to invert the RSA function for the ciphertext $c = 3$ using the oracle $\mathcal{O}_h(y,N)$

y	$\mathcal{O}(y, N)$	l	h
3	0	0	10 403
$3 \cdot 2^7$	1	0	5201.5
$3 \cdot 4^7$	1	2600.7	5201.5
$3 \cdot 8^7$	1	3901.1	5201.5
$3 \cdot 16^7$	0	4551.3	5201.5
$3 \cdot 32^7$	0	4551.3	4876.4
$3 \cdot 64^7$	1	4551.3	4713.8
$3 \cdot 128^7$	0	4632.5	4713.8
$3 \cdot 256^7$	1	4632.5	4673.2
$3 \cdot 512^7$	1	4652.9	4673.2
$3 \cdot 1024^7$	1	4663.0	4673.2
$3 \cdot 2048^7$	1	4668.1	4673.2
$3 \cdot 4096^7$	1	4670.7	4673.2
$3 \cdot 8192^7$	0	4671.9	4673.2
-	-	4671.9	4672.5

So the preimage of 3 under the RSA function

$$x \longmapsto x^7 \ (\text{mod } 10\,403)$$

is 4672.

16.4 RANDOM SELF-REDUCTIONS

We remarked earlier, when considering the Merkle–Hellman scheme and other schemes based on complexity theory, that the problem with these schemes is that the associated problems were hard in the worst case but easy on average. The obvious question to ask oneself is how does one know that problems such as the RSA problem or the DDH problem also do not have this property? For example given an RSA modulus N and a public exponent e it might be hard to solve

$$c = m^e \ (\text{mod } N)$$

for a random c in the worst case, but it could be easy on average.

It turns out that one can prove that problems such as RSA for a fixed modulus N or DDH for a fixed group G are hard on average. The technique to do this is based on a random self-reduction from one given problem instance to another random problem instance. This means that if we can solve the problem on average then we can solve the problem in the worst case. Hence, the worst case behaviour of the problem and the average case behaviour of the problem must be similar.

Lemma 16.7 *The RSA problem is random self-reducible.*

Proof
Suppose we are given c and are asked to solve

$$c = m^e \ (\text{mod } N),$$

where the idea is that this is a 'hard' problem instance. We reduce this to an 'average' problem instance by choosing $s \in (\mathbb{Z}/N\mathbb{Z})^*$ at random and setting

$$c' = s^e c.$$

We then try to solve

$$c' = m'^e \pmod{N}.$$

If we are unsuccessful we choose another value of s until we hit the 'average' type problem. If the average case was easy then we could solve $c' = m'^e \pmod{N}$ for m' and then set

$$m = \frac{m'}{s}$$

and terminate.

Q.E.D.

One can also show that the DDH problem is random self-reducible, in the sense that testing whether

$$(x, y, z) = (g^a, g^b, g^c)$$

is a valid Diffie–Hellman triple, i.e. whether $c = a \cdot b$, does not depend on the particular choices of a, b and c. To see this consider the related triple

$$(x', y', z') = (g^{a_1}, g^{b_1}, g^{c_1}) = (x^v g^{u_1}, y g^{u_2}, z^v y^{u_1} x^{v u_2} g^{u_1 u_2})$$

for random u_1, u_2, v. Now if (x, y, z) is a valid Diffie–Hellman triplet then so is (x', y', z'), and vice versa.

One can show that the distribution of (x', y', z') will be uniform over all valid Diffie–Hellman triples if the original triple is a valid Diffie–Hellman triple, whilst the distribution will be uniform over all triples (and not just Diffie–Hellman ones) in the case where the original triple was not a valid Diffie–Hellman triple.

16.5 RANDOMIZED ALGORITHMS

We end this chapter with a discussion of randomized algorithms; first we give some definitions of algorithm types, then we relate these to complexity classes and finally we give some examples.

Recall that definitions are usually given for decision problems, so assume we have a property which we wish to test to be true or false. There are the following definitions of algorithm types, all taking their names from gambling cities.

- **Monte-Carlo Algorithm**

  - Always outputs FALSE if the answer is actually FALSE.
  - Answers TRUE with probability $\geq 1/2$.
  - Otherwise answers FALSE, even though the actual answer is TRUE.

- **Atlantic City Algorithm**

  - Outputs TRUE with probability $\geq 2/3$ of being correct.
  - Outputs FALSE with probability $\geq 2/3$ of being correct.

- **Las Vegas Algorithm**

    - Will terminate with the correct answer with probability $\geq 1/2$.

    - Otherwise will not terminate.

In the above definitions we assume that the algorithm runs in polynomial time in terms of the size of the input data. We can clearly extend these definitions to non-decision problems quite easily.

We now turn our attention to the randomized complexity classes. We assume we have a problem instance I and a possible witness w whose length is a polynomial function of the length of the instance I. We wish to determine whether $I \in S$.

Definition 16.8 *A problem $\mathcal{DP}$ is said to lie in class $\mathcal{RP}$ if there is an algorithm A, which on input of a problem instance I and a witness w will perform as follows:*

- *If $I \in S$ then for at least half of all possible witnesses w the algorithm A outputs that $I \in S$.*

- *If $I \notin S$ then for all witnesses w the algorithm A outputs $I \notin S$.*

Note that we have, since we can replace 'at least half' with 'at least one', that

$$\mathcal{RP} \subset \mathcal{NP}.$$

We also clearly have $\mathcal{P} \subset \mathcal{RP}$.

The class $\mathcal{RP}$ is important since it gives us a probabilistic algorithm to decide whether $I \in S$ for any value of S. We generate k random witnesses w_i and call $A(I, w_i)$ for $i = 1, \ldots, k$. Then if $A(I, w_i)$ returns $I \in S$ for at least one value of w_i then we return $I \in S$, otherwise we return $I \notin S$. This latter statement will then be false around $1/2^k$ of the time. Relating this to our definitions based on gambling cities we see that

If $\mathcal{DP} \in \mathcal{RP}$ there exists a Monte-Carlo algorithm for $\mathcal{DP}$.

We now define another class.

Definition 16.9 *A problem $\mathcal{DP}$ is said to lie in class $\mathcal{BPP}$ if there is an algorithm A, which on input of a problem instance I and a witness w will perform as follows:*

- *If $I \in S$ then for at least $2/3$ of all possible witnesses w the algorithm A outputs $I \in S$.*

- *If $I \notin S$ then for at least $2/3$ of all possible witnesses w the algorithm A outputs $I \notin S$.*

We see that

If $\mathcal{DP} \in \mathcal{BPP}$ there exists an Atlantic City algorithm for $\mathcal{DP}$.

Finally we define the class $\mathcal{ZPP}$ as

$$\mathcal{ZPP} = \mathcal{RP} \cap \text{co} - \mathcal{RP},$$

with

If $\mathcal{DP} \in \mathcal{ZPP}$ there exists a Las Vegas algorithm for $\mathcal{DP}$.

We have the inclusions

$$\mathcal{P} \subset \mathcal{ZPP} \subset \mathcal{RP} \subset \mathcal{NP} \cap \mathcal{BPP}.$$

The Fermat test and the Miller–Rabin test for primality are examples of Monte-Carlo algorithms to test for compositeness. Recall these tests on input of a number N do one of two things:

- If N is prime will always output FALSE (or probably prime).

- If N is composite will output TRUE with probability $\geq 1/2$, otherwise will output FALSE.

Hence

$$\text{COMPOSITES} \in \mathcal{RP}.$$

By repeating the Monte-Carlo test we can amplify the probability of being correct to be arbitrarily close to one.

The Adleman–Huang algorithm for primality proving is an example of a Las Vegas algorithm to test for primality. The input to this problem is a number N. If the input is composite then the algorithm may not terminate, but if it does terminate then it will tell us correctly whether N is prime or not. Hence

$$\text{PRIMALITY} \in \mathcal{ZPP}.$$

The historically earlier ECPP algorithm, on which the test of Adleman and Huang is based, is not guaranteed to terminate on input of a prime number, but in practice it always does.

Chapter Summary

- Complexity theory deals with the worst case behaviour of algorithms to solve a given decision problem.

- Some problems are easy on average, but there exist certain instances which are very hard to solve. We do not wish to base our cryptographic systems on such problems.

- Cryptographic systems based on knapsack problems have been particularly notorious from this perspective, as one can often use lattice basis reduction to break them.

- Problems which we do base public key cryptography on, such as the RSA problem or the discrete logarithm problem, have the property that even computing single bits of the answer seems to be as hard as computing the whole answer.

- Problems such as RSA and the DDH problem are hard on average, since they posses random self-reductions from a given instance of the problem to a random instance of the problem.

Further Reading

A nice introduction to complexity theory can be found in Chapter 2 of Bach and Shallit. A discussion of the relationships between theoretical complexity theory and cryptographic concepts such as zero-knowledge proofs can be found in the book by Goldreich. A discussion of knapsack based systems and how to break them using lattices can be found in the survey article by Odlyzko.

E. Bach and S. Shallit. *Algorithmic Number Theory, Volume 1: Efficient Algorithms.* MIT Press, 1996.

O. Goldreich. *Modern Cryptography, Probabilistic Proofs and Pseudo-randomness.* Springer-Verlag, 1999.

A. Odlyzko. *The Rise and Fall of Knapsack Cryptosystems.* In *Cryptology and Computational Number Theory*, Proc. Symposia in Applied Maths, Volume 42, 1990.

Review Exercises

16.1.1   Describe the complexity classes $\mathcal{P}$, $\mathcal{NP}$ and co $-\mathcal{NP}$.

16.1.2   What is a super-increasing knapsack?

16.1.3   How does the Merkle–Hellman cryptosystem translate a super-increasing knapsack into a hard knapsack problem?

16.1.4   What is meant by a hard predicate for a function and how is this concept related to the concept of semantic security?

16.1.5   Explain the difference between a Monte-Carlo, an Atlantic City and a Las Vegas algorithm.

16.1.6   Describe the following algorithms as either Monte-Carlo, Atlantic City or Las Vegas:

        a)   Pollard's rho algorithm.
        b)   Miller–Rabin primality test.
        c)   Shank's algorithm for square roots in $\mathbb{F}_p$.

Programming Exercises

16.2.1   Implement the Merkle–Hellman scheme and the lattice based attack on this scheme. Investigate how successful the lattice based attack actually is in practice.

Standard Exercises

16.3.1   Show, for the RSA problem, that

$$\mathcal{O}_h(c, N) = \mathcal{O}_1(c \cdot 2^e \ (\text{mod } N), N),$$
$$\mathcal{O}_1(c, N) = \mathcal{O}_h(c \cdot 2^{-e} \ (\text{mod } N), N).$$

16.3.2   [**Requires knowledge of graph theory**.]   Show that the recursive algorithm to determine whether a graph is 3-colourable given in the text will visit, on average, less than 197 vertices no matter what the size of the graph is.

16.3.3   Show that in our definition of $\mathcal{BPP}$, or Atlantic City algorithms, one can replace the constants $2/3$ by any proportion in the range $(1/2, 1)$.

16.3.4   Show that if one-way functions exist then $\mathcal{P} \neq \mathcal{NP}$.

CHAPTER 17

Provable Security: With Random Oracles

Chapter Goals

- To describe the random oracle model.

- To show how the random oracle model can be used to prove certain signature schemes are secure.

- To show why chosen ciphertext attacks require our public key encryption algorithms to have redundancy in the ciphertext.

- To explain RSA-OAEP and give a proof sketch.

- To describe how to turn ElGamal encryption into a secure system.

17.1 INTRODUCTION

The modern approach to showing that certain protocols are secure is one based on provable security. This name is in fact a misnomer since the techniques used do not actually prove security, in the sense of perfect security mentioned earlier. Instead, the proponents of provable security aim to prove that if an adversary is able to break a certain notion of the security of a system then one could use the adversary to do something believed to be impossible.

For example one tries to prove that if one can break the semantic security of RSA in a chosen ciphertext attack then one is also able to factor integers. Hence, such a proof is a relativized result, it is a proof of security relative to the hardness of factoring integers.

The major contribution of the area of provable security has really been in actually defining what is meant by a secure encryption or signature algorithm. Many of the concepts we have already introduced such as existential forgery, semantic security, indistinguishability of encryptions, adaptive chosen ciphertext attacks have all arisen due to the study of provable security.

Let us explain the techniques of provable security by explaining what one means in a concrete example. We suppose we are given an adversary which is a probabilistic algorithm which breaks some security property of RSA (for example semantic security of RSA) with a certain non-negligible probability. Already this leads us to some definitional work, what do we mean by non-negligible probability?

We hence need to define what we mean much better. We now assume that the scheme has a security parameter k, which measures how big the key size is. For example in RSA the security parameter could be the number of bits in the modulus N. The adversary is said to be successful with non-negligible probability if it succeeds in its task with probability greater than

$$1/p(k),$$

where p is some polynomial in k.

For the moment let us assume that our adversary A is a passive adversary, i.e. for RSA encryption it makes no decryption queries. We now wish to present a new algorithm B_A which takes as input an integer N and which calls the adversary a polynomial, in k, number of times. This new algorithm's aim could be to output the factors of N, with again a non-negligible probability. The algorithm B_A would show that the existence of such an adversary A would imply a polynomial-time factoring algorithm, which succeeded with a non-negligible probability. Since we do not believe a polynomial-time factoring algorithm is achievable with current knowledge we can conclude that such an adversary is also unachievable with current knowledge.

You have already seen the above technique used when we showed that a successful passive adversary against the ElGamal encryption scheme would imply an efficient algorithm to solve the DDH problem, or when we showed that a passive adversary against the Goldwasser–Micali scheme would imply an efficient algorithm to solve the QUADRES problem.

To recap, given an algorithm A we create a new algorithm B_A which uses A as a subroutine. The input to B_A is the hard mathematical problem we wish to solve, whilst the input to A is some cryptographic problem. The difficulty arises when A is an active adversary, in this case A is allowed to call a decryption or signature oracle for the input public keys. The algorithm B_A, if it wants to use algorithm A as a subroutine, needs to supply the answers to A's oracle queries. Algorithm B_A now has a number of problems:

- Its responses must appear valid, in that encryptions should decrypt and signatures should verify, otherwise algorithm A would notice its oracle was lying. Hence, algorithm B_A could no longer guarantee that algorithm A was successful with non-negligible probability.

- The responses of the oracle should be consistent with the probability distributions of responses that A expects if the oracles were true decryption/encryption oracles. Again, otherwise A would notice.

- The responses of the oracles should be consistent across all the calls made by the adversary A.

- Algorithm B_A needs to supply these answers without knowing the secret key. For example in the case of RSA, if B_A wants to find the factors of N, it can hardly use these factors to respond to algorithm A before it has found the factors.

This last point is the most crucial one. We are essentially asking B_A to decrypt or sign a message without knowing the private key, but this is meant to be impossible since our scheme is meant to be secure.

To get around this problem it has become common practice to use something called the 'random oracle model'. A random oracle is an idealized hash function which on input of a new query will pick, uniformly at random, some response from its output domain, and which if asked the same query twice will always return the same response.

In the random oracle model we assume our adversary A makes no use of the explicit hash function defined in the scheme under attack. In other words the adversary A runs, and is successful, even if we replace the real hash function by a random oracle. The algorithm B_A responds to the decryption oracle and/or signature queries of A by cheating and 'cooking' the responses of the random oracle to suit his own needs. To see how this is done in practice look at the next section on proofs of security of signature algorithms.

A proof in the random oracle model is an even more relativized proof than that which we considered before. Such a proof says that assuming some problem is hard, say factoring, then an adversary cannot exist which makes no use of the underlying hash function. This does not imply that an adversary does not exist which uses the real specific hash function as a means of breaking the cryptographic system.

In all our proofs and definitions we are very loose. We try to convey the flavour of the arguments rather than the precise details. Those who want more precise definitions should look at the original papers. One should be warned however that in this field definitions can alter quite subtly from one paper to the next, this is because most of the real importance is in the definitions rather than the proofs themselves.

17.2 SECURITY OF SIGNATURE ALGORITHMS

We first consider proofs of security of digital signature algorithms because they are conceptually somewhat simpler.

The first main technique we shall introduce is the forking lemma, due to Stern and Pointcheval. This applies to certain types of signature schemes which use a hash function as follows: To sign a message

- the signer produces a, possibly empty, commitment σ_1,

- the signer computes $h = H(\sigma_1 \| m)$,

- the signer computes σ_2 which is the 'signature' on σ_1 and h.

We label the output of the signature schemes as $(\sigma_1, H(\sigma_1 \| m), \sigma_2)$ so as to keep track of the exact hash query. For example we have

- DSA : $\sigma_1 = \varnothing$, $h = H(m)$,

$$\sigma_2 = (r, (h + xr)/k \pmod q),$$

where $r = \left(g^k \pmod p\right) \pmod q$.

- EC-DSA : $\sigma_1 = \varnothing, h = H(m)$,

$$\sigma_2 = (r, (h + xr)/k \ (\text{mod } q)),$$

where $r = x\text{-coord}([k]G)$.

- Schnorr signatures: $\sigma_1 = g^k, h = H(\sigma_1 \| m)$

$$\sigma_2 = xh + k \ (\text{mod } q).$$

In all of these schemes the hash function is assumed to have codomain equal to $\mathbb{F}_q$.

Recall in the random oracle model the hash function is allowed to be cooked up by the algorithm B_A to do whatever it likes. Suppose an adversary A can produce an existential forgery on a message m with non-negligible probability in the random oracle model. Hence, the output of the adversary is

$$(m, \sigma_1, h, \sigma_2).$$

We can assume that the adversary makes the critical hash query

$$h = H(\sigma_1 \| m),$$

since otherwise we can make the query for the adversary ourselves.

Algorithm B_A now runs the adversary A twice, with the same random tape and a slightly different random oracle. The adversary A runs in polynomial time and so makes polynomially many hash queries. If all hash queries were answered the same as before then algorithm A would output exactly the same signature. However, algorithm B_A answers these random oracle queries just as before, but chooses one hash query at random to answer differently. With non-negligible probability this will be the critical hash query and so (with non-negligible probability) the adversary B_A will obtain two signatures on the same message which have different hash query responses. In other words we obtain

$$(m, \sigma_1, h, \sigma_2) \text{ and } (m, \sigma_1, h', \sigma_2').$$

We then try to use these two outputs of algorithm A to solve the hard problem which is the goal of algorithm B_A. The exact details and a thorough proof of this technique can be found in the paper by Stern and Pointcheval mentioned in the Further Reading section at the end of this chapter.

17.2.1 Passive Adversary Examples

We concern ourselves with some applications.

17.2.1.1 Schnorr Signatures: The technique of the forking lemma allows us to show

Theorem 17.1 *In the random oracle model, assuming discrete logarithms are hard to compute for the group G, no passive adversary against Schnorr signatures can exist for the group G.*

Proof
Let the input to algorithm B_A be a discrete logarithm problem $y = g^x$ which we wish to solve. So let us assume we run our adversary A on input of the public key y and try to use the forking lemma argument. With non-negligible probability we obtain two signatures

$$\left(m, \sigma_1 = g^k, h, \sigma_2 = xh + k \ (\text{mod } q) \right)$$

and

$$\left(m, \sigma_1' = g^{k'}, h', \sigma_2' = xh' + k' \ (\text{mod } q) \right),$$

where $h = H(\sigma_1 \| m)$ is the oracle query from the first run of A and $h' = H(\sigma_1' \| m)$ is the oracle query from the second run of A.

The algorithm B_A's goal is to recover x. It concludes that we must have $k = k'$ since we have $\sigma_1 = \sigma_1'$. So it concludes that

$$Ax = B \ (\text{mod } q),$$

where

$$A = h - h' \ (\text{mod } q),$$
$$B = \sigma_2 - \sigma_2' \ (\text{mod } q).$$

It will also know that $A \neq 0$, since otherwise the two hash values would be equal. This then means that B_A can solve the required discrete logarithm problem by computing

$$x = A^{-1}B \ (\text{mod } q).$$

Q.E.D.

We shall later show that Schnorr signatures are also secure against active adversaries in the random oracle model.

17.2.1.2 DSA Signatures: The above argument for Schnorr signatures does not apply to DSA as we shall now show.

Let the input to algorithm B_A be a discrete logarithm problem $y = g^x$ which we wish to solve. So let us assume we run our adversary A on input of the public key y and try to use the forking lemma argument. With non-negligible probability we obtain two signatures

$$(m, \sigma_1 = \varnothing, h, \sigma_2 = (r, s)) \text{ and } (m, \sigma_1' = \varnothing, h', \sigma_2' = (r', s')),$$

where $h = H(m)$ is the oracle query from the first run of A, $h' = H(m)$ is the oracle query from the second run of A and

$$r = g^k \ (\text{mod } p) \ (\text{mod } q),$$
$$r' = g^{k'} \ (\text{mod } p) \ (\text{mod } q),$$
$$s = (h + xr)/k \ (\text{mod } q),$$
$$s' = (h' + xr')/k' \ (\text{mod } q).$$

The algorithm B_A's goal is to recover x. We can no longer conclude that $k = k'$, since we do not even know that $r = r'$. Hence, the proof technique does not apply. In fact there is no known proof of security for DSA signatures.

We can try and repair this by using a modified form of DSA by applying the hash function to m and r instead of just m. In the context of the notation used in our description of the forking lemma this would imply that $\sigma_1 = r$, $h = H(m\|r)$ and $\sigma_2 = (h + xr)/k \pmod{q}$.

Even with this modification, to make DSA more like Schnorr signatures, we cannot prove security. Our forking lemma argument would imply that we obtain two signatures with

$$r = g^k \pmod{p} \pmod{q},$$
$$r' = g^{k'} \pmod{p} \pmod{q},$$
$$s = (h + xr)/k \pmod{q},$$
$$s' = (h' + xr')/k' \pmod{q},$$

and with $r = r'$. But we still could not imply that $k = k'$ since this does not follow from the equation

$$g^k \pmod{p} \pmod{q} = g^{k'} \pmod{p} \pmod{q}.$$

It is the reduction modulo q which is getting in the way, if we removed this then our signature scheme could be shown to be secure. But we would lose the property of small signature size which DSA has.

17.2.1.3 EC-DSA Signatures: A similar problem arises with EC-DSA and the forking lemma argument. But now a small modification allows us to give a proof of security for the modified scheme, in certain situations. We again assume that we apply the hash function to m and r instead of just m. We then obtain by running our adversary twice and using the forking lemma

$$r = x\text{-coord}([k]P) \pmod{q},$$
$$r' = x\text{-coord}([k']P) \pmod{q},$$
$$s = (h + xr)/k \pmod{q},$$
$$s' = (h' + xr')/k' \pmod{q},$$

where again we have $r = r'$ and $h = H(m\|r)$ and $h' = H(m\|r')$ are the two critical hash queries. If q is larger than the size of the finite field, from $r = r'$ we can now conclude that $k = \pm k'$ and so we deduce that

$$(s \mp s')k = h - h' \pmod{q}.$$

We therefore obtain two possibilities for k and we recover two possibilities for x. The actual answer is produced by checking which one of our two possibilities for x satisfies $[x]P = Y$. So we have shown:

Theorem 17.2 *In the random oracle model the above* **modified** *version of EC-DSA is secure against passive adversaries, assuming that the discrete logarithm problem in $E(\mathbb{F}_p)$ is hard and*

$$q = \#E(\mathbb{F}_p) > p.$$

Notice how this result only applies to a certain subset of all elliptic curves.

17.2.2   Active Adversaries

To provide a proof for active adversaries we need to show how the algorithm B_A will answer the signature queries of the algorithm A. To do this we use the random oracle model again, in that we use the ability of B_A to choose the output of the hash function. Notice that this may mean that the input to the hash function must be unknown up until the message is signed. If the hash function is only applied to the message m and not some other quantity (such as σ_1 above) then algorithm A could have already queried the hash oracle for the input m before the signature is created, and then algorithm B_A would not be able to change the response from the previous one.

The process of B_A signing signatures for A without A being able to tell and without B_A having the private key is called a simulation of the signing queries. This simulation essentially means that an active attack can be no more powerful than a passive attack, in the random oracle model, since any active attacker can be turned into a passive attacker by simply simulating the signing queries.

17.2.2.1   Schnorr Signatures: Providing a simulation of the signing queries for Schnorr signatures is particularly easy, and the simulator is closely related to our zero-knowledge protocol of Section 13.3. We assume that the simulator keeps a list L of all previous random oracle queries. On input of a message m the simulator does the following:

1. Computes random values of s and h such that $1 \le s, h < q$.

2. Sets $r = g^s y^{-h}$.

3. If $(r \| m, h') \in L$ for $h' \ne h$ then the simulator returns to step 1.

4. Sets $L = L \cup (r \| m, h)$, i.e. the hash oracle should now always return h on input of $(r \| m)$.

5. Output the 'signature' (h, s).

You should check that the above does produce a valid signature, and that assuming h is a random oracle the above simulation cannot be distinguished by algorithm A from a true signature algorithm. Hence we have:

Theorem 17.3 *In the random oracle model, assuming discrete logarithms are hard to compute for the group G, no active adversary against Schnorr signatures can exist for the group G.*

No similar security statement is known for DSA. A security proof is known for EC-DSA where, instead of modelling the hash function as a generic object and reducing the security to a discrete logarithm problem, one models the group operation as a generic object and reduces the security of EC-DSA to the collision resistance of the actual hash function used.

17.2.3   RSA with Full Domain Hash

One should notice that in the previous discussion of the Schnorr, DSA and EC-DSA signature schemes we assumed that the hash function H is a function with codomain $\mathbb{F}_q$. Such hash functions are hard to construct in practice, but the above arguments assume this property.

A similar situation occurs with a variant of RSA signatures called RSA-FDH, or *full domain hash*. In this we assume a hash function

$$H : \{0,1\}^* \longrightarrow (\mathbb{Z}/N\mathbb{Z})^*,$$

where N is the RSA modulus. Again such hash functions are hard to construct in practice, but if we assume they can exist and we model them by a random oracle then we can prove the following RSA signature algorithm is secure.

Let N denote an RSA modulus with public exponent e and private exponent d. Let f denote the function

$$f : \begin{cases} (\mathbb{Z}/N\mathbb{Z})^* \longrightarrow (\mathbb{Z}/N\mathbb{Z})^* \\ \qquad x \longmapsto x^e. \end{cases}$$

The RSA problem is given $y = f(x)$ determine x. In the RSA-FDH signature algorithm on being given a message m we produce the signature

$$s = H(m)^d = f^{-1}(H(m)).$$

One can then prove the following theorem.

Theorem 17.4 *In the random oracle model if an active adversary A exists which produces an existential forgery for RSA-FDH, which requires q_H hash queries and q_S signature queries, then there is an algorithm which given y can invert the RSA function on y with probability $1/q_H$.*

Proof
We describe an algorithm B_A which on input of $y \in (\mathbb{Z}/N\mathbb{Z})^*$ outputs $x = f^{-1}(y)$. Algorithm B_A first chooses a value of $t \in [1, \ldots, q_H]$ and throughout keeps a numbered record of all the hash queries made. Algorithm B_A runs algorithm A and responds to the hash queries for the input m_i as follows:

- If A makes a hash query, and this is the tth such query then B_A replies with y and updates the internal hash list so that $y = H(m_t)$.

- If A makes a hash query m_i with $i \neq t$, then B_A computes a random $s_i \in (\mathbb{Z}/N\mathbb{Z})^*$ and updates the internal hash list so that $H(m_i) = s_i^e \pmod{N} = h_i$, keeping a record of the value of s_i. Algorithm B_A then responds with h_i.

If A makes a signing query for a message m_i before making a hash query on the message m_i then B_A first makes the hash query for algorithm A. Then signing queries are responded to as:

- If message m_i is equal to m_t then algorithm B_A stops and returns fail.

- If $m_i \neq m_t$ then B_A returns s_i as a response to the signature query.

Let A terminate with output (m, s) and without loss of generality we can assume that A made a hash oracle query for the message m. Now if $m \neq m_t$ then B_A terminates and admits failure. But if $m = m_t$ then we have

$$f(s) = H(m_t) = y.$$

Hence we have succeeded in inverting f.

In analysing algorithm B_A one notices that if A terminates successfully then (m, s) is an existential forgery and so m was not asked of the signing oracle. The value of t is independent of the view of A, so A cannot try and always ask for the signature of message m_t in the algorithm rather than not ask for the signature. Hence, roughly speaking, the probability of success is around $1/q_H$, i.e. the probability that the existential forgery was on the message m_t and not on some other one.

Q.E.D.

17.2.4 RSA-PSS

Another way of securely using RSA as a signature algorithm is to use a system called RSA-PSS, or *probabilistic signature scheme*. This scheme can also be proved secure in the random oracle model under the RSA assumption. We do not give the details of the proof here but simply explain the scheme, since it is becoming increasingly important due to its adoption by standards bodies. The advantage of RSA-PSS over RSA-FDH is that one only requires a hash function with a traditional codomain, e.g. bit strings of length t, rather than a set of integers modulo another number.

As usual one takes an RSA modulus N, a public exponent e and a private exponent d. Suppose the security parameter is k, i.e. N is a k bit number. We define two integers k_0 and k_1 so that

$$k_0 + k_1 \le k - 1.$$

For example one could take $k_i = 128$ or 160.

We then define two hash functions, one which expands data and one which compresses data:

$$G : \{0,1\}^{k_1} \longrightarrow \{0,1\}^{k-k_1-1}$$
$$H : \{0,1\}^* \longrightarrow \{0,1\}^{k_1}.$$

We let

$$G_1 : \{0,1\}^{k_1} \longrightarrow \{0,1\}^{k_0}$$

denote the function which returns the first k_0 bits of $G(w)$ for $w \in \{0,1\}^{k_1}$ and we let

$$G_2 : \{0,1\}^{k_1} \longrightarrow \{0,1\}^{k-k_0-k_1-1}$$

denote the function which returns the last $k - k_0 - k_1 - 1$ bits of $G(w)$ for $w \in \{0,1\}^{k_1}$. To sign a message m:

- Generate a random value $r \in \{0,1\}^{k_0}$.
- Put $w = H(m\|r)$.
- Set $y = 0\|w\|(G_1(w) \oplus r)\|G_2(w)$.
- Output $s = y^d \pmod{N}$.

To verify a signature (s, m):

- Compute $y = s^e \pmod{N}$.

- Split y into the components

$$b\|w\|\alpha\|y$$

  where b is one bit long, w is k_1 bits long, α is k_0 bits long and y is $k - k_0 - k_1 - 1$ bits long.

- Compute $r = \alpha \oplus G_1(w)$.

- The signature verifies if

$$b = 0 \text{ and } G_2(w) = y \text{ and } H(m\|r) = w.$$

If we allow the modelling of the hash functions G and H by random oracles then one can show that the above signature algorithm is secure, in the sense that the existence of a successful algorithm to find existential forgeries could be used to produce an algorithm to invert the RSA function. For the proof of this one should consult the EuroCrypt '96 paper of Bellare and Rogaway mentioned in the Further Reading section at the end of this chapter.

17.3 SECURITY OF ENCRYPTION ALGORITHMS

We have seen that it is easy, under the DDH assumption, to produce semantically secure public key encryption schemes assuming only passive adversaries. For example the ElGamal encryption scheme satisfies these properties. We have also seen that a semantically secure system based on the QUADRES problem is easy to produce, assuming only passive adversaries, but this system of Goldwasser and Micali has terrible message expansion properties. It is much harder to produce discrete logarithm based systems which are secure against active adversaries or which are semantically secure under the RSA assumption.

In this section we first present some historical attempts at producing ElGamal based encryption algorithms which aimed to be secure against active adversaries. These are important as they show a basic design criteria. We then go on to describe the main RSA based system which is secure against active adversaries in the random oracle model, namely RSA-OAEP.

17.3.1 Immunization of ElGamal Based Encryption

Recall that ElGamal encryption is given by

$$(g^k, m \cdot y^k)$$

where $y = g^x$ is the public key. Such a system can be proved to have semantic security under the DDH assumption using quite elementary techniques, as we showed in Chapter 15. However, we also showed that such a system is not secure against active adversaries since the ciphertext was trivially malleable.

It was soon realized that the problem with active attacks was that it was too easy for the adversary to write down a valid ciphertext, and not just a related one. The reasoning went that if it was hard for the adversary to write down a valid ciphertext without having first encrypted the plaintext to produce the ciphertext, then the adversary would have no advantage in mounting a chosen ciphertext attack. After all, why would an adversary want to decrypt a ciphertext if the only way he could produce a ciphertext was to encrypt some plaintext?

This meant one needed a decryption function which on input of a ciphertext would either output the corresponding plaintext or would output an `Invalid Ciphertext` message. For this to happen some redundancy needs to be added to the ciphertext which could be checked by the decryptor, to check whether the ciphertext was valid. Compare this with our discussion on encryption functions in Chapter 4, where we argued that a ciphertext should contain no redundancy. But there we were only interested in passive attacks, here we are trying to defend against much more powerful adversaries.

Zheng and Seberry were the first to explore this philosophy for practical crypto-systems, which pervades the modern approach to public key encryption function design. Their overall approach is important, so we present these early attempts at producing secure public key encryption schemes as illustrative of the approach.

The first thing to notice is that public key encryption is usually used to convey a key to encrypt a large message, hence it is not necessary to encrypt a message which lies in the group G (as in ElGamal). We can still use the ElGamal idea to transport a key, which we can then use to produce a session key to encrypt the actual message.

We first describe some notation:

- G is a public group of prime order q generated by g.

- $V(h)$ takes a group element h and generates a random bit string from h. The function V is often called a key derivation function.

- H is a hash function producing an l-bit output.

- $y = g^x$ will be the public key corresponding to the private key x.

17.3.1.1   Zheng–Seberry Scheme 1:   To encrypt a message m one computes

1. $k \in_R \{1, \ldots, q-1\}$.

2. $z = V(y^k)$.

3. $t = H(m)$.

4. $c_1 = g^k$.

5. $c_2 = z \oplus (m\|t)$.

6. Output (c_1, c_2).

When we decrypt a ciphertext we perform the following steps

1. $z' = V(c_1{}^x)$.

2. $w = z' \oplus c_2$.

3. t' is the last l bits of w.

4. m' is the first $\#w - l$ bits of w.

5. If $H(m') = t'$ then output m'.

6. Output `Invalid Ciphertext`.

The idea here is that we have added an extra piece of information to the ElGamal ciphertext, namely the encryption of the hash of the plaintext. Since it is meant to be hard to invert the hash function it should be hard to write down a valid ciphertext without knowing the corresponding plaintext. The addition of the hash adds the required redundancy which is then tested by the decryption function.

17.3.1.2 Zheng–Seberry Scheme 2: The second system uses a universal one-way hash function, which is essentially a parametrized set of hash functions H_i, where $i \le \ell$. One can think of this in some ways as a keyed hash function or as a MAC.

More formally a universal one-way hash function is a keyed hash function H_k such that if the adversary is given x and then a hidden key k is chosen at random it should be hard for the adversary to be able to compute a y such that

$$H_k(y) = H_k(x).$$

To encrypt a message m in the second of Zheng and Seberry's schemes we compute

1. $k \in_R \{1, \ldots, q - 1\}$.

2. Let z denote the $\#m$ leftmost bits of $V(y^k)$.

3. Let s denote the ℓ rightmost bits of $V(y^k)$.

4. $c_1 = g^k$.

5. $c_2 = H_s(m)$.

6. $c_3 = z \oplus m$.

7. Output (c_1, c_2, c_3).

We leave it to the reader to write down the associated decryption function. The above system is similar to the first but the hash of the message is no longer encrypted, it is now sent in the clear. But now one has an added difficultly since we do not know which hash function, or key, has been used to generate the hash value. The above system is very close to the system called DHIES which is currently considered the best practical ElGamal based encryption function.

17.3.1.3 Zheng–Seberry Scheme 3: In the third and final scheme produced by Zheng and Seberry one uses a DSA-like signature to 'sign' the message which is encrypted. The scheme works like a combination of an ElGamal-like encryption followed by a DSA signature, however the public key for the DSA signature is ephemeral and becomes part of the ciphertext. Again we leave it for the reader to write down the decryption algorithm.

1. $k, t \in_R \{1, \ldots, q - 1\}$.

2. $r = y^{k+t}$.

3. $z = G(r)$.

4. $c_1 = g^k$.

5. $c_2 = g^t$.

6. $c_3 = (H(m) + xr)/k \pmod{q}$.

7. $c_4 = z \oplus m$.

8. Output (c_1, c_2, c_3, c_4).

Zheng and Seberry proved their schemes secure under a very strong conjectural assumption, namely that the space of ciphertexts was 'sole samplable'. This is an assumption akin to assuming that the encryption algorithm is plaintext aware. However, the first of the above schemes can be shown to be trivially insecure as follows. Suppose in the **find** stage our adversary outputs two messages m_1 and m_2. Then a hidden bit b is chosen and the adversary is given the encryption of m_b. This is equal to

$$c = (c_1, c_2) = \left(g^k, z \oplus (m_b \| H(m_b)) \right).$$

The adversary in its **guess** stage can now perform the following operations. First it generates a new message m_3, different from m_1 and m_2, but of the same length. Then the adversary asks the decryption oracle to decrypt the ciphertext

$$(c_1, c_2 \oplus (m_1 \| H(m_1)) \oplus (m_3 \| H(m_3))).$$

When $b = 1$ the above ciphertext will be a valid encryption of m_3 and so the decryption oracle will return m_3. However, when $b = 0$ the above ciphertext is highly unlikely to be a valid encryption of anything, let alone m_3. This gives us a polynomial-time test, for an adaptive adversary, to detect the value of the hidden bit b.

17.3.2 RSA-OAEP

Recall that the raw RSA function does not provide a semantically secure encryption scheme, even against passive adversaries. To make a system which is secure we need either to add redundancy to the plaintext before encryption or to add some other form of redundancy to the ciphertext. In addition the padding used needs to be random so as to make a non-deterministic encryption algorithm. This is done in RSA by using a padding scheme, and over the years a number of padding systems have been proposed. However, some of the older ones are now considered weak.

By far the most successful padding scheme in use today was invented by Bellare and Rogaway and is called OAEP or Optimized Asymmetric Encryption Padding. OAEP is a padding scheme which can be used with any function which is a one-way trapdoor permutation, in particular the RSA function. When used with RSA it is often denoted RSA-OAEP.

Originally it was thought the RSA-OAEP was a plaintext-aware encryption algorithm, but this claim has since been shown to be wrong. However, one can show in the random oracle model that RSA-OAEP is semantically secure against adaptive chosen ciphertext attacks.

We first give the description of OAEP in general. Let f be any k-bit to k-bit trapdoor one-way permutation, e.g. for $k = 1024$ one could let f be the RSA function $c = m^e$. Let k_0 and k_1 denote numbers such that a work effort of 2^{k_0} or 2^{k_1} is impossible (e.g. $k_0, k_1 > 128$). Put $n = k - k_0 - k_1$ and let

$$G : \{0,1\}^{k_0} \longrightarrow \{0,1\}^{n+k_1}$$
$$H : \{0,1\}^{n+k_1} \longrightarrow \{0,1\}^{k_0}$$

be hash functions. Let m be a message of n bits in length. We then encrypt using the function

$$E(m) = f\left(\{m \parallel 0^{k_1} \oplus G(R)\} \parallel \{R \oplus H(m0^{k_1} \oplus G(R))\}\right).$$

where

- $m \parallel 0^{k_1}$ means m followed by k_1 zero bits,

- R is a random bit string of length k_0,

- $\parallel$ denotes concatenation.

One can view OAEP as a two-stage Feistel network as Fig. 17.1 demonstrates.

Fig. 17.1   OAEP as a Feistel network

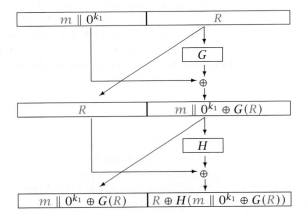

To decrypt a message given $E(m)$ and the trapdoor to f we can compute

$$A = \{T \parallel \{R \oplus H(T)\}\} = \left\{\{m \parallel 0^{k_1} \oplus G(R)\} \parallel \{R \oplus H(m \parallel 0^{k_1} \oplus G(R))\}\right\}.$$

So we know

$$T = m \parallel 0^{k_1} \oplus G(R).$$

Hence we can compute $H(T)$ and recover R from $R \oplus H(T)$. But then given R we can compute $G(R)$ and recover m. Note we need to check whether $T \oplus G(R)$ ends in k_1 zeros, if it does not then we should reject this ciphertext as invalid.

The main result about RSA-OAEP is:

Theorem 17.5 *In the random oracle model, if we model G and H by random oracles then RSA-OAEP is semantically secure against adaptive chosen ciphertext attacks if the RSA assumption holds.*

Proof
We sketch the proof and leave the details for the interested reader to look up. We first rewrite the RSA function f as

$$f : \begin{cases} \{0,1\}^{n+k_1} \times \{0,1\}^{k_0} \longrightarrow (\mathbb{Z}/N\mathbb{Z})^* \\ (s,t) \longmapsto (s\|t)^e \pmod N. \end{cases}$$

Note it is impossible to mathematically write the RSA function like this, but let us assume that we can. We then define RSA-OAEP as

$$s = (m\|0^{k_1}) \oplus G(r), \quad t = r \oplus H(s).$$

The RSA assumption can be proved to be equivalent to the partial one-wayness of the function f, in the sense that the problem of recovering s from $f(s,t)$ is as hard as recovering (s,t) from $f(s,t)$. So for the rest of our sketch we try to turn an adversary A for breaking RSA-OAEP into an algorithm B_A which solves the partial one-wayness of the RSA function. In particular B_A is given $c^* = f(s^*, t^*)$, for some fixed RSA modulus N, and is asked to compute s^*.

Algorithm B_A now calls the **find** stage of A to produce two messages m_0 and m_1. A bit b is then chosen by B_A and B_A now assumes that c^* is the encryption of m_b. The ciphertext c^* is now given to the **guess** stage of A, and A tries to guess the bit b. Whilst algorithm A is running the algorithm B_A must answer the oracle queries for the hash function G, the hash function H and the decryption oracle. To maintain consistency, B_A keeps two lists, an H-List and a G-List of all prior calls to the oracles for H and G respectively.

The oracle queries are answered by B_A as follows:

- Query $G(y)$:
  For any query δ in the H-List one checks whether

$$c^* = f(\delta, y \oplus H(\delta)).$$

  – If this holds then we have inverted f as required, we can still continue with the simulation of G and set

$$G(y) = \delta \oplus (m_b \| 0^{k_1}).$$

  – If this equality does not hold for any value of δ then we choose $G(y)$ uniformly at random from the codomain of G.

- Query $H(\delta)$:
  A random value is chosen from the codomain of H and set to this value. We also check whether for any y in the G-List we have

$$c^* = f(\delta, y \oplus H(\delta)),$$

  if so we have managed to partially invert the function f as required.

- Query decryption of c :
  We look in the G-List and the H-List for a pair y, δ such that if we set

$$\sigma = \delta, \tau = y \oplus H(\delta) \text{ and } \mu = G(y) \oplus \delta,$$

then $c = f(\sigma, \tau)$ and the k_1 least significant bits of μ are equal to zero. If this is the case then we return the plaintext consisting of the n most significant bits of μ, otherwise we return `Invalid Ciphertext`.

Notice that if a ciphertext which was generated in the correct way (by calling G, H and the encryption algorithm) is then passed to the above decryption oracle, we will obtain the original plaintext back.

We have to show that the above decryption oracle is able to 'fool' the adversary A enough of the time. In other words when the oracle is passed a ciphertext, which had not been generated by a prior call to the necessary G and H, we need to show that it produces a value which is consistent with the running of the adversary A.

Finally we need to show that if the adversary A has a non-negligible chance of breaking the semantic security of RSA-OAEP then one has a non-negligible probability that B_A can partially invert f.

These last two facts are proved by careful analysis of the probabilities associated with a number of events. Recall that B_A assumes that $c^* = f(s^*, t^*)$ is an encryption of m_b. Hence, there should exist an r^* which satisfies

$$r^* = H(s^*) \oplus t^*,$$
$$G(r^*) = s^* \oplus (m_b \| 0^{k_1}).$$

One first shows that the probability of the decryption simulator failing is negligible. Then one shows that the probability that s^* is actually asked of the H oracle is non-negligible, as long as the adversary A has a non-negligible probability of finding the bit b. But as soon as s^* is asked of H then we spot this and can therefore break the partial one-wayness of f.

The actual technical probability arguments are rather involved and we refer the reader to the paper of Fujisaki, Okamoto, Pointcheval and Stern where the full proof is given.

Q.E.D.

17.3.3 Turning CPA Schemes into CCA2 Schemes

Suppose we have a public key encryption scheme which is semantically secure against chosen plaintext attacks, such as ElGamal. Such a scheme by definition needs to be non-deterministic hence we write the encryption function as

$$E(m, r),$$

where m is the message to be encrypted and r is the random input and we denote the decryption function by $D(c)$. Hence, for ElGamal encryption we have

$$E(m, r) = (g^r, m \cdot h^r).$$

Fujisaki and Okamoto showed how to turn such a scheme into an encryption scheme which is semantically secure against adaptive adversaries. Their result only applies in the random oracle model and works by showing that the resulting scheme is plaintext aware. We do not go into the details of the proof at all, but simply give the transformation which is both simple and elegant.

We take the encryption function above and alter it by setting

$$E'(m, r) = E(m\|r, H(m\|r))$$

where H is a hash function. The decryption algorithm is also altered in that we first compute

$$m' = D(c)$$

and then we check that

$$c = E(m', H(m')).$$

If this last equation holds we recover m from $m' = m\|r$, if the equation does not hold then we return `Invalid Ciphertext`.

For ElGamal we therefore obtain the encryption algorithm

$$(g^{H(m\|r)}, (m\|r) \cdot h^{H(m\|r)}),$$

which is only marginally less efficient than raw ElGamal encryption.

Chapter Summary

- The main technique in provable security is to show how the existence of an adversary against the cryptographic scheme under consideration can be used to solve some supposedly hard problem. Since one believes the problem to be hard, one then concludes that such an adversary cannot exist.

- The random oracle model is a computational model used as a proof technique in provable security. A proof in the random oracle model does not mean the system is secure in the real world, it only provides evidence that it may be secure.

- In the random oracle model one can use the forking lemma to show that certain discrete logarithm signature schemes are secure. To obtain proofs in the case of active adversaries one uses the random oracle to simulate the signing queries of the adversary.

- One can also show in the random oracle model that the two main RSA based signature schemes used in 'real life' are also secure, namely RSA-FDH and RSA-PSS.

- Proving encryption algorithms to be secure is slightly more tricky, early attempts of Zheng and Seberry made use of non-standard assumptions.

- In the random oracle model one can prove that the standard RSA encryption method, namely RSA-OAEP, is secure.

Further Reading

Provable security is a rapidly expanding field, and the number of papers grows with each passing year. A good description of the forking lemma and its applications is given in the article of Pointcheval and Stern. The random oracle model and a number of applications including RSA-FDH and RSA-PSS are given in the papers of Bellare and Rogaway. The full proof of the security of RSA-OAEP is given in the paper of Fujisaki and others.

M. Bellare and P. Rogaway. *Random oracles are practical: a paradigm for designing efficient protocols.* In Proc. 1st Annual Conf. on Comp. and Comms. Security, ACM, 62–73, 1993.

M. Bellare and P. Rogaway. *The exact security of digital signatures – How to sign with RSA and Rabin.* In Advances in Cryptology – EuroCrypt '96. Springer-Verlag LNCS 1070, 399–416, 1996.

E. Fujisaki, T. Okamoto, D. Pointcheval and J. Stern. *RSA-OAEP is secure under the RSA assumption.* In Advances in Cryptology – CRYPTO 2001, Springer-Verlag LNCS 2139, 260–274, 2001.

D. Pointcheval and J. Stern. *Security arguments for digital signatures and blind signatures.* J. Cryptology, **13**, 361–396, 2000.

Review Exercises

17.1.1   What is meant by a non-negligible function?

17.1.2   What is the random oracle model and why does a proof in the random oracle model not apply in the real world?

17.1.3   What is the forking lemma and how is it used to prove that Schnorr signatures are secure in the random oracle model?

17.1.4   Why cannot we use the forking lemma to show that DSA is secure in the random oracle model?

17.1.5   Why, to make an encryption scheme secure against active attacks, do designers add some form redundancy?

17.1.6   What is the padding scheme used in RSA-OAEP?

17.1.7   How is the padding scheme of RSA-OAEP related to a Feistel cipher?

Standard Exercises

17.2.1   How easy is it to construct a hash function whose codomain is $(\mathbb{Z}/N\mathbb{Z})^*$, for use in RSA-FDH?

17.2.2   Write down the corresponding decryption algorithms for the second and third of the Zheng and Seberry schemes mentioned in the text.

17.2.3   The proof of RSA-OAEP assumes that f, the RSA function, is a k-bit to k-bit trapdoor one-way permutation. Is this a valid assumption, and if not does this lead to an attack on RSA-OAEP?

CHAPTER 18

Provable Security: Without Random Oracles

Chapter Goals

- To cover some of the more modern schemes which can be proved secure without recourse to the random oracle model.

- To examine the strong RSA assumption and the interactive Hash Diffie–Hellman assumption.

- To explain the GHR and Cramer–Shoup signature algorithms.

- To explain the Cramer–Shoup encryption algorithm.

- To introduce the DHIES encryption algorithm.

18.1 INTRODUCTION

In the previous chapter we looked at signature and encryption schemes which can be proved secure in the so-called 'random oracle model'. The random oracle model does not model the real world of computation. A proof in the random oracle model only provides evidence that a scheme may be secure in the real world, it does not guarantee security in the real world. We can interpret a proof in the random oracle model as saying that if an adversary against the real-world scheme exists then that adversary must make use of the specific hash function employed.

In this chapter we sketch recent work on how researchers have tried to construct signature and encryption algorithms which do not depend on the random oracle model. We shall only consider schemes which are practical, and we shall only sketch the proof ideas. Readers interested in the details of proofs or in other schemes should consult the extensive literature in this area.

What we shall see is that whilst quite natural encryption algorithms can be proved secure without the need for random oracles, the situation is quite different for signature algorithms. This is the opposite case to what we saw when we used random oracles to model hash functions. In the previous chapter it was the signature algorithms which looked more natural compared with the encryption algorithms. This should not be surprising, signature algorithms make extensive use of hash functions for their security.

Hence, we should expect that they impose stricter restraints on such hash functions, which may not be actually true in the real world.

However, the removal of the use of random oracles comes at a price. We need to make stronger intractability assumptions than we have otherwise made. In the next section we outline two such new intractability assumptions. These new assumptions are related to assumptions we have met before, for example that DDH is hard or that the RSA problem is hard, but these new problems are much less studied than the ones we have met before. They are also easier problems than ones we have met before, hence the assumption that the problems are hard is a much stronger assumption than before.

18.2   SOME NEW PROBLEMS

18.2.1   The Strong RSA Assumption

We have already met and studied the RSA assumption, which is the assumption that the following problem is hard:

Definition 18.1 (RSA Problem) *Given an RSA modulus* $N = p \cdot q$, *an exponent* e *with* $\gcd(e, \phi(N)) = 1$ *and a random* $c \in (\mathbb{Z}/N\mathbb{Z})^*$ *find* $m \in (\mathbb{Z}/N\mathbb{Z})^*$ *such that*

$$m^e = c.$$

The *strong RSA assumption* is the assumption that the following problem is hard:

Definition 18.2 (Flexible RSA Problem) *Given an RSA modulus* $N = p \cdot q$ *and a random* $c \in (\mathbb{Z}/N\mathbb{Z})^*$ *find* $e > 1$ *and* $m \in (\mathbb{Z}/N\mathbb{Z})^*$ *such that*

$$m^e = c.$$

Clearly if we can solve the RSA problem then we can solve the flexible RSA problem. This means that the strong RSA assumption is a stronger intractability assumption than the standard RSA assumption, in that it is conceivable that in the future we may be able to solve the flexible RSA problem but not the RSA problem proper. However, at present we conjecture that both problems should be equally as hard.

18.2.2   The Interactive Hash Diffie–Hellman Assumption

The interactive Hash Diffie–Hellman assumption is that a certain analogue of the decision Diffie–Hellman problem is hard. We first define what we mean by the HDH, or Hash Diffie–Hellman problem. Suppose we are given a finite cyclic abelian group G and a hash function H. The Hash Diffie–Hellman problem is to detect on input of

$$g^x, g^y \text{ and } h$$

whether

$$h = H(g^x \| g^{xy}).$$

Note this assumption combines information about the interaction between a hash function and the standard DDH assumption.

Now, assume that our adversary against HDH was given an oracle for the hidden number y which returned

$$HDH_y(X) = H(X\|X^y).$$

The interactive HDH assumption is built from the HDH assumption by modelling what an adaptive active adversary could do by using the above oracle. Clearly we need to stop the adversary calling the HDH_y oracle on the input value g^x since that would result in the instant solution of the HDH problem. Hence, we restrict the adversary in that it is not allowed to execute

$$HDH_y(g^x),$$

but all other calls to the HDH oracle are allowed. The interactive HDH assumption is that, even with access to the above oracle, the adversary still cannot solve the HDH problem.

Note the hash function is required in the definition of an adaptive attack. To see why, suppose we use the analogous definition for an adaptive attack against the decision Diffie–Hellman assumption. On input of $a = g^x, b = g^y$ and $c = g^z$ the adversary could query the non-hashed Diffie–Hellman oracle with the query

$$DH_y(g \cdot a) = DH_y(g \cdot g^x)$$

this would return

$$g^{y(x+1)} = b \cdot g^{xy}.$$

We could then divide out by b and test whether

$$g^{xy} = c.$$

Combining the hash function with the Diffie–Hellman assumption into one assumption also will allow us, in the DHIES scheme below, to remove the need for a random oracle proof. However, we still have something a little strange since it may be possible that the precise hash function we use in the scheme has some funny interaction with the exact finite abelian group used in the scheme, which together makes the HDH problem in this instance easy. One could therefore argue that the use of the HDH assumption as opposed to the random oracle model brings the same philosophical problems.

18.3 SIGNATURE SCHEMES

We have already remarked that signature schemes which are provably secure, without the random oracle model are hard to come by. They also appear somewhat contrived compared with the schemes such as RSA-PSS, DSA or Schnorr which are used in real life. The first such provably secure signature scheme in the standard model was by Goldwasser, Micali and Rivest. This was however not very practical as it relied on messages being associated with leaves of a binary tree, and each node in the tree needed to be authenticated with respect to its parent. This made the resulting scheme far too slow.

In this section we consider two modern provably secure signature schemes which are 'practical'. However, we shall see with both of them that they still come with some problems which do not occur in more standard signature schemes.

18.3.1 Gennaro–Halevi–Rabin Signature Scheme

In 1999 Gennaro, Halevi and Rabin came up with a provably secure signature scheme, called the GHR signature scheme, which does not require the random oracle model for its security. The security of this scheme is based on the strong RSA assumption.

As the key generation step one takes an RSA modulus

$$N = p \cdot q$$

where p and q are chosen to be safe primes, in that both $(p-1)/2$ and $(q-1)/2$ should also be prime. This restriction on p and q implies that finding an odd integer which is not co-prime to

$$\phi(N) = (p - 1)(q - 1)$$

is as hard as factoring. In addition to N the public key also consists of a random element $s \in (\mathbb{Z}/N\mathbb{Z})^*$.

To sign a message m the signer, who knows the factors of N, can compute a value σ such that

$$\sigma^{H(m)} = s \pmod{N}.$$

The above equation serves also as the verification equation.

One can see how the scheme is related to the strong RSA assumption immediately. However, the scheme requires a very special type of hash function. To see why, suppose an active adversary wanted a signature on a message m_1 and he could find another message m_2 such that

$$H(m_2) = a \cdot H(m_1).$$

Now suppose the active attacker asked the signer for a signature on m_2. The signer outputs σ_2 such that

$$\sigma_2^{H(m_2)} = s \pmod{N}.$$

The attacker can now forge a signature on the message m_1 by computing

$$\sigma_1 = \sigma_2^a \pmod{N},$$

since

$$
\begin{aligned}
\sigma_1^{H(m_1)} &= (\sigma_2^a)^{H(m_1)} \pmod{N} \\
&= \sigma_2^{aH(m_1)} \pmod{N} \\
&= \sigma_2^{H(m_2)} \pmod{N} \\
&= s.
\end{aligned}
$$

The authors of the above signature scheme propose that the easiest way to avoid this type of attack would be for the hash function to be such that it always returned a random prime number. One would still require that finding collisions in the hash function was hard. Whilst it is possible to design hash functions which only output prime numbers they are not well studied and are not 'natural' hash functions.

18.3.2   The Cramer–Shoup Signature Scheme

The Cramer–Shoup signature scheme is still based on the strong RSA assumption and is provably secure, without the need for the random oracle model. Like the previous GHR signature scheme the signer needs to generate prime numbers, but these do not have to be the output of the hash function. Hence, the Cramer–Shoup scheme can make use of a standard hash function, such as SHA-1. In our discussion below we shall assume H is a 'standard' hash function which outputs bit strings of 160 bits, which we interpret as 160-bit integers as usual.

Again to generate the public key, we create an RSA modulus N which is the produce of two safe primes p and q. We also choose two random elements

$$h, x \in Q_N,$$

where as usual Q_N is the set of quadratic residues modulo N. We also create a random 160-bit prime e'. The public key consists of

$$(N, h, x, e')$$

whilst the private key is the factors p and q.

To sign a message the signer generates another 160-bit prime number e and another random element $y' \in Q_N$. The signer then computes, since they know the factors of N, the solution y to the equation

$$y = \left(xh^{H(x')}\right)^{1/e} \pmod{N},$$

where x' satisfies

$$x' = y'^{e'} h^{-H(m)}.$$

The output of the signer is

$$(e, y, y').$$

To verify a message the verifier first checks that e' is an odd number satisfying

$$e \neq e'.$$

Then the verifier computes

$$x' = y'^{e'} h^{-H(m)}$$

and then checks that

$$x = y^e h^{-H(x')}.$$

On the assumption that H is a collision resistant hash function and the strong RSA assumption holds, one can prove that the above scheme is secure against active adversaries. We sketch the most important part of the proof, but the full details are left to the interested reader to look up.

Assume the adversary makes t queries to a signing oracle. We want to use the adversary A to create an algorithm B_A to break the strong RSA assumption for the modulus N. Before setting up the public key for input to algorithm A, the algorithm B_A first decides on what prime values e_i it will output in the signature queries. Then, having knowledge of the e_i, the algorithm B_A concocts values for the h and x in the public key, so that it always knows the e_ith root of h and x.

So when given a signing query for a message m_i, algorithm B_A can then compute a valid signature, without knowing the factorization of N, by generating $y'_i \in Q_N$ at random and then computing

$$x'_i = y'^{e'}_i h^{-H(m_i)} \pmod{N}$$

and then

$$y_i = x^{1/e_i}(h^{1/e_i})^{H(x'_i)} \pmod{N},$$

the signature being given by

$$(m_i, y_i, y'_i).$$

The above basic signing simulation is modified in the full proof, depending on what type of forgery algorithm A is producing. But the basic idea is that B_A creates a public key to enable it to respond to every signing query in a valid way.

18.4   ENCRYPTION ALGORITHMS

Unlike the case of signature schemes, for encryption algorithms one can produce provably secure systems which are practical and close to those used in 'real life', without assuming the random oracle model. In fact the second of the two schemes we consider in this section, namely DHIES, is the public key encryption algorithm based on the discrete logarithm problem in finite fields or elliptic curves which is given in various standards documents.

One problem with DHIES is that its security is partly based on the difficulty of solving the interactive HDH problem. This is not as well studied a problem as the usual DDH problem, so first we shall present a provably secure scheme whose security rests on the usual DDH problem.

18.4.1   The Cramer–Shoup Encryption Scheme

The Cramer–Shoup encryption scheme requires as domain parameters a finite abelian group G of prime order q. In addition we require a universal one-way family of hash functions. Recall, this is a family $\{H_i\}$ of hash functions for which it is hard for an adversary to choose an input x, then to draw a random hash function H_i, and then to find a different input y so that

$$H_i(x) = H_i(y).$$

A public key in the Cramer–Shoup scheme is chosen as follows. First the following random elements are selected

$$g_1, g_2 \in G,$$
$$x_1, x_2, y_1, y_2, z \in \mathbb{Z}/q\mathbb{Z}.$$

The user then computes the following elements

$$c = g_1{}^{x_1} g_2{}^{x_2},$$
$$d = g_1{}^{y_1} g_2{}^{y_2},$$
$$h = g_1{}^{z}.$$

The user finally chooses a hash function H from the universal one-way family of hash functions and outputs the public key

$$(g_1, g_2, c, d, h, H),$$

whilst keeping the private key secret

$$(x_1, x_2, y_1, y_2, z).$$

The encryption algorithm proceeds as follows, which is very similar to ElGamal encryption. The message m is considered as an element of G. The sender then chooses a random ephemeral key $r \in \mathbb{Z}/q\mathbb{Z}$ and computes

$$u_1 = g_1{}^{r},$$
$$u_2 = g_2{}^{r},$$
$$e = m \cdot h^{r},$$
$$\alpha = H(u_1 \| u_2 \| e),$$
$$v = c^{r} d^{r\alpha}.$$

The ciphertext is then the quadruple

$$(u_1, u_2, e, v).$$

On receiving this ciphertext the owner of the private key can recover the message as follows: First they compute $\alpha = H(u_1 \| u_2 \| e)$ and test whether

$$u_1{}^{x_1 + y_1 \alpha} u_2{}^{x_2 + y_2 \alpha} = v.$$

If this equation does not hold then the ciphertext should be rejected. If this equation holds then the receiver can decrypt the ciphertext by computing

$$m = \frac{e}{u_1{}^{z}}.$$

To show that the scheme is provably secure, under the assumption that the DDH problem is hard and that H is chosen from a universal one-way family of hash functions, we assume we have an adversary A against the scheme and show how to use A in another algorithm B_A which tries to solve the DDH problem.

One way to phrase the DDH problem is as follows: Given $(g_1, g_2, u_1, u_2) \in G$ determine whether either this quadruple is a random quadruple or we have $u_1 = g_1{}^{r}$

and $u_2 = g_2{}^r$ for some value of $r \in \mathbb{Z}/q\mathbb{Z}$. So algorithm B_A will take as input a quadruple $(g_1, g_2, u_1, u_2) \in G$ and try to determine whether this is a random quadruple or a quadruple related to the Diffie–Hellman problem.

Algorithm B_A first needs to choose a public key, which it does in a non-standard way, by first selecting the random elements

$$x_1, x_2, y_1, y_2, z_1, z_2 \in \mathbb{Z}/q\mathbb{Z}.$$

Algorithm B_A then computes the following elements

$$c = g_1{}^{x_1} g_2{}^{x_2},$$
$$d = g_1{}^{y_1} g_2{}^{y_2},$$
$$h = g_1{}^{z_1} g_2{}^{z_2}.$$

Finally B_A chooses a hash function H from the universal one-way family of hash functions and outputs the public key

$$(g_1, g_2, c, d, h, H).$$

Notice that the part of the public key corresponding to h has been chosen differently than in the real scheme, but that algorithm A will not be able to detect this change.

Algorithm B_A now runs the **find** stage of algorithm A, responding to decryption queries of (u_1', u_2', e', v') by computing

$$m = \frac{e'}{u_1'^{z_1} u_2'^{z_2}},$$

after performing the standard check on validity of the ciphertext. The output of the **find** stage will be two plaintexts m_0, m_1.

After running the **find** stage, algorithm B_A chooses a bit b at random and computes the target ciphertext as

$$e = m_b \cdot (u_1{}^{z_1} u_2{}^{z_2}),$$
$$\alpha = H(u_1 \| u_2 \| e),$$
$$v = u_1{}^{x_1 + y_1 \alpha} u_2{}^{x_2 + y_2 \alpha}.$$

The target ciphertext is then the quadruple

$$(u_1, u_2, e, v).$$

Notice that when the input to B_A is a legitimate DDH quadruple then the target ciphertext will be a valid encryption, but when the input to B_A is not a legitimate DDH quadruple then the target ciphertext is highly likely to be an invalid ciphertext.

This target ciphertext is then passed to the **guess** stage of the adversary A. If this adversary outputs the correct value of b then we suspect that the input to B_A is a valid DDH quadruple, whilst if the output is wrong then we suspect that the input to B_A is not valid. This produces a statistical test to detect whether the input to B_A was valid or not. By repeating this test a number of times we can produce as accurate a statistical test as we want.

Note, that the above is only a sketch. We need to show that the view of the adversary A in the above game is no different from that in a real attack on the system, otherwise A would know something was not correct. For example we need to show that the responses B_A makes to the decryption queries of A cannot be distinguished from a true decryption oracle. For further details one should consult the full proof in the paper mentioned in the Further Reading section.

Notice that, whilst very similar to ElGamal encryption, the Cramer–Shoup encryption scheme is much less efficient. Hence, whilst provably secure it is not used much in practice due to the performance disadvantages. The DHIES scheme considered next is also provably secure without the random oracle model, although the underlying intractability assumption is less studied, however DHIES is only slightly less efficient than the ElGamal encryption scheme from Chapter 7.

18.4.2   The DHIES Encryption Scheme

The DHIES encryption scheme is very similar to the type of immunization techniques originally proposed by Zheng and Seberry. However, one can prove that DHIES is secure against adaptive chosen ciphertext attack, assuming the three components are themselves secure, the three components being

- A finite cyclic abelian group in which the interactive Hash Diffie–Hellman (HDH) assumption holds.

- A symmetric key based encryption function which is semantically secure against adaptive chosen plaintext attacks.

- A message authentication code, or keyed hash function, for which an active adversary cannot find the MAC of an 'unasked message'. One should think of this last concept as a MAC version of existential forgery.

The DHIES scheme of Bellare and Rogaway integrates all three of the above components giving rise to the schemes name, Diffie–Hellman Integrated Encryption Scheme. Originally the scheme was called DHAES, for Diffie–Hellman Augmented Encryption Scheme, but this caused confusion with the Advanced Encryption Standard.

Key generation for DHIES is just like that of ElGamal encryption. The domain parameters are a cyclic finite abelian group G of prime order q, a generator g, a symmetric encryption function $\{E_k, D_k\}$, a MAC function which we shall denote by MAC_k and a hash function H. The hash function and the group need to be chosen so that the interactive HDH assumption holds.

To generate a public/private key pair we generate a random $x \in \mathbb{Z}/q\mathbb{Z}$ and compute the public key

$$f = g^x.$$

To encrypt a message m we generate a random per message ephemeral key k and compute

$$v = f^k \text{ and } u = g^k.$$

Then we pass this into the hash function to obtain two keys, one for the symmetric encryption algorithm and one for the MAC function,

$$(k_1, k_2) = H(u \| v).$$

We then compute

$$c = E_{k_1}(m),$$
$$t = MAC_{k_2}(c).$$

The ciphertext is transmitted as the triple

$$u \| c \| t.$$

Notice that this scheme allows arbitrary long messages to be encrypted efficiently using a public key scheme. The u acts as a key transport mechanism, the encryption is performed using a symmetric encryption function, the protection against adaptive adversaries for the whole scheme is provided by the addition of the MAC t.

On receiving the ciphertext $u \| c \| t$ the legitimate private key holder can compute

$$v = u^x.$$

Then the two keys k_1 and k_2 can be computed via

$$(k_1, k_2) = H(u \| v).$$

The ciphertext is then rejected if the MAC does not verify, i.e. we should have

$$t = MAC_{k_2}(c).$$

Finally, the plaintext is recovered from

$$m = D_{k_1}(c).$$

We now sketch how to prove that DHIES is secure against adaptive adversaries, assuming the interactive HDH assumption holds and the symmetric encryption and MAC functions are chosen appropriately. To do this we assume an adversary A against DHIES and show how this can be used to either solve the interactive HDH assumption or to break the symmetric encryption scheme or to forge a MAC.

We will construct an algorithm B_A whose goal is to solve the interactive HDH assumption. The algorithm B_A is given as input

$$g^x, g^y \text{ and } h$$

and is asked to detect whether

$$h = H(g^y \| g^{xy}).$$

Algorithm B_A is also given an oracle $\mathcal{O}$ for the hidden number x which returns

$$HDH_x(X) = H(X \| X^x).$$

Algorithm B_A sets up the public key

$$f = g^x.$$

It calls the **find** stage of algorithm A to obtain two messages m_0 and m_1. Then B_A chooses a random bit b and defines the keys k_1, k_2 from h via

$$k_1 \| k_2 = h.$$

Algorithm B_A then computes

$$c = E_{k_1}(m_b),$$
$$t = MAC_{k_2}(c).$$

Finally B_A computes the ciphertext

$$(g^y, c, t),$$

and passes it to the **guess** stage of algorithm A. Eventually A will return its guess as to the hidden bit b.

   If this guess is correct then B_A concludes that the input was likely to be a valid HDH input; if the guess is incorrect then B_A concludes that the input was likely not be a valid HDH input. The proof of the security shows that either B_A detects the validity or invalidity of the HDH input or it manages to break the semantic security of the symmetric encryption function or it manages to create a forgery for the MAC function. The details of the proof are quite interesting but are left for the interested reader.

   The only issue we shall discuss is how algorithm B_A answers the decryption queries of algorithm A. We give a simplified explanation, the full details are slightly more involved. Recall B_A has access to an oracle $\mathcal{O}$ for the HDH problem for the hidden key x. On obtaining the ciphertext query

$$u_i \| c_i \| t_i$$

the algorithm B_A calls its HDH oracle to compute

$$(k_1, k_2) = \mathcal{O}(u_i) = H(u_i \| u_i^x).$$

The simulation can then check the validity of the ciphertext and return the correct plaintext just as the genuine decryptor would do. The problem with the above is we need to deal with the case where the decryption oracle is called with a ciphertext for which $u_i = g^y$, since this is an invalid query for the HDH oracle according to the earlier definition of game that B_A is playing to break the HDH assumption. For how to overcome this problem one should consult the original paper.

   Notice that the *interactive* nature of the interactive HDH assumption was required to simulate the decryption oracle. This has led people to criticize the proof since it reduces the security of the DHIES scheme to a completely non-standard intractability assumption. This is the only interactive intractability assumption that one can find in the literature. One could also argue that it has the same problems associated with the random oracle model, as the HDH assumption hides any non-trivial interaction between the hash function and the decision Diffie-Hellman assumption. Despite these shortcomings in the proof for DHIES, the scheme is used in real life since it is highly efficient.

Chapter Summary

- Signature schemes which are secure without the random oracle model are less natural than those which are secure in the random oracle model. This is probably because signatures make crucial use of hash functions which are easy to model by random oracles.

- The strong RSA assumption is a natural weakening of the standard RSA assumption.

- The interactive Hash Diffie-Hellman assumption is a considerable weakening of the usual DDH assumption. The HDH assumption combines interactions between the hash function used and the Diffie-Hellman problem within the given group. The interactive nature also creates an intractability assumption which is completely non-standard.

- The Cramer-Shoup encryption scheme is provably secure, without the random oracle model, assuming the DDH problem is hard. It is around three times slower than the usual ElGamal encryption algorithm.

- The DHIES encryption scheme is also provably secure, without the random oracle model. However, its security is based in the interactive Hash Diffie-Hellman assumption. The advantage of DHIES is that it is very efficient, this has led it to be adopted by a number of standards bodies.

Further Reading

The schemes mentioned in this chapter can be found in the following papers.

M. Abdalla, M. Bellare and P. Rogaway. *DHAES: An encryption scheme based on the Diffie-Hellman problem*. Submission to IEEE P1363a standard.

R. Cramer and V. Shoup. *A practical public key cryptosystem provably secure against adaptive chosen ciphertext attack*. In Advances in Cryptology - CRYPTO '98, Springer-Verlag LNCS 1462, 13-25, 1998.

R. Cramer and V. Shoup. *Signature schemes based on the strong RSA assumption*. ACM Transactions on Information and Systems Security, 3, 161-185, 2000.

R. Gennaro, S. Halevi and T. Rabin. *Secure hash-and-sign signatures without the random oracle.* In Advances in Cryptology – EuroCrypt '99, Springer-Verlag LNCS 1592, 123–139, 1999.

Standard Exercises

18.1.1   Try to invent an efficient hash function to use with the scheme of Gennaro, Halevi and Rabin. Are there any computational assumptions which allow you to prove, for your hash function, that it is hard to find collisions?

18.1.2   In the signing simulations for the Cramer–Shoup signature algorithm we needed to compute a value of Q_N at random without knowing the factorization of N. Since testing for membership of Q_N is believed to be as hard as factoring, how can this stage of the simulation be efficiently accomplished?

18.1.3   In the Cramer–Shoup encryption algorithm, show that a valid ciphertext will always pass the test given by the equation,

$$u_1{}^{x_1+y_1\alpha} u_2{}^{x_2+y_2\alpha} = v.$$

18.1.4   In the proof sketch for the Cramer–Shoup encryption scheme, show that the target ciphertext given to the **guess** stage of the adversary is a valid ciphertext when the input to B_A is a valid DDH quadruple.

Appendix A
Basic Mathematical Terminology

This appendix is presented as a series of notes which summarizes most of the mathematical terminology needed in this book. In this appendix we present the material in a more formal manner than we did in Chapter 1 and the rest of the book.

A.1 SETS

Here we recap on some basic definitions etc. which we list here for completeness.

Definition A.1 *For two sets A, B we define the union, intersection, difference and Cartesian product by*

$$A \cup B = \{x : x \in A \text{ or } x \in B\},$$
$$A \cap B = \{x : x \in A \text{ and } x \in B\},$$
$$A \setminus B = \{x : x \in A \text{ and } x \notin B\},$$
$$A \times B = \{(x, y) : x \in A \text{ and } y \in B\}.$$

The statement $A \subset B$ means that

$$x \in A \Rightarrow x \in B.$$

Using these definitions one can prove in a standard way all the basic results of set theory that one shows in school using Venn diagrams. For example

Lemma A.2 *If $A \subset B$ and $B \subset C$ then $A \subset C$.*

Proof

Let x be an element of A, we wish to show that x is an element of C. Now as $A \subset B$ we have that $x \in B$, and as $B \subset C$ we then deduce that $x \in C$.

Q.E.D.

Notice that this is a proof whereas an argument using Venn diagrams is not a proof. Using Venn diagrams merely shows you were not clever enough to come up with a picture which proved the result false.

A.2   RELATIONS

Next we define relations and some properties that they have. Relations, especially equivalence relations, play an important part in algebra and it is worth considering them at this stage so it is easier to understand what is going on later.

Definition A.3 *A (binary) relation on a set A is a subset of the Cartesian product $A \times A$.*

This we explain with an example:

Consider the relationship 'less than or equal to' between natural numbers. This obviously gives us the set

$$LE = \{(x, y) : x, y \in \mathbb{N}, \ x \text{ is less than or equal to } y\}.$$

In much the same way every relationship that you have met before can be written in this set-theoretic way. An even better way to put the above is to define the relation less than or equal to to be the set

$$LE = \{(x, y) : x, y \in \mathbb{N}, \ x - y \notin \mathbb{N} \setminus \{0\}\}.$$

Obviously this is a very cumbersome notation so for a relation R on a set S we write

$$x \, R \, y$$

if $(x, y) \in R$, i.e. if we now write $\leq$ for LE we obtain the usual notation $1 \leq 2$ etc.

Relations which are of interest in mathematics usually satisfy one or more of the following four properties:

Definition A.4

A relation R on a set S is reflexive if for all $x \in S$ we have $(x, x) \in R$.

A relation R on a set S is symmetric if $(x, y) \in R$ implies that $(y, x) \in R$.

A relation R on a set S is anti-symmetric if $(x, y) \in R$ and $(y, x) \in R$ implies that $x = y$.

A relation R on a set S is transitive if $(x, y) \in R$ and $(y, z) \in R$ implies that $(x, z) \in R$.

We return to our example of $\leq$. This relation $\leq$ is certainly reflexive as $x \leq x$ for all $x \in \mathbb{N}$. It is not symmetric as $x \leq y$ does not imply that $y \leq x$, however it is anti-symmetric as $x \leq y$ and $y \leq x$ imply that $x = y$. You should note that it is transitive as well.

Relations like $\leq$ occur so frequently that we give them a name:

Definition A.5 *A relation which is reflexive, transitive and anti-symmetric is called a partial order relation.*

Definition A.6 *A relation which is transitive and anti-symmetric and which for all x, y we have either $(x, y) \in R$ or $(y, x) \in R$ is called a total order relation.*

Another important type of relationship is that of an equivalence relation:

Definition A.7 *A relation which is reflexive, symmetric and transitive is called an equivalence relation.*

The obvious example of $\mathbb{N}$ and the relation 'is equal to' is an equivalence relation and hence gives this type of relation its name. One of the major problems in any science is that of classification of sets of objects. This amounts to placing the objects into mutually disjoint subsets. An equivalence relation allows us to place equivalent elements into disjoint subsets. Each of these subsets is called an equivalence class. If the properties we are interested in are constant over each equivalence class then we may as well restrict our attention to the equivalence classes themselves. This often leads to greater understanding. In the jargon this process is called factoring out by the equivalence relation. It occurs frequently in algebra to define new objects from old, e.g. quotient groups. The following example is probably the most familiar being a description of modular arithmetic:

Let m be a fixed positive integer. Consider the equivalence relation on $\mathbb{Z}$ which says x is related to y if $(x - y)$ is divisible by m. This is an equivalence relation, which you should check. The equivalence classes we denote by

$$\overline{0} = \{\ldots, -2m, -m, 0, m, 2m, \ldots\},$$
$$\overline{1} = \{\ldots, -2m + 1, -m + 1, 1, m + 1, 2m + 1, \ldots\},$$
$$\ldots \quad \ldots$$
$$\overline{m - 1} = \{\ldots, -m - 1, -1, m - 1, 2m - 1, 3m - 1, \ldots\}.$$

Note that there are m distinct equivalence classes, one for each of the possible remainders on division by m. The classes are often called the residue classes modulo m. The resulting set $\{\overline{0}, \ldots, \overline{m - 1}\}$ is often denoted by $\mathbb{Z}/m\mathbb{Z}$ as we have divided out by all multiples of m. If m is a prime number, say p, then the resulting set is often denoted $\mathbb{F}_p$ as the resulting object is a field.

A.3   FUNCTIONS

We give two definitions of functions; the first is wordy and is easier to get hold of, the second is set-theoretic.

Definition A.8 *A function is a rule which maps the elements of one set, the domain, with those of another, the codomain. Each element in the domain must map to one and only one element in the codomain.*

The point here is that the function is not just the rule, e.g. $f(x) = x^2$, but also the two sets that one is using. A few examples will suffice.

1. The rule $f(x) = \sqrt{x}$ is not a function from $\mathbb{R}$ to $\mathbb{R}$ since the square root of a negative number is not in $\mathbb{R}$. It is also not a function from $\mathbb{R}_{\geq 0}$ to $\mathbb{R}$ since every

element of the domain has two square roots in the codomain. But it is a function from $\mathbb{R}_{\geq 0}$ to $\mathbb{R}_{\geq 0}$.

2. The rule $f(x) = 1/x$ is not a function from $\mathbb{R}$ to $\mathbb{R}$ but it is a function from $\mathbb{R} \setminus \{0\}$ to $\mathbb{R}$.

3. Note not every element of the codomain need have an element mapping to it. Hence, the rule $f(x) = x^2$ taking elements of $\mathbb{R}$ to elements of $\mathbb{R}$ is a function.

Our definition of a function is unsatisfactory as it would also require a definition of what a rule is. In keeping with the spirit of everything else we have done we give a set-theoretic description.

Definition A.9 *A function from the set A to the set B is a subset F of $A \times B$ such that:*

1. *If $(x, y) \in F$ and $(x, z) \in F$ then $y = z$.*

2. *For all $x \in A$ there exists a $y \in B$ such that $(x, y) \in F$.*

The set A is called the domain, the set B the codomain. The first condition means that each element in the domain maps to at most one element in the codomain. The second condition means that each element of the domain maps to at least one element in the codomain. Given a function f from A to B and an element x of A then we denote by $f(x)$ the unique element in B such that $(x, f(x)) \in f$.

One can compose functions, if the definitions make sense. Say one has a function f from A to B and a function g from B to C then the function $g \circ f$ is the function with domain A and codomain C consisting of the elements $(x, g(f(x)))$.

Lemma A.10 *Let f be a function from A to B, let g be a function from B to C and h be a function from C to D, then we have*

$$h \circ (g \circ f) = (h \circ g) \circ f.$$

Proof
Let (a, d) belong to $(h \circ g) \circ f$. Then their exists an $(a, b) \in f$ and a $(b, d) \in (h \circ g)$ for some $b \in B$, by definition of composition of functions. Again by definition there exists a $c \in C$ such that $(b, c) \in g$ and $(c, d) \in h$. Hence $(a, c) \in (g \circ f)$, which shows $(a, d) \in h \circ (g \circ f)$. Hence

$$(h \circ g) \circ f \subset h \circ (g \circ f).$$

Similarly one can show the other inclusion.

Q.E.D.

One function, the identity function, is particularly important:

Definition A.11 *The identity function id_A on a set A is the set $\{(x, x) : x \in A\}$.*

Lemma A.12 *For any function f from A to B we have*

$$f \circ \mathrm{id}_B = \mathrm{id}_A \circ f = f.$$

Proof

Let x be an element of A, then

$$(f \circ \mathrm{id}_A)(x) = f(\mathrm{id}_A(x)) = f(x) = \mathrm{id}_B(f(x)) = (\mathrm{id}_B \circ f)(x).$$

Q.E.D.

Two properties that we shall use all the time are the following:

Definition A.13

A function f from A to B is said to be injective (or 1:1) if for any two elements, x, y of A with $f(x) = f(y)$ we have $x = y$.

A function f from A to B is said to be surjective (or onto) if for every element $b \in B$ there exists an element $a \in A$ such that $f(a) = b$.

A function which is both injective and surjective is called bijective (or a 1:1 correspondence). We shall now give some examples.

1. The function from $\mathbb{R}$ to $\mathbb{R}$ given by $f(x) = x + 2$ is bijective.

2. The function from $\mathbb{N}$ to $\mathbb{N}$ given by $f(x) = x + 2$ is injective but not surjective as the elements $\{0, 1\}$ are not the image of anything.

3. The function from $\mathbb{R}$ to $\mathbb{R}_{\geq 0}$ given by $f(x) = x^2$ is surjective as every non-negative real number has a square root in $\mathbb{R}$ but it is not injective as if $x^2 = y^2$ then we could have $x = -y$.

The following gives us a good reason to study bijective functions.

Lemma A.14 *A function $f : A \to B$ is bijective if and only if there exists a function $g : B \to A$ such that $f \circ g$ and $g \circ f$ are the identity function.*

We leave the proof of this lemma as an exercise. Note, applying this lemma to the resulting g means that g is also bijective. Such a function as g in the above lemma is called an inverse of f and is usually denoted f^{-1}. Note that a function only has an inverse if it is bijective.

A.4   PERMUTATIONS

We let A be a finite set of cardinality n, without loss of generality we can assume that $A = \{1, 2, \ldots, n\}$. A bijective function from A to A is called a permutation. The set of all permutations on a set of cardinality n is denoted by S_n.

Suppose $A = \{1, 2, 3\}$, then we have the permutation $f(1) = 2$, $f(2) = 3$ and $f(3) = 1$. This is a very cumbersome way to write a permutation. Mathematicians (being lazy people) have invented the following notation, the function f above is written as

$$\begin{pmatrix} 1 & 2 & 3 \\ 2 & 3 & 1 \end{pmatrix}.$$

What should be noted about this notation (which applies for arbitrary n) is that all the numbers between 1 and n occur exactly once on each row. The first row is always given as the numbers 1 to n in increasing order. Any such matrix with these properties represents a permutation, and all permutations can be represented by such a matrix. This leads us to the elementary

Lemma A.15 *The cardinality of the set S_n is $n!$.*

Proof
This is a well-known argument. There are n choices for the first element in the second row of the above matrix. Then there are $n - 1$ choices for the second element in the second row and so on.

Q.E.D.

As permutations are nothing but functions we can compose them (this is called in the jargon multiplying the permutations). Remembering that $g \circ f$ means apply the function f and then apply the function g we see that

$$\begin{pmatrix} 1 & 2 & 3 \\ 2 & 3 & 1 \end{pmatrix} \circ \begin{pmatrix} 1 & 2 & 3 \\ 3 & 2 & 1 \end{pmatrix}$$

means $1 \to 3 \to 1$, $2 \to 2 \to 3$ and $3 \to 1 \to 2$. Hence, the result of composing (multiplying) the above two permutations is

$$\begin{pmatrix} 1 & 2 & 3 \\ 1 & 3 & 2 \end{pmatrix}. \tag{A.1}$$

Mathematicians are, as we said, by nature lazy people and this notation we have introduced is still a little too much. For instance we always write down the numbers $1, \ldots, n$ in the top row of each matrix to represent a permutation. Also some columns are redundant, for instance the first column of the permutation (A.1). We now introduce another notation for permutations which is concise and clear. We first need to define what a cycle is.

Definition A.16 *By a cycle or n-cycle we mean the object $(x_1, \ldots, x_n)$ with distinct $x_i \in \mathbb{N} \setminus \{0\}$. This represents the permutation $f(x_1) = x_2$, $f(x_2) = x_3$, $\ldots$, $f(x_{n-1}) = x_n$, $f(x_n) = x_1$ and for $x \notin \{x_1, \ldots, x_n\}$ we have $f(x) = x$.*

For instance we have

$$\begin{pmatrix} 1 & 2 & 3 \\ 2 & 3 & 1 \end{pmatrix} = (1, 2, 3) = (2, 3, 1) = (3, 1, 2).$$

Notice that a cycle is not a unique way of representing a permutation. As another example we have

$$\begin{pmatrix} 1 & 2 & 3 \\ 3 & 2 & 1 \end{pmatrix} = (1, 3)(2) = (3, 1)(2).$$

The identity permutation is represented by $()$. Again, as mathematicians are lazy we always write $(1, 3)(2) = (1, 3)$. This can lead to ambiguities as $(1, 2)$ could represent a function from

$$\{1, 2\} \text{ to } \{1, 2\}$$

or

$$\{1, 2, \ldots, n\} \text{ to } \{1, 2, \ldots, n\}.$$

Which function it represents is usually however clear from the context.

Two cycles $(x_1, \ldots, x_n)$ and $(y_1, \ldots, y_n)$ are called disjoint if $\{x_1, \ldots, x_n\} \cap \{y_1, \ldots, y_n\} = \varnothing$. It is easy to show that if σ and τ are two disjoint cycles then

$$\sigma \circ \tau = \tau \circ \sigma.$$

Note this is not true for cycles which are not disjoint, e.g.

$$(1,2,3,4) \circ (3,5) = (1,2,3,5,4) \neq (1,2,5,3,4) = (3,5) \circ (1,2,3,4).$$

What really makes cycles interesting is the following

Lemma A.17 *Every permutation can be written as a product of disjoint cycles.*

Proof
Let σ be a permutation on $\{1, \ldots, n\}$. Let σ_1 denote the cycle

$$(1, \sigma(1), \sigma(\sigma(1)), \ldots, \sigma(\ldots \sigma(1) \ldots)),$$

where we keep applying σ until we get back to 1. We then take an element x of $\{1, \ldots, n\}$ such that $\sigma_1(x) = x$ and consider the cycle σ_2 given by

$$(x, \sigma(x), \sigma(\sigma(x)), \ldots, \sigma(\ldots \sigma(x) \ldots)).$$

We then take an element of $\{1, \ldots, n\}$ which is fixed by σ_1 and σ_2 to create a cycle σ_3. We continue this way until we have used all elements of $\{1, \ldots, n\}$. The resulting cycles $\sigma_1, \ldots, \sigma_t$ are obviously disjoint and their product is equal to the cycle σ.

Q.E.D.

What is nice about this proof is that it is constructive. Given a permutation we can follow the procedure in the proof to obtain the permutation as a product of disjoint cycles.

Consider the permutation

$$\sigma = \begin{pmatrix} 1 & 2 & 3 & 4 & 5 & 6 & 7 & 8 & 9 \\ 2 & 3 & 7 & 6 & 8 & 4 & 1 & 5 & 9 \end{pmatrix}.$$

We have $\sigma(1) = 2$, $\sigma(2) = 3$, $\sigma(3) = 7$ and $\sigma(7) = 1$ so the first cycle is

$$\sigma_1 = (1,2,3,7).$$

The next element of $\{1, \ldots, 9\}$ which we have not yet considered is 4. We have $\sigma(4) = 6$ and $\sigma(6) = 4$ so $\sigma_2 = (4,6)$. Continuing in this way we find $\sigma_3 = (5,8)$ and $\sigma_4 = (9)$. Hence we have

$$\sigma = (1,2,3,7)(4,6)(5,8)(9) = (1,2,3,7)(4,6)(5,8).$$

A.5 OPERATIONS

In mathematics one meets lots of binary operations: ordinary addition and multiplication, composition of functions, matrix addition and multiplication, multiplication of permutations, etc., the list is somewhat endless. All of these binary operations have a lot in common, they also have many differences, for instance, for two real numbers x and y we have $x \cdot y = y \cdot x$, but for two 2 by 2 matrices with real entries, A and B, it is not true that we always have $A \cdot B = B \cdot A$. To study the similarities and differences between these operations we formalize the concept below. We then prove some results which are true of operations given some basic properties, these results can then be applied to any of the operations above which satisfy the given properties. Hence our abstraction will allow us to prove results in many areas at once.

Definition A.18 *A (binary) operation on a set A is a function from the domain $A \times A$ to the codomain A.*

So if $A = \mathbb{R}$ we could have the function $f(x, y) = x + y$. Writing $f(x, y)$ all the time can become a pain so we often write a symbol between the x and the y to denote the operation, e.g.

$$x \cdot y \quad x + y \quad x\, y$$
$$x \circ y \quad x \odot y \quad x \diamond y$$
$$x \wedge y \quad x \vee y \quad x \star y.$$

Most often we write $x + y$ and $x \cdot y$, we refer to the former as additive notation and the latter as multiplicative notation. One should bear in mind that we may not be actually referring to ordinary multiplication and addition when we use these terms/notations.

Operations can satisfy various properties:

Definition A.19 (Associative) *An operation $\diamond$ is said to be associative if for all x, y and z we have*

$$(x \diamond y) \diamond z = x \diamond (y \diamond z).$$

Operations which are associative include all those examples mentioned above. Non-associative operations do exist but cryptographers have very little interest in them. Note that for an associative operation the expression

$$w \diamond x \diamond y \diamond z$$

is well defined, as long as we do not move the relative position of any of the terms it does not matter which operation we carry out first.

Definition A.20 (Commutative) *An operation $\vee$ is said to be commutative if for all x and y we have*

$$x \vee y = y \vee x.$$

Ordinary addition, multiplication and matrix addition is commutative, but multiplication of matrices and permutations is not.

Definition A.21 (Identity) *An operation $\cdot$ on the set A is said to have an identity if there exists an element e of A such that for all x we have*

$$e \cdot x = x \cdot e = x.$$

The first thing we notice is that all the example operations above possess an identity, but that ordinary subtraction on the set $\mathbb{R}$ does not possess an identity. The following shows that there can be at most one identity for any given operation.

Lemma A.22 *If an identity exists then it is unique. It is then called 'the' identity.*

Proof

Suppose there are two identities e and e'. As e is an identity we have $e \cdot e' = e'$ and as e' is an identity we have $e \cdot e' = e$. Hence, we have $e' = e \cdot e' = e$.

Q.E.D.

Usually if we are using an additive notation then we denote the identity by 0 to correspond with the identity for ordinary addition, and if we are using the multiplicative notation then we denote the identity by either 1 or e.

Definition A.23 (Inverses) *Let $+$ be an operation on a set A with identity 0. Let $x \in A$. If there is a $y \in A$ such that*

$$x + y = y + x = 0$$

then we call y an inverse of x.

In the additive notation it is usual to write the inverse of x as $-x$. In the multiplicative notation it is usual to write the inverse as x^{-1}.

All elements in $\mathbb{R}$ have inverses with respect to ordinary addition. All elements in $\mathbb{R}$ except zero have inverses with respect to ordinary multiplication. Every permutation has an inverse with respect to multiplication of permutations. However, only square matrices of non-zero determinant have inverses with respect to matrix multiplication.

The next result shows that an element can have at most one inverse assuming the operation is associative.

Lemma A.24 *Consider an associative operation on a set A with identity e. Let $x \in A$ have an inverse y, then this inverse is unique, we call it 'the' inverse.*

Proof

Suppose their are two such inverses y and y' then

$$y = ye = y(xy') = (yx)y' = ey' = y'.$$

Note how we used the associativity property above.

Q.E.D.

We shall assume from now on that all operations we shall encounter are associative. Say one wishes to perform the same operation over and over again, for example

$$x \vee x \vee x \vee \cdots \vee x \vee x.$$

If our operation is written additively then we write for $n \in \mathbb{N}$, $n \cdot x$ for $x + \cdots + x$, whilst if our operation is written multiplicatively we write x^n for $x \cdots x$.

The following result can be proved by induction:

Lemma A.25 (Law of Powers) *For any operation $\circ$ which is associative we have*

$$g^m \circ g^n = g^{m+n}, \quad (g^m)^n = g^{m \cdot n}.$$

We can extend the notation to all $n \in \mathbb{Z}$, if x has an inverse (and the operation an identity), by $(-n) \cdot x = n \cdot (-x)$ and $x^{-n} = (x^{-1})^n$.

The following lemma is obvious, but often causes problems as it is slightly counter-intuitive. To get it in your brain consider the case of matrices.

Lemma A.26 *Consider a set with an associative operation which has an identity, e. If* $x, y \in G$ *possess inverses then we have*

1. $(x^{-1})^{-1} = x$.

2. $(xy)^{-1} = y^{-1}x^{-1}$.

Proof
For the first we notice

$$x^{-1} \cdot x = e = x \cdot x^{-1}.$$

Hence by definition of inverses the result follows. For the second we have

$$x \cdot y \cdot (y^{-1} \cdot x^{-1}) = x \cdot (y \cdot y^{-1}) \cdot x^{-1} = x \cdot e \cdot x^{-1} = x \cdot x^{-1} = e,$$

and again the result follows by the definition of inverses.

Q.E.D.

We have the following dictionary to translate between additive and multiplicative notations:

Additive	Multiplicative
$x + y$	xy
0	1 or e
$-x$	x^{-1}
$n \cdot x$	x^n

A.6 GROUPS

Definition A.27 *A group is a set G with a binary operation* $\circ$ *such that*

1. $\circ$ *is associative.*

2. $\circ$ *has an identity element in G.*

3. *Every element of G has an inverse.*

Note we have not said that the binary operation is closed as this is implicit in our definition of what an operation is. If the operation is also commutative then we say that we have a commutative, or abelian, group.

The following are all groups, as an exercise you should decide on the identity element, what the inverse of each element is, and which groups are abelian.

1. The integers $\mathbb{Z}$ under addition (written $\mathbb{Z}^+$).

2. The rationals $\mathbb{Q}$ under addition (written $\mathbb{Q}^+$).

3. The reals $\mathbb{R}$ under addition (written $\mathbb{R}^+$).

4. The complexes $\mathbb{C}$ under addition (written $\mathbb{C}^+$).

5. The rationals (excluding zero) $\mathbb{Q} \setminus \{0\}$ under multiplication (written $\mathbb{Q}^*$).

6. The reals (excluding zero) $\mathbb{R} \setminus \{0\}$ under multiplication (written $\mathbb{R}^*$).

7. The complexes (excluding zero) $\mathbb{C} \setminus \{0\}$ under multiplication (written $\mathbb{C}^*$).

8. The set of n vectors over $\mathbb{Z}, \mathbb{Q}, \ldots$, etc. under vector addition.

9. The set of $n \times m$ matrices with integer, rational, real or complex entries under matrix addition (written $M_{n \times m}(\mathbb{Z})$, etc.).

10. The general linear group (the matrices of non-zero determinant) over the rationals, reals or complexes under matrix multiplication (written $GL_n(\mathbb{Q})$, etc.).

11. The special linear group (the matrices of determinant ± 1) over the integers, rationals etc. (written $SL_n(\mathbb{Z})$, etc.).

12. The set of permutations on n elements, written S_n and often called the symmetric group on n letters.

13. The set of continuous (differentiable) functions from $\mathbb{R}$ to $\mathbb{R}$ under pointwise addition.

14. etc.

The list is endless, a group is one of the most basic concepts in mathematics.

Not all mathematical objects are however groups. Consider the following list of sets and operations which are not groups. You should decide why they are not groups.

1. The natural numbers $\mathbb{N}$ under ordinary addition or multiplication.

2. The integers $\mathbb{Z}$ under subtraction or multiplication.

We now give a number of definitions related to groups.

Definition A.28

The order of a group is the number of elements in the underlying set G and is denoted $|G|$ or $\#G$.

The order of an element $g \in G$ is the least positive integer n such that $g^n = e$, if such an n exists otherwise we say that g has infinite order.

A cyclic group G is a group which has an element g such that each element of G can be written in the form g^n for some $n \in \mathbb{Z}$ (in multiplicative notation). If this is the case then one can write $G = \langle g \rangle$ and one says that g is a generator of the group G.

Note, the only element in a group with order one is the identity element and if x is an element of a group then x and x^{-1} have the same order.

Lemma A.29 *If $G = \langle g \rangle$ and g has finite order n then the order of G is n.*

Proof

Every element of G can be written as g^m for some $m \in \mathbb{Z}$, but as g has order n there are only n distinct such values, as

$$g^{n+1} = g^n \circ g = e \circ g = g.$$

So the group G has only n elements.

Q.E.D.

Let us relate this back to the permutations which we introduced earlier. Recall that the set of permutations forms a group under composition. It is easy to see that if $\sigma \in S_n$ is a k-cycle then σ has order k in S_n. One can also easily see that if σ is a product of disjoint cycles then the order of σ is the least common multiple of the orders of the constituent cycles.

A subset S of G is said to generate G if every element of G can be written as a product of elements of S. For instance

- the group S_3 is generated by the set $\{(1, 2), (1, 2, 3)\}$,

- the group $\mathbb{Z}^+$ is generated by the element 1,

- the group $\mathbb{Q}^*$ is generated by the set of prime numbers, it therefore has an infinite number of generators.

Note that the order of a group says nothing about the number of generators it has.

An important set of finite groups which are easy to understand is groups obtained by considering the integers modulo a number m. Recall that we have $\mathbb{Z}/m\mathbb{Z} = \{0, 1, \ldots, m - 1\}$. This is a group with respect to addition, when we take the non-negative remainder after forming the sum of two elements. It is not a group with respect to multiplication in general, even when we exclude 0. We can, however, get around this by setting

$$(\mathbb{Z}/m\mathbb{Z})^* = \{x \in \mathbb{Z}/m\mathbb{Z} : (m, x) = 1\}.$$

This latter set is a group with respect to multiplication, when we take the non-negative remainder after forming the product of two elements. The order of $(\mathbb{Z}/m\mathbb{Z})^*$ is denoted $\phi(m)$, the Euler ϕ function. This is an important function in the theory of numbers. As an example we have

$$\phi(p) = p - 1,$$

if p is a prime number. We shall return to this function later.

We now turn our attention to subgroups.

Definition A.30 *A subgroup H of a group G is a subset of G which is also a group with respect to the operation of G. We write in this case $H < G$.*

Note that by this definition $GL_n(\mathbb{R})$ is not a subgroup of $M_n(\mathbb{R})$, although $GL_n(\mathbb{R}) \subset M_n(\mathbb{R})$. The operation on $GL_n(\mathbb{R})$ is matrix multiplication whilst that on $M_n(\mathbb{R})$ is matrix addition.

However we do have the subgroup chains:

$$\mathbb{Z}^+ < \mathbb{Q}^+ < \mathbb{R}^+ < \mathbb{C}^+,$$
$$\mathbb{Q}^* < \mathbb{R}^* < \mathbb{C}^*.$$

If we also identify $x \in \mathbb{Z}$ with the diagonal matrix $\mathrm{diag}(x, \ldots, x)$ then we also have that $\mathbb{Z}^+$ is a subgroup of $M_n(\mathbb{Z})$ and so on.

As an important example, consider the set $2\mathbb{Z}$ of even integers, this is a subgroup of $\mathbb{Z}^+$. If we write $\mathbb{Z}^+ = 1\mathbb{Z}$, then we have $n\mathbb{Z} < m\mathbb{Z}$ if and only if m divides n, where $m\mathbb{Z} = \{\ldots, -2m, -m, 0, m, 2m, \ldots\}$. We hence obtain various chains of subgroups of $\mathbb{Z}^+$,

$$18\mathbb{Z} < 6\mathbb{Z} < 2\mathbb{Z} < \mathbb{Z}^+,$$
$$18\mathbb{Z} < 9\mathbb{Z} < 3\mathbb{Z} < \mathbb{Z}^+,$$
$$18\mathbb{Z} < 6\mathbb{Z} < 3\mathbb{Z} < \mathbb{Z}^+.$$

We now show that these are the only such subgroups of $\mathbb{Z}^+$.

Lemma A.31 *The only subgroups of $\mathbb{Z}^+$ are $n\mathbb{Z}$ for some positive integer n.*

Proof

Let H be a subgroup of $\mathbb{Z}^+$. As H is non-empty it must contain an element x and its inverse $-x$. Hence H contains at least one positive element n. Let n denote the least such positive element of H and let m denote an arbitrary non-zero element of H. By Euclidean division, there exist $q, r \in \mathbb{Z}$ with $0 \le r < n$ such that

$$m = qn + r.$$

Hence $r \in H$, by choice of n this must mean $r = 0$. Therefore all elements of H are of the form nq which is what was required.

Q.E.D.

So every subgroup of $\mathbb{Z}^+$ is an infinite cyclic group. This last lemma combined with the earlier subgroup chains gives us a good definition of what a prime number is.

Definition A.32 *A prime number is a (positive) generator of a non-trivial subgroup of $\mathbb{Z}^+$, i.e. $H \ne \mathbb{Z}^+$ or 0, for which no subgroup of $\mathbb{Z}^+$ contains H except $\mathbb{Z}^+$ and H itself.*

What is good about this definition is that we have not referred to the multiplicative structure of $\mathbb{Z}$ to define the primes. Also it is obvious that neither zero nor one is a prime number. In addition the above definition allows one to generalize the notion of primality to other settings, for how this is done consult any standard textbook on abstract algebra.

A.6.1   Normal Subgroups and Cosets

A normal subgroup is particularly important in the theory of groups. The name should not be thought of as meaning that these are the subgroups that normally arise, the name is a historic accident. To define a normal subgroup we first need to define what is meant by conjugate elements.

Definition A.33 *Two elements x, y of a group G are said to be conjugate if there is an element $g \in G$ such that $x = g^{-1}yg$.*

It is obvious that two conjugate elements have the same order. If N is a subgroup of G we define, for any $g \in G$,

$$g^{-1}Ng = \{g^{-1}xg : x \in N\},$$

which is another subgroup of G, called a conjugate of the subgroup N.

Definition A.34 *A subgroup $N < G$ is said to be normal if $g^{-1}Ng \subset N$ for all $g \in G$. If this is the case then we write $N \lhd G$.*

For any group G we have $G \lhd G$ and $\{e\} \lhd G$ and if G is an abelian group then every subgroup of G is normal. The importance of normal subgroups comes from the fact that these are subgroups that we can factor out by. This is related to the cosets of a subgroup which we now go on to introduce.

Definition A.35 *Let G be a group and $H < G$ (H is not necessarily normal). Fix an element $g \in G$ then we define the left coset of H with respect to g to be the set*

$$gH = \{gh : h \in H\}.$$

Similarly we define the right coset of H with respect to g to be the set

$$Hg = \{hg : h \in H\}.$$

Let H denote a subgroup of G then one can show that the set of all left (or right) cosets of H in G forms a partition of G, but we leave this to the reader. In addition if $a, b \in G$ then $aH = bH$ if and only if $a \in bH$, which is also equivalent to $b \in aH$, a fact which we also leave to the reader to show. Note that we can have two equal cosets $aH = bH$ without having $a = b$.

What these latter facts show is that if we define the relation R_H on the group G with respect to the subgroup H by

$$(a, b) \in R_H \text{ if and only if } a = bh \text{ for some } h \in H,$$

then this relation is an equivalence relation. The equivalence classes are just the left cosets of H in G.

The number of left cosets of a subgroup H in G we denote by $(G : H)_L$, the number of right cosets we denote by $(G : H)_R$. We are now in a position to prove the most important theorem of elementary group theory, namely Lagrange's Theorem.

Theorem A.36 (Lagrange's Theorem) *Let H be a subgroup of a finite group G then*

$$|G| = (G : H)_L \cdot |H|$$
$$(G : H)_R \cdot |H|.$$

Before we prove this result we state some obvious important corollaries;

Corollary A.37

We have $(G : H)_L = (G : H)_R$; this common number we denote by $(G : H)$ and call it the index of the subgroup H in G.

The order of a subgroup and the index of a subgroup both divide the order of the group.

If G is a group of prime order, then G has only the subgroups G and $\langle e \rangle$.

We now return to the proof of Lagrange's Theorem.

Proof
We form the following collection of distinct left cosets of H in G which we define inductively. Put $g_1 = e$ and assume we are given i cosets by $g_1 H, \ldots, g_i H$. Now take an element g_{i+1} not lying in any of the left cosets $g_j H$ for $j \leq i$. After a finite number of such steps we have exhausted elements in the group G. So we have disjoint union of left cosets which cover the whole group.

$$G = \bigcup_{1 \leq i \leq (G:H)_L} g_i H.$$

We also have for each i, j that $|g_i H| = |g_j H|$, this follows from the fact that the map

$$H \longrightarrow gH$$
$$h \longmapsto gh$$

is a bijective map of sets. Hence

$$|G| = \sum_{1 \leq i \leq (G:H)_L} |g_i H| = (G : H)_L |H|.$$

The other equality follows using the same argument.

Q.E.D.

We can also deduce from the corollaries the following

Lemma A.38 *If G is a group of prime order then it is cyclic.*

Proof
If $g \in G$ is not the identity then $\langle g \rangle$ is a subgroup of G of order ≥ 2. But then it must have order $|G|$ and so G is cyclic.

Q.E.D.

We can use Lagrange's Theorem to write down the subgroups of some small groups. For example, consider the group S_3 this has order 6 so by Lagrange's Theorem its subgroups must have order $1, 2, 3$ or 6. It is easy to see that the only subgroups are therefore:

- one subgroup of order 1; namely $\langle (1) \rangle$,

- three subgroups of order 2; namely $\langle (1, 2) \rangle$, $\langle (1, 3) \rangle$ and $\langle (2, 3) \rangle$,

- one subgroup of order 3; namely $\langle (1, 2, 3) \rangle$,

- one subgroup of order 6, which is S_3 obviously.

A.6.2 Factor or Quotient Groups

Throughout this subsection let G be a group with a normal subgroup N. The following elementary lemma, whose proof we again leave to the reader, gives us our justification for looking at normal subgroups.

Lemma A.39 *Let $H < G$ then the following are equivalent:*

1. $xH = Hx$ for all $x \in G$.

2. $x^{-1}Hx = H$ for all $x \in G$.

3. $H \lhd G$.

4. $x^{-1}hx \in H$ for all $x \in G$ and $h \in H$.

By G/N we denote the set of left cosets of N, note that these are the same as the right cosets of N. We note that two cosets, $g_1 N$ and $g_2 N$ are equal if and only if $g_1^{-1} g_2 \in N$.

We wish to turn G/N into a group, the so-called factor group or quotient group. Let $g_1 N$ and $g_2 N$ denote any two elements of G/N then we define the product of their left cosets to be $(g_1 g_2)N$.

We first need to show that this is a well-defined operation, i.e. if we replace g_1 by g_1' and g_2 by g_2' with $g_1^{-1}g_1' = n_1 \in N$ and $g_2^{-1}g_2' = n_2 \in N$ then our product still gives the same coset. In other words we wish to show

$$(g_1g_2)N = (g_1'g_2')N.$$

Now let $x \in (g_1g_2)N$ then $x = g_1g_2n$ for some $n \in N$. Then $x = g_1'n_1^{-1}g_2'n_2^{-1}n$. But as G is normal (left cosets = right cosets) we have $n_1'^{-1}g_2' = g_2'n_3$ for some $n_3 \in N$. Hence

$$x = g_1'g_2'n_3n_2^{-1}n \in g_1'g_2'N.$$

This proves the first inclusion, the other follows similarly. We conclude that our operation on G/N is well defined. One can also show that if N is an arbitrary subgroup of G and we define the operation on the cosets above then this is only a well-defined operation if N is a normal subgroup of G.

So we have a well-defined operation on G/N, we now need to show that this operation satisfies the axioms of a group:

- As an identity we take $eN = N$, since for all $g \in G$ we have

$$eN \cdot gN = (eg)N = gN.$$

- As an inverse of (gN) we take $g^{-1}N$ as

$$gN.g^{-1}N = (gg^{-1})N = eN = N.$$

- Associativity follows from

$$(g_1N)(g_2N \cdot g_3N) = g_1N((g_2g_3)N) = (g_1(g_2g_3))N$$
$$= ((g_1g_2)g_3)N = ((g_1g_2)N)g_3N$$
$$= (g_1N \cdot g_2N)(g_3N).$$

We now present some examples.

1. Let G be an arbitrary finite group of order greater than one, let H be a subgroup of G. Then $H = G$ and $H = \{e\}$ are always normal subgroups of G.

2. If $H = G$ then there is only one coset and so we have $G/G = \{G\}$ is a group of order one.

3. If $H = \{e\}$ then the cosets of H are the one-element subsets of G. That is $G/\{e\} = \{\{g\} : g \in G\}$.

4. Put $G = S_3$ and $N = \{(1), (1,2,3), (1,3,2)\}$, then N is a normal subgroup of G. The cosets of N in G are N and $(1,2)N$ with

$$((1,2)N)^2 = (1,2)^2N = (1)N = N.$$

Hence $S_3/\langle(1,2,3)\rangle$ is a cyclic group of order 2.

5. If G is abelian then every subgroup H of G is normal, so one can always form the quotient group G/H.

6. Since $(\mathbb{Z}, +)$ is abelian we have that $m\mathbb{Z}$ is always a normal subgroup. Forming the quotient group $\mathbb{Z}/m\mathbb{Z}$ we obtain the group of integers modulo m under addition.

A.6.3   Homomorphisms

Let G_1 and G_2 be two groups, we wish to look at the functions from G_1 to G_2. Obviously one could look at all such functions, however by doing this we would lose all the structure that the group laws give us. We restrict ourselves to maps which preserve this group law.

Definition A.40 *A homomorphism from a group G_1 to a group G_2 is a function f with domain G_1 and codomain G_2 such that for all $x, y \in G_1$ we have*

$$f(x \cdot y) = f(x) \cdot f(y).$$

Note multiplication on the left is with the operation of the group G_1 whilst the multiplication on the right is with respect to the operation of G_2. As examples we have

1. The identity map $\mathrm{id}_G : G \to G$, where $\mathrm{id}_G(g) = g$ is a group homomorphism.

2. Consider the function $\mathbb{R}^+ \to \mathbb{R}^*$ given by $f(x) = e^x$. This is a homomorphism as for all $x, y \in \mathbb{R}$ we have

    $$e^{x+y} = e^x e^y.$$

3. Consider the map from $\mathbb{C}^*$ to $\mathbb{R}^*$ given by $f(z) = |z|$. This is also a homomorphism.

4. Consider the map from $\mathrm{GL}_n(\mathbb{C})$ to $\mathbb{C}^*$ given by $f(A) = \det(A)$, this is a group homomorphism as $\det(AB) = \det(A) \cdot \det(B)$ for any two elements of $\mathrm{GL}_n(\mathbb{C})$.

Two elementary properties of homomorphisms are summarized in the following lemma.

Lemma A.41 *Let $f : G_1 \to G_2$ be a homomorphism of groups, then*

1. *$f(e_1) = e_2$.*

2. *For all $x \in G_1$ we have $f(x^{-1}) = (f(x))^{-1}$.*

Proof
For the first result we have $e_2 f(x) = f(x) = f(e_1 x) = f(e_1) f(x)$ and so

$$e_2 = f(x)f(x)^{-1} = f(e_1)f(x)f(x)^{-1} = f(e_1)$$

as required.
   Now for the second we have

$$f(x^{-1})f(x) = f(x^{-1}x) = f(e_1) = e_2,$$

so the result follows by definition.

Q.E.D.

   For any homomorphism f from G_1 to G_2 there are two special subgroups associated with f.

Definition A.42

The kernel of f is the set

$$\mathrm{Ker} f = \{x \in G_1 : f(x) = e_2\}.$$

The image of f is the set

$$\mathrm{Im} f = \{y \in G_2 : y = f(x), \ x \in G_1\}.$$

Lemma A.43 $\mathrm{Ker} f$ *is a normal subgroup of* G_1.

Proof

We first show that it is a subgroup. It is certainly non-empty as $e_1 \in \mathrm{Ker} f$ as $f(e_1) = e_2$. Now if $x \in \mathrm{Ker} f$ then $f(x^{-1}) = f(x)^{-1} = e_2^{-1} = e_2$, hence $x^{-1} \in \mathrm{Ker} f$. Hence to show that $\mathrm{Ker} f$ is a subgroup we only have to show that for all $x, y \in \mathrm{Ker} f$ we have $xy^{-1} \in \mathrm{Ker} f$. But this is easy as if $x, y \in \mathrm{Ker} f$ then we have

$$f(xy^{-1}) = f(x)f(y^{-1}) = e_2 e_2 = e_2,$$

and we are done.

We now show that $\mathrm{Ker} f$ is in fact a normal subgroup of G_1. We need to show that if $x \in \mathrm{Ker} f$ then $g^{-1}xg \in \mathrm{Ker} f$ for all $g \in G_1$. So let $x \in \mathrm{Ker} f$ and let $g \in G_1$, then we have

$$f(g^{-1}xg) = f(g^{-1})f(x)f(g) = f(g)^{-1}e_2 f(g) = f(g)^{-1}f(g) = e_2,$$

so we are done.

Q.E.D.

Lemma A.44 $\mathrm{Im} f$ *is a subgroup of* G_2.

Proof

$\mathrm{Im} f$ is certainly non-empty as $f(e_1) = e_2$. Now suppose $y \in \mathrm{Im} f$ so there is an $x \in G_2$ such that $f(x) = y$, then $y^{-1} = f(x)^{-1} = f(x^{-1})$ and $x^{-1} \in G_1$ so $y^{-1} \in \mathrm{Im} f$.

Now suppose $y_1, y_2 \in \mathrm{Im} f$, hence for some x_1, x_2 we have

$$y_1 y_2^{-1} = f(x_1)f(x_2^{-1}) = f(x_1 x_2^{-1}).$$

Hence $\mathrm{Im} f < G_2$.

Q.E.D.

It is clear that $\mathrm{Im} f$ in some sense measures whether the homomorphism f is surjective as f is surjective if and only if $\mathrm{Im} f = G_2$. Actually the set $G_2/\mathrm{Im} f$ is a better measure of the surjectivity of the function. What we also have is that $\mathrm{Ker} f$ measures how far from injective f is, due to the following result.

Lemma A.45 *A homomorphism, f, is injective if and only if* $\mathrm{Ker} f = \{e_1\}$.

Proof

Assume f is injective, then we know that if $f(x) = e_2 = f(e_1)$ then $x = e_1$ and so $\mathrm{Ker} f = \{e_1\}$.

Now assume that $\mathrm{Ker} f = \{e_1\}$ and let $x, y \in G_1$ be such that $f(x) = f(y)$. Then

$$f(xy^{-1}) = f(x)f(y^{-1}) = f(x)f(y)^{-1} = f(x)f(x)^{-1} = e_2.$$

So $xy^{-1} \in \mathrm{Ker} f$, but then $xy^{-1} = e_1$ and so $x = y$. So f is injective.

Q.E.D.

Bijective homomorphisms allow us to categorize groups more effectively, as the following definition elaborates.

Definition A.46 *A homomorphism f is said to be an isomorphism if it is bijective. Two groups are said to be isomorphic if there is an isomorphism between them, in which case we write $G_1 \cong G_2$.*

Note this means that isomorphic groups have the same number of elements. Indeed for all intents and purposes one may as well assume that isomorphic groups are equal, since they look the same up to relabelling of elements.

Isomorphisms satisfy the following properties,

- If $f : G_1 \to G_2$ and $g : G_2 \to G_3$ are isomorphisms then $g \circ f$ is also an isomorphism, i.e. isomorphisms are transitive.

- If $f : G_1 \to G_2$ is an isomorphism then so is $f^{-1} : G_2 \to G_1$, i.e. isomorphisms are symmetric.

From this we see that the relation 'is isomorphic to' is an equivalence relation on the class of all groups. This justifies our notion of isomorphic being like equal.

Let G_1, G_2 be two groups, then we define the product group $G_1 \times G_2$ to be the set $G_1 \times G_2$ of ordered pairs (g_1, g_2) with $g_1 \in G_1$ and $g_2 \in G_2$. The group operation on $G_1 \times G_2$ is given componentwise:

$$(g_1, g_2) \circ (g_1', g_2') = (g_1 \circ g_1', g_2 \circ g_2').$$

The first $\circ$ refers to the group $G_1 \times G_2$, the second to the group G_1 and the third to the group G_2. Some well-known groups can actually be represented as product groups. For example, consider the map

$$\mathbb{C}^+ \longrightarrow \mathbb{R}^+ \times \mathbb{R}^+$$
$$z \longmapsto (\mathrm{Re}(z), \mathrm{Im}(z)).$$

This map is obviously a bijective homomorphism, hence we have $\mathbb{C}^+ \cong \mathbb{R}^+ \times \mathbb{R}^+$.

We now come to a crucial theorem which says that the concept of a quotient group is virtually equivalent to the concept of a homomorphic image.

Theorem A.47 (First Isomorphism Theorem for Groups) *Let f be a homomorphism from a group G_1 to a group G_2. Then*

$$G_1 / \mathrm{Ker} f \cong \mathrm{Im} f.$$

The proof of this result can be found in any introductory text on abstract algebra. Note that $G_1 / \mathrm{Ker} f$ makes sense as $\mathrm{Ker} f$ is a normal subgroup of G.

A.7 RINGS

A ring is an additive finite abelian group with an extra operations, usually denoted by multiplication such that the multiplication operation is associative and has an inverse.

The addition and multiplication operations are linked via the distributive law,

$$a \cdot (b + c) = a \cdot b + a \cdot c = (b + c) \cdot a.$$

If the multiplication operation is commutative then we say we have a commutative ring. The following are examples of rings.

- integers under addition and multiplication,

- polynomials with coefficients in $\mathbb{Z}$, denoted $\mathbb{Z}[X]$,

- integers modulo a number m, denoted $\mathbb{Z}/m\mathbb{Z}$.

Although one can consider subrings they turn out to be not so interesting. Of more interest are the ideals of the ring, these are additive subgroups $I < R$ such that

$$i \in I \text{ and } r \in R \text{ implies } i \cdot r \in I.$$

Examples of ideals in a ring are the principal ideals which are those additive subgroups generated by a single ring element. For example if $R = \mathbb{Z}$ then the principal ideals are the ideals $m\mathbb{Z}$, for each integer m.

Just as with normal subgroups and groups, where we formed the quotient group, we can with ideals and rings form the quotient ring. If we take $R = \mathbb{Z}$ and $I = m\mathbb{Z}$ for some integer m then the quotient ring is the ring $\mathbb{Z}/m\mathbb{Z}$ of integers modulo m under addition and multiplication modulo m. This leads us naturally to the Chinese Remainder Theorem.

Theorem A.48 (CRT) *Let* $m = p_1^{z_1} \dots p_t^{z_t}$ *be the prime factorization of* m, *then the following map is a ring isomorphism*

$$f : \begin{array}{ccc} \mathbb{Z}/m\mathbb{Z} & \longrightarrow & \mathbb{Z}/p_1^{z_1}\mathbb{Z} \times \cdots \times \mathbb{Z}/p_t^{z_t}\mathbb{Z} \\ x & \longmapsto & (x \ (\mathrm{mod}\ p_1^{z_1}), \dots, x \ (\mathrm{mod}\ p_t^{z_t})). \end{array}$$

Proof
This can be proved by induction on the number of prime factors of m. We leave the details to the interested reader.

We shall now return to the Euler ϕ function mentioned earlier. Remember $\phi(n)$ denotes the order of the group $\mathbb{Z}/n\mathbb{Z}^*$. We would like to be able to calculate this value easily.

Lemma A.49 *Let* $m = p_1^{z_1} \dots p_t^{z_t}$ *be the prime factorization of* m. *Then we have*

$$\phi(m) = \phi(p_1^{z_1}) \dots \phi(p_t^{z_t}).$$

Proof
This follows from the Chinese Remainder Theorem, as the ring isomorphism

$$\mathbb{Z}/m\mathbb{Z} \cong \mathbb{Z}/p_1^{z_1}\mathbb{Z} \times \cdots \times \mathbb{Z}/p_t^{z_t}\mathbb{Z}$$

induces a group isomorphism

$$(\mathbb{Z}/m\mathbb{Z})^* \cong (\mathbb{Z}/p_1^{z_1}\mathbb{Z})^* \times \cdots \times (\mathbb{Z}/p_t^{z_t}\mathbb{Z})^*.$$

Q.E.D.

To compute the Euler ϕ function all we now require is:

Lemma A.50 *Let p be a prime number, then $\phi(p^e) = p^{e-1}(p-1)$.*

Proof
There are $p^e - 1$ elements of $\mathbb{Z}$ satisfying $1 \le k < p^e$, of these we must eliminate those of the form $k = rp$ for some r. But $1 \le rp < p^e$ implies $1 \le r < p^{e-1}$, hence there are $p^{e-1} - 1$ possible values of r. So we obtain

$$\phi(p^e) = (p^e - 1) - (p^{e-1} - 1)$$

from which the result follows.

Q.E.D.

An ideal I of a ring is called prime if $x \cdot y \in I$ implies either $x \in I$ or $y \in I$. Notice, the ideals $I = m\mathbb{Z}$ of the ring $\mathbb{Z}$ are prime if and only if m is plus or minus a prime number.

The prime ideals are special as if we take the quotient of a ring by a prime ideal then we obtain a field. Hence, $\mathbb{Z}/p\mathbb{Z}$ is a field. This brings us naturally on to the subject of fields.

A.8   FIELDS

A field is essentially two abelian groups stuck together using the distributive law. More formally:

Definition A.51 *A field is an additive abelian group F, such that $F \setminus \{0\}$ also forms an abelian group with respect to another operation (which is usually written multiplicatively). The two operations, addition and multiplication, are linked via the distributive law:*

$$a \cdot (b + c) = a \cdot b + a \cdot c = (b + c) \cdot a.$$

Many fields that one encounters have infinitely many elements. Every finite field either contains $\mathbb{Q}$ as a subfield, in which case we say it has characteristic zero, or it contains $\mathbb{F}_p$ as a subfield in which case we say it has characteristic p. The only fields with finitely many elements have p^r elements when p is a prime. We denote such fields by $\mathbb{F}_{p^r}$, for each value of r there is only one such field up to isomorphism. Such finite fields are often called Galois Fields.

Let F be a field, we denote by $F[X]$ the ring of polynomials in a single variable X with coefficients in the field F. The set $F(X)$ of rational functions in X is the set of functions of the form

$$f(X)/g(X),$$

where $f(X), g(X) \in F[X]$ and $g(X)$ is not the zero polynomial. The set $F(X)$ is a field with respect to the obvious addition and multiplication. One should note the difference in the notation of the brackets, $F[X]$ and $F(X)$.

Let f be a polynomial of degree n with coefficients in $\mathbb{F}_p$ which is irreducible. Let θ denote a root of f. Consider the set

$$\mathbb{F}_p(\theta) = \{a_0 + a_1\theta + \cdots + a_{n-1}\theta^{n-1} : a_i \in \mathbb{F}_p\}.$$

Given two elements of $\mathbb{F}_p(\theta)$ one adds them componentwise and multiplies them as polynomials in θ but then one takes the remainder of the result on division by $f(\theta)$. The set $\mathbb{F}_p(\theta)$ is a field, there are field-theoretic isomorphisms

$$\mathbb{F}_{p^n} = \mathbb{F}_p(\theta) = \mathbb{F}_p[X]/(f),$$

where (f) represents the ideal

$$\{f \cdot g : g \in \mathbb{F}_p[X]\}.$$

To be more concrete let us look at the specific example given by choosing a value of $p \equiv 3 \pmod 4$ and $f(X) = X^2 + 1$. Now since $p \equiv 3 \pmod 4$ the polynomial f is irreducible over $\mathbb{F}_p[X]$ and so the quotient $\mathbb{F}_p[X]/(f)$ forms a field, which is isomorphic to $\mathbb{F}_{p^2}$.

Let i denote a root of the polynomial $X^2 + 1$. The field $\mathbb{F}_{p^2} = \mathbb{F}_p(i)$ consists of numbers of the form

$$a + bi$$

where a and b are integers modulo p. We add such numbers as

$$(a + bi) + (c + di) = (a + c) + (b + d)i.$$

We multiply such numbers as

$$(a + bi)(c + di) = (ac + (ad + bc)i + bdi^2) = (ac - bd) + (ad + bc)i.$$

Here is another example. Let θ denote a root of the polynomial $x^3 + 2$, then an element of

$$\mathbb{F}_{7^3} = \mathbb{F}_7(\theta)$$

can be represented by

$$a + b\theta + c\theta^2.$$

Multiplication of two such elements gives

$$
\begin{aligned}
(a + b\theta + c\theta^2)(a' + b'\theta + c'\theta^2) &= aa' + \theta(a'b + b'a) + \theta^2(ac' + bb' + ca') \\
&\quad + \theta^3(bc' + cb') + cc'\theta^4 \\
&= (aa' - 2bc' - 2cb') + \theta(a'b + b'a - 2cc') \\
&\quad + \theta^2(ac' + bb' + ca').
\end{aligned}
$$

A.9   VECTOR SPACES

Definition A.52 *Given a field K a vector space (or a K-vector space) V is an abelian group (also denoted V) and an external operation $K \times V \to V$ (called scalar multiplication) which satisfies the following axioms: For all $\lambda, \mu \in K$ and all $x, y \in V$ we have*

1. $\lambda(\mu x) = (\lambda\mu)x.$

2. $(\lambda + \mu)x = \lambda x + \mu x.$

3. $1_K x = x.$

4. $\lambda(x + y) = \lambda x + \lambda y.$

One often calls the elements of V the vectors and the elements of K the scalars. Note that we are not allowed to multiply or divide two vectors. We shall start with some examples:

- For a given field K and an integer $n \geq 1$, let $V = K^n = K \times \cdots \times K$ be the n-fold Cartesian product. This is a vector space over K with respect to the usual addition of vectors and multiplication by scalars. A special case of $n = 1$ shows that any field is a vector space over itself. When $K = \mathbb{R}$ and $n = 2$ we obtain the familiar system of geometric vectors in the plane. When $n = 3$ and $K = \mathbb{R}$ we obtain 3-dimensional vectors. Hence you can already see the power of vector spaces as they allow us to consider n-dimensional space in a concrete way.

- Let K be a field and consider the set of polynomials over K, namely $K[X]$. This is a vector space with respect to addition of polynomials and multiplication by elements of K.

- Let K be a field and E any set at all. Define V to be the set of functions $f : E \to K$. Given $f, g \in V$ and $\lambda \in K$ one can define the sum $f + g$ and scalar product λf via

$$(f + g)(x) = f(x) + g(x) \text{ and } (\lambda f)(x) = \lambda f(x).$$

We leave the reader the simple task to check that this is a vector space.

- The set of all continuous functions $f : \mathbb{R} \to \mathbb{R}$ is a vector space over $\mathbb{R}$. This follows from the fact that if f and g are continuous then so is $f + g$ and λf for any $\lambda \in \mathbb{R}$. Similarly the set of all differentiable functions $f : \mathbb{R} \to \mathbb{R}$ also forms a vector space.

A.9.1   Vector Sub-spaces

Let V be a K-vector space and let W be a subset of V. W is said to be a vector subspace (or just subspace) of V if

1. W is a subgroup of V with respect to addition.

2. W is closed under scalar multiplication.

By this last condition we mean $\lambda x \in W$ for all $x \in W$ and all $\lambda \in K$. What this means is that a vector subspace is a subset of V which is also a vector space with respect to the same addition and multiplication laws as are on V. There are always two trivial subspaces of a space, namely $\{0\}$ and V itself. Here are some more examples:

- Let $V = K^n$ and $W = \{(\xi_1, \ldots, \xi_n) \in K^n : \xi_n = 0\}.$

- Let $V = K^n$ and $W = \{(\xi_1, \ldots, \xi_n) \in K^n : \xi_1 + \cdots + \xi_n = 0\}.$

- $V = K[X]$ and $W = \{f \in K[X] : f = 0 \text{ or } \deg f \le 10\}$.

- $\mathbb{C}$ is a natural vector space over $\mathbb{Q}$, and $\mathbb{R}$ is a vector subspace of $\mathbb{C}$.

- Let V denote the set of all continuous functions from $\mathbb{R}$ to $\mathbb{R}$ and W the set of all differentiable functions from $\mathbb{R}$ to $\mathbb{R}$. Then W is a vector subspace of V.

A.9.2 Properties of Elements of Vector Spaces

Before we go any further we need to define certain properties which sets of elements of vector spaces can possess. For the following definitions let V be a K-vector space and let $x_1, \ldots, x_n$ and x denote elements of V.

Definition A.53

x is said to be a linear combination of $x_1, \ldots, x_n$ if there exists scalars $\lambda_i \in K$ such that

$$x = \lambda_1 x_1 + \cdots + \lambda_n x_n.$$

The elements $x_1, \ldots, x_n$ are said to be linearly independent if the relation

$$\lambda_1 x_1 + \cdots + \lambda_n x_n = 0$$

implies that $\lambda_1 = \cdots = \lambda_n = 0$. If $x_1, \ldots, x_n$ are not linearly independent then they are said to be linearly dependent.

A subset A of a vector space is linearly independent or free if whenever $x_1, \ldots, x_n$ are finitely many elements of A, they are linearly independent.

A subset A of a vector space V is said to span (or generate) V if every element of V is a linear combination of finitely many elements from A.

If there exists a finite set of vectors spanning V then we say that V is finite-dimensional.

We now give some examples of the last concept.

- The vector space $V = K^n$ is finite-dimensional. For let

$$e_i = (0, \ldots, 0, 1, 0, \ldots, 0)$$

  be the n-tuple with 1 in the ith-place and 0 elsewhere. Then V is spanned by the vectors $e_1, \ldots, e_n$. Note the analogy with the geometric plane.

- $\mathbb{C}$ is a finite-dimensional vector space over $\mathbb{R}$, and $\{1, \sqrt{-1}\}$ is a spanning set.

- $\mathbb{R}$ and $\mathbb{C}$ are not finite-dimensional vector spaces over $\mathbb{Q}$. This is obvious since $\mathbb{Q}$ has countably many elements, any finite-dimensional subspace over $\mathbb{Q}$ will also have countably many elements. However it is a basic result in analysis that both $\mathbb{R}$ and $\mathbb{C}$ have uncountably many elements.

Now some examples about linear independence:

- In the vector space $V = K^n$ the n-vectors $e_1, \ldots, e_n$ defined earlier are linearly independent.

- In the vector space $\mathbb{R}^3$ the vectors $x_1 = (1, 2, 3)$, $x_2 = (-1, 0, 4)$ and $x_3 = (2, 5, -1)$ are linearly independent.

- On the other hand, the vectors $y_1 = (2, 4, -3)$, $y_2 = (1, 1, 2)$ and $y_3 = (2, 8, -17)$ are linearly dependent as we have $3y_1 - 4y_2 - y_3 = 0$.

- In the vector space (and ring) $K[X]$ over the field K the infinite set of vectors

$$\{1, X, X^2, X^3, \ldots\}$$

is linearly independent.

A.9.3 Dimension and Bases

Definition A.54 *A subset A of a vector space V which is linearly independent and spans the whole of V is called a basis.*

Given a basis then each element in V can be written in a unique way: for if $x_1, \ldots, x_n$ is a basis and suppose that we can write x as a linear combination of the x_i in two ways i.e. $x = \lambda_1 x_1 + \cdots + \lambda_n x_n$ and $x = \mu_1 x_1 + \cdots + \mu_n x_n$. Then we have

$$0 = x - x = (\lambda_1 - \mu_1)x_1 + \cdots + (\lambda_n - \mu_n)x_n$$

and as the x_i are linearly independent we obtain $\lambda_i - \mu_i = 0$, i.e. $\lambda_i = \mu_i$.
 We have the following examples.

- The vectors $e_1, \ldots, e_n$ of K^n introduced earlier form a basis of K^n. This basis is called the standard basis of K^n.

- The set $\{1, i\}$ is a basis of the vector space $\mathbb{C}$ over $\mathbb{R}$.

- The infinite set $\{1, X, X^2, X^2, \ldots\}$ is a basis of the vector space $K[X]$.

By way of terminology we call the vector space $V = \{0\}$ the trivial or zero vector space. All other vector spaces are called non-zero. To make the statements of the following theorems easier we shall say that the zero vector space has the basis set $\varnothing$.

Theorem A.55 *Let V be a finite-dimensional vector space over a field K. Let C be a finite subset of V which spans V and let A be a subset of C which is linearly independent. Then V has a basis, B, such that $A \subset B \subset C$.*

Proof

We can assume that V is non-zero. Consider the collection of all subsets of C which are linearly independent and contain A. Certainly such subsets exist since A is itself an example. So choose one such subset B with as many elements as possible. By construction B is linearly independent. We now show that B spans V.

 Since C spans V we only have to show that every element $x \in C$ is a linear combination of elements of B. This is trivial when $x \in B$ so assume that $x \notin B$. Then $B' = B \cup \{x\}$ is a subset of C larger than B, whence B' is linearly dependent, by choice of B. If $x_1, \ldots, x_r$ are the distinct elements of B this means that there is a linear relation

$$\lambda_1 x_1 + \cdots + \lambda_r x_r + \lambda x = 0,$$

in which not all the scalars, λ_i, λ, are zero. In fact $\lambda \neq 0$. So we may rearrange to express x as a linear combination of elements of B, as λ has an inverse in K.

Q.E.D.

Corollary A.56 *Every finite-dimensional vector space, V, has a basis.*

Proof
We can assume that V is non-zero. Let C denote a finite spanning set of V and let $A = \varnothing$ and then apply the above theorem.

Q.E.D.

The last theorem and its corollary are true if we drop the assumption of finite dimensional. However then we require much more deep machinery to prove the result. The following result is crucial to the study of vector spaces as it allows us to define the dimension of a vector space. One should think of dimension of a vector space as the same as dimension of the 2-D or 3-D space one is used to.

Theorem A.57 *Suppose a vector space V contains a spanning set of m elements and a linearly independent set of n elements. Then $m \geq n$.*

Proof
Let $A = \{x_1, \ldots, x_m\}$ span V, and let $B = \{y_1, \ldots, y_n\}$ be linearly independent and suppose that $m < n$. Hence we wish to derive a contradiction.

We successively replace the xs by the ys, as follows. Since A spans V, there exists scalars $\lambda_1, \ldots, \lambda_m$ such that

$$y_1 = \lambda_1 x_1 + \cdots + \lambda_m x_m.$$

At least one of the scalars, say λ_1, is non-zero and we may express x_1 in terms of y_1 and $x_2, \ldots, x_m$. It is then clear that $A_1 = \{y_1, x_2, \ldots, x_m\}$ spans V.

We repeat the process m times and conclude that $A_m = \{y_1, \ldots, y_m\}$ spans V. (One can formally dress this up as induction if one wants to be precise, which we will not bother with.)

By hypothesis $m < n$ and so A_m is not the whole of B and y_{m+1} is a linear combination of $y_1, \ldots, y_m$, as A_m spans V. This contradicts the fact that B is linearly independent.

Q.E.D.

Let V be a finite-dimensional vector space. Suppose A is a basis of m elements and B a basis of n elements. By applying the above theorem twice (once to A and B and once to B and A) we deduce that $m = n$. From this we conclude the following theorem.

Theorem A.58 *Let V be a finite-dimensional vector space. Then all bases of V have the same number of elements, we call this number the dimension of V (written $\dim V$).*

It is clear that $\dim K^n = n$. This agrees with our intuition that a vector with n components lives in an n-dimensional world, and that $\dim \mathbb{R}^3 = 3$. Note when referring to dimension we sometimes need to be clear about the field of scalars. If we wish to emphasise the field of scalars we write $\dim_K V$. This can be important, for example if we consider the complex numbers we have

$$\dim_{\mathbb{C}} \mathbb{C} = 1, \quad \dim_{\mathbb{R}} \mathbb{C} = 2, \quad \dim_{\mathbb{Q}} \mathbb{C} = \infty.$$

The following results are left as exercises.

Theorem A.59 *If V is a (non-zero) finite-dimensional vector space, of dimension n, then*

1. *Given any linearly independent subset A of V, there exists a basis B such that $A \subset B$.*

2. *Given any spanning set C of V, there exists a basis B such that $B \subset C$.*

3. *Every linearly independent set in V has $\leq n$ elements.*

4. *If a linearly independent set has exactly n elements then it is a basis.*

5. *Every spanning set has $\geq n$ elements.*

6. *If a spanning set has exactly n elements then it is a basis.*

Theorem A.60 *Let W be a subspace of a finite-dimensional vector space V. Then $\dim W \leq \dim V$, with equality holding if and only if $W = V$.*

Appendix B
Java Examples

In this appendix we give some examples of how one uses standard Java libraries, such as that included with the Java programming language, to use some of the concepts in this book. The standard library classes shipped with Java 1.2 and onwards provide support for digital signatures and hash functions.

To obtain support for encryption you need to also install a Java Cryptographic Engine (or JCE). As of Java 1.4 one of these, namely SUN JCE, comes shipped with the standard library classes. However, the SUN JCE is not fully available worldwide due to export regulations. We have therefore in our examples used the Cryptix JCE available from

www.cryptix.org.

This is meant to be compatible to the SUN JCE, but it also supports a wider range of algorithms, including many we have not mentioned in this book. In addition it is available worldwide without restriction.

We do not give code for actually implementing algorithms such as RSA, DES etc. We simply show how you can use these when they are provided by another programmer following a standard API. You should still however try to implement your own versions of RSA etc. since actually implementing these functions often leads to greater understanding of their uses and limitations.

All of our sample code makes use of the following function which takes an array of bytes and returns the string corresponding to its hexadecimal representation:

```java
static String To_Hex(byte[] bs)
    {
      StringBuffer str = new StringBuffer();
```

```
     for(int i=0; i < bs.length; i++)
       {
         String b = Integer.toHexString(bs[i]);
         if(b.length() < 2) b = "0" + b;
         str.append( b.substring(b.length()-2) );
       }
     return str.toString();
   }
```

B.1 BLOCK CIPHERS

We first show how one uses DES, Triple DES (called DESede in Java) and Rijndael using the Cryptix JCE. The following program demonstrates how keys are created and how one deals with different encryption modes such as CBC Mode and ECB Mode.

To use a block cipher you need to specify the algorithm type such as DES, the mode of operation such as CBC Mode and the padding system to be used. The padding system used in the code below is called PKCS 5 and is defined in the fifth Public Key Cryptography Standards (hence PKCS) published by RSA Laboratories.

Notice how once you know how to use one block cipher you know how to use them all.

```
import java.security.*;
import javax.crypto.*;
import javax.crypto.spec.*;
import javax.crypto.interfaces.*;

import cryptix.jce.provider.CryptixCrypto;

public class Symmetric_Demo
{
  /* Notice how this is algorithm independent */
  static void Encrypt(String Alg,String Mode,String Padding)
              throws NoSuchAlgorithmException,
                     InvalidKeyException,
                     IllegalBlockSizeException,
                     NoSuchPaddingException,
                     BadPaddingException,
                     InvalidAlgorithmParameterException,
                     NoSuchProviderException
    {
      System.out.println("\nDemo of "+Alg+" "+Mode+" "+Padding);

      KeyGenerator keygen = KeyGenerator.getInstance(Alg);

      if (Alg.equals("DES"))            { keygen.init(56); }
      else if (Alg.equals("Rijndael"))  { keygen.init(128); }
```

```
    else                                       { keygen.init(168); }

    SecretKey sKey = keygen.generateKey();

    Cipher cipher;

    // Create the cipher
    cipher = Cipher.getInstance(Alg+"/"+Mode+"/"+Padding);

    // Initialize the cipher for encryption
    IvParameterSpec spec = null;
    if (Mode.equals("CBC"))
        { SecureRandom sr=new SecureRandom();
          byte[] iv=new byte[cipher.getBlockSize()];
          sr.nextBytes(iv);
          spec=new IvParameterSpec(iv);
          cipher.init(Cipher.ENCRYPT_MODE, sKey, spec);
        }
    else
        { cipher.init(Cipher.ENCRYPT_MODE, sKey); }

    // Our cleartext
    byte[] cleartext = "This is just an example".getBytes();

    System.out.println("PlainText : "+To_Hex(cleartext));

    // Encrypt the cleartext
    byte[] ciphertext = cipher.doFinal(cleartext);

    System.out.println("CipherText : "+To_Hex(ciphertext));

    // Initialize the same cipher for decryption
    if (Mode.equals("CBC"))
        { cipher.init(Cipher.DECRYPT_MODE, sKey, spec); }
    else
        { cipher.init(Cipher.DECRYPT_MODE, sKey); }

    // Decrypt the ciphertext
    byte[] cleartext1 = cipher.doFinal(ciphertext);

    System.out.println("DecryptedText : "+To_Hex(cleartext1));
  }


public static void main(String[] args)
            throws NoSuchAlgorithmException,
                NoSuchProviderException,
```

```
                            InvalidAlgorithmParameterException,
                            InvalidKeyException,
                            InvalidKeyException,
                            IllegalBlockSizeException,
                            NoSuchPaddingException,
                            BadPaddingException
  {
    Provider c_jce = new CryptixCrypto();
    int result = Security.addProvider(c_jce);
    if (result==-1)
      { System.out.println("Provider already exists.\n"); }
    else
      { System.out.println("Provider added.\n"); }

    // ECB Mode
    Encrypt("DES","ECB","PKCS5Padding");
    Encrypt("DESede","ECB","PKCS5Padding");
    Encrypt("Rijndael","ECB","PKCS5Padding");

    // CBC Mode
    Encrypt("DES","CBC","PKCS5Padding");
    Encrypt("DESede","CBC","PKCS5Padding");
    Encrypt("Rijndael","CBC","PKCS5Padding");
  }
}
```

B.2 PUBLIC KEY ENCRYPTION

The following program shows how one can use the Cryptix JCE to perform RSA and
ElGamal encryption. Notice how the code is very similar to the Block Cipher code
above. The mode of operation is chosen to be ECB Mode and the padding system is
that used in PKCS 1.

```
import java.security.*;
import javax.crypto.*;

import cryptix.jce.provider.CryptixCrypto;

public class Assymetric_Demo
{
  /* Notice how this is algorithm independent */
  static void Encrypt(String Alg,String Mode,String Padding)
            throws NoSuchAlgorithmException,
                   InvalidKeyException,
                   IllegalBlockSizeException,
                   NoSuchPaddingException,
                   BadPaddingException,
```

```
                    InvalidAlgorithmParameterException,
                    NoSuchProviderException
  {
     System.out.println("\nDemo of "+Alg+" "+Mode+" "+Padding);

     KeyPairGenerator Kgen = KeyPairGenerator.getInstance(Alg);
     Kgen.initialize(512);

     KeyPair kpair = Kgen.generateKeyPair();

     Cipher cipher;

     // Create the cipher
     cipher = Cipher.getInstance(Alg+"/"+Mode+"/"+Padding);

     // Initialize the cipher for encryption
     cipher.init(Cipher.ENCRYPT_MODE, kpair.getPublic());

     // Our cleartext
     byte[] cleartext = "This is just an example".getBytes();

     System.out.println("PlainText : "+To_Hex(cleartext));

     // Encrypt the cleartext
     byte[] ciphertext = cipher.doFinal(cleartext);

     System.out.println("CipherText : "+To_Hex(ciphertext));

     cipher.init(Cipher.DECRYPT_MODE, kpair.getPrivate());

     // Decrypt the ciphertext
     byte[] cleartext1 = cipher.doFinal(ciphertext);

     System.out.println("DecryptedText : "+To_Hex(cleartext1));
  }


public static void main(String[] args)
             throws NoSuchAlgorithmException,
                    NoSuchProviderException,
                    InvalidAlgorithmParameterException,
                    InvalidKeyException,
                    InvalidKeyException,
                    IllegalBlockSizeException,
                    NoSuchPaddingException,
                    BadPaddingException
  {
     Provider c_jce = new CryptixCrypto();
```

```
      int result = Security.addProvider(c_jce);
      if (result==-1)
        { System.out.println("Provider already exists.\n"); }
      else
        { System.out.println("Provider added.\n"); }

      Encrypt("ElGamal","ECB","PKCS#1");
      Encrypt("RSA","ECB","PKCS#1");
    }
}
```

B.3 HASH FUNCTIONS

The following code shows how hash functions can be applied using the standard Java library classes provided with the Java JDK, i.e. no JCE is required. The code explains how SHA-1 and MD5 can be called. Again the library classes abstract away which hash function is being used, since both SHA-1 and MD5 use the same calling sequence when they are applied.

```
import java.security.*;
import java.io.*;

public class Hash_Demo
{
  /* Notice how this is algorithm independent */
  static void Digest_Demo(String Alg)
                throws NoSuchAlgorithmException,
                       UnsupportedEncodingException
    {
      byte[] data;
      int i;
      data=new byte[100];

      System.out.println("\nDemo of "+Alg);
      MessageDigest MD=MessageDigest.getInstance(Alg);

      for (i=0; i<100; i++) { data[i]=(byte) i; }
      MD.update(data);
      byte[] hash=MD.digest();
      System.out.println(To_Hex(hash));

      for (i=0; i<100; i++) { data[i]=(byte) (i+10); }
      MD.update(data);
      hash=MD.digest();
      System.out.println(To_Hex(hash));

      System.out.flush();
```

```
        }


    public static void main(String[] args)
                   throws NoSuchAlgorithmException,
                            UnsupportedEncodingException
      {
        Digest_Demo("SHA");
        Digest_Demo("MD5");
      }
  }
```

B.4   DIGITAL SIGNATURES

The following code shows how data can be signed using the standard Java library classes. These classes support both DSA and RSA, although the latter one appears to be a naive hash based RSA algorithm. To use a provably secure RSA based signature algorithm such as RSA-PSS one needs to use the Cryptix JCE.

With DSA there are inbuilt domain parameters, i.e. the p, q and g. However we also show how you can generate your own using the Java BigInteger class.

```
import java.security.*;
import java.security.spec.*;
import java.security.interfaces.*;
import java.math.BigInteger;
import java.io.*;

import cryptix.jce.provider.CryptixCrypto;

public class Signature_Demo
{
  /* Notice how this is algorithm independent */
  static void Do_Signature(Signature Alg,
                         PrivateKey priv,PublicKey pub)
                 throws InvalidKeyException,
                        SignatureException,
                        UnsupportedEncodingException
    {
      /* Get Message */
      byte[] message=new byte[100];
      for (int i=0; i<100; i++) { message[i]=(byte) i; }

      /* Now do some signing */
      Alg.initSign(priv);
      Alg.update(message);
      byte[] signature=Alg.sign();
```

```
        System.out.println("Signature = " + To_Hex(signature));

        /* Now do the Verifying */
        Alg.initVerify(pub);
        Alg.update(message);
        boolean verifies = Alg.verify(signature);
        System.out.println("Signature Verifies : " + verifies);
        System.out.flush();
    }


    static void RSA_Sig(String Alg)
                throws    NoSuchAlgorithmException,
                          NoSuchProviderException,
                          InvalidKeyException,
                          SignatureException,
                          UnsupportedEncodingException

    {
        System.out.println("\n\n"+Alg+" Demo");

        SecureRandom random= new SecureRandom();
        KeyPairGenerator KGen=KeyPairGenerator.getInstance("RSA");

        KeyPair pair = KGen.generateKeyPair();
        PrivateKey priv=pair.getPrivate();
        PublicKey  pub=pair.getPublic();

        System.out.println("Private key is " +
            ((RSAPrivateKey) priv).getPrivateExponent().toString());

        System.out.println("Public key is " +
            ((RSAPublicKey) pub).getPublicExponent().toString());

        System.out.println("Modulus is " +
            ((RSAPublicKey) pub).getModulus().toString());

        /* Now do some signing */
        Signature rsa=Signature.getInstance(Alg);

        Do_Signature(rsa,priv,pub);
    }



    /* flag = 1 implies use the inbuilt Domain Parameters
            = 0 implies generate our own Domain Parameters
```

```
*/
static void DSA(int flag)
            throws NoSuchAlgorithmException,
                   NoSuchProviderException,
                   InvalidAlgorithmParameterException,
                   InvalidKeyException,
                   SignatureException,
                   UnsupportedEncodingException
  {
    System.out.println("\n\nDSA Demo");

    SecureRandom random= new SecureRandom();

    /* Generate Domain Parameters */
    KeyPairGenerator KGen=KeyPairGenerator.getInstance("DSA");
    if (flag==0)
      { /* Generate our own Domain Parameters */

        BigInteger p,q,g,t,one=BigInteger.ONE;

        /* Find q */
        q=new BigInteger(160,20,random);

        /* Find p */
        do
           { t=new BigInteger(1024-160,random);
             p=q.multiply(t);   p=p.add(one);
           }
        while (   !p.isProbablePrime(20)
              || (p.bitLength()!=1024) );

        /* Find g */
        do
          { g=new BigInteger(1024,random);
            g=g.modPow(t,p);
          }
        while (g.equals(one));

        DSAParameterSpec dsaSpec
                            = new DSAParameterSpec(p,q,g);
        KGen.initialize(dsaSpec,random);
      }
    else
      { KGen.initialize(1024,random); }

    /* Now Generate the Key Pair */
    KeyPair pair = KGen.generateKeyPair();
    PrivateKey priv=pair.getPrivate();
```

```java
        PublicKey  pub=pair.getPublic();

        DSAParams Params=((DSAPublicKey) pub).getParams();
        System.out.println(" p = " + Params.getP().toString());
        System.out.println(" q = " + Params.getQ().toString());
        System.out.println(" g = " + Params.getG().toString());


        System.out.println("Private key is "
              + ((DSAPrivateKey) priv).getX().toString());

        System.out.println("Public key is "
              + ((DSAPublicKey) pub).getY().toString());

        /* Now do some signing */
        Signature dsa=Signature.getInstance("SHA1withDSA");

        Do_Signature(dsa,priv,pub);
    }


  public static void main(String[] args)
                throws NoSuchAlgorithmException,
                    NoSuchProviderException,
                    InvalidAlgorithmParameterException,
                    InvalidKeyException,
                    SignatureException,
                    UnsupportedEncodingException,
                    InvalidKeyException
    {
        Provider c_jce = new CryptixCrypto();
        int result = Security.addProvider(c_jce);
        if (result==-1)
          { System.out.println("Provider already exists.\n"); }
        else
          { System.out.println("Provider added.\n"); }

        RSA_Sig("SHA1withRSA");      // Uses only standard API
        RSA_Sig("RSASSA-PSS/SHA-1"); // Needs Cryptix

        DSA(1);                      // Uses only standard API
        DSA(0);                      // Uses only standard API
    }
}
```

B.5 ZERO-KNOWLEDGE PROOFS AND COMMITMENTS

We end this appendix by giving a more involved example which does not use the Java cryptographic API directly. In this example we implement the commitment protocol from Chapter 13 which was used in our voting protocol. In addition we also implement the non-interactive proof that the commitment is a commitment to either plus one or minus one.

The reason for including this example is to show how the Java `BigInteger` class can be used to create some of the more advanced schemes in this book which are not implemented in the standard libraries. The following code makes no use of any features of the SUN or Cryptix JCE, and hence can be run using only the standard Java library classes.

B.5.1 Parameters.java

This first class simply holds the Domain Parameters for our commitment scheme, which essentially consist of a DSA public key.

```java
import java.security.*;
import java.security.interfaces.*;
import java.math.BigInteger;

class Parameters
{
  private BigInteger p,q,g,h;

  public Parameters(SecureRandom random)
          throws NoSuchAlgorithmException
    {
      /* Get the SUN Installed Domain Parameters */
      KeyPairGenerator KGen=KeyPairGenerator.getInstance("DSA");
      KGen.initialize(1024,random);
      KeyPair pair = KGen.generateKeyPair();
      DSAPublicKey pub=(DSAPublicKey) pair.getPublic();
      DSAParams Params=pub.getParams();

      p=Params.getP();
      q=Params.getQ();
      g=Params.getG();
      h=pub.getY();
    }

  public BigInteger getP()    { return p; }
  public BigInteger getQ()    { return q; }
  public BigInteger getG()    { return g; }
  public BigInteger getH()    { return h; }
}
```

B.5.2   Private_Commitment.java

This second class holds the private values associated to a commitment,

$$b = g^a h^c.$$

```
import java.math.BigInteger;

class Private_Commitment
{
  private BigInteger a,c,b;
  private Parameters PK;

  public Private_Commitment(Parameters P)
    { PK=P; }

  public void assign(BigInteger a1,BigInteger b1,BigInteger c1)
    { a=a1;   b=b1; c=c1;   }

  public BigInteger getA()        { return  a; }
  public BigInteger getB()        { return  b; }
  public BigInteger getC()        { return  c; }
  public Parameters get_Params()  { return PK;   }
}
```

B.5.3   Public_Commitment.java

This third class holds the public value of the commitment only.

```
import java.math.BigInteger;

class Public_Commitment
{
  private BigInteger b;
  private Parameters PK;

  public Public_Commitment(Parameters P)
    { PK=P; }

  public void assign(BigInteger b1)  { b=b1; }
  public Parameters get_Params()     { return PK;   }
  public BigInteger getB()           { return b; }
}
```

B.5.4   Commitment_Factory.java

This fourth class creates a public/private commitment pair. The idea is that the committer uses this class to create a pair, they can then publish the public commitment and keep the private commitment safe until they need to reveal their committed value.

```java
import java.math.BigInteger;
import java.security.*;

class Commitment_Factory
{
  private Parameters PK;
  private Public_Commitment Pub;
  private Private_Commitment Priv;

  public Commitment_Factory(Parameters P)
     { PK=P; }

  public void Commit(int cc,SecureRandom random)
                throws ArithmeticException
     {
        BigInteger q=PK.getQ();
        BigInteger p=PK.getP();
        BigInteger g=PK.getG();
        BigInteger h=PK.getH();

        if (cc!=1 && cc!=-1)
            { throw new ArithmeticException(
                          "Commitment should be +/- 1");
            }

        BigInteger a,b,c,t1,t2;
        a=new BigInteger(q.bitLength(),random);
        a=a.mod(q);

        c=BigInteger.ONE;
        if (cc<0) { c=c.negate(); }

        t1=g.modPow(a,p);
        t2=h.modPow(c,p);
        b=t1.multiply(t2);
        b=b.mod(p);

        Pub=new Public_Commitment(PK);
        Pub.assign(b);

        Priv=new Private_Commitment(PK);
        Priv.assign(a,b,c);
     }

  public Public_Commitment getPublic() { return Pub; }
  public Private_Commitment getPrivate() { return Priv; }
}
```

B.5.5 Proof.java

Now we can present the class which generates a proof on input of a private commitment and which will verify a proof on input of a public commitment. Notice the use of the standard Java library classes to call the SHA-1 hash function.

```java
import java.math.BigInteger;
import java.security.*;

class Proof
{
  private BigInteger d1,d2,r1,r2,alpha1,alpha2;

  public Proof() { ; }

  public void Assign_Proof( BigInteger D1,BigInteger D2,
                            BigInteger R1,BigInteger R2,
                            BigInteger A1,BigInteger A2)
    { d1=D1;      d2=D2;
      r1=R1;      r2=R2;
      alpha1=A1;  alpha2=A2;
    }

  public BigInteger get_d1()     { return d1; }
  public BigInteger get_d2()     { return d2; }
  public BigInteger get_r1()     { return r1; }
  public BigInteger get_r2()     { return r2; }
  public BigInteger get_alpha1() { return alpha1; }
  public BigInteger get_alpha2() { return alpha2; }

  public void Make_Proof(Private_Commitment priv,
                         SecureRandom random)
              throws NoSuchAlgorithmException
    {
      Parameters P=priv.get_Params();
      BigInteger p=P.getP();
      BigInteger q=P.getQ();
      BigInteger g=P.getG();
      BigInteger h=P.getH();

      // Form the Commitment
      BigInteger r,d,w;
      r=new BigInteger(q.bitLength(),random);  r=r.mod(q);
      d=new BigInteger(q.bitLength(),random);  d=d.mod(q);
      w=new BigInteger(q.bitLength(),random);  w=w.mod(q);

      BigInteger t1,t2,t3;
      t1=g.modPow(r,p);
```

```
t2=g.modPow(w,p);

BigInteger a,b,c;
a=priv.getA();
b=priv.getB();
c=priv.getC();
if (c.equals(BigInteger.ONE))
   { t3=b.multiply(h);
     t3=t3.mod(p);
   }
else
   { t3=h.modInverse(p);
     t3=t3.multiply(b);
     t3=t3.mod(p);
   }
t3=t3.modPow(d,p);
t3=t3.modInverse(p);

t1=t1.multiply(t3); t1=t1.mod(p);
if (c.equals(BigInteger.ONE))
  { alpha1=t1; alpha2=t2; }
else
  { alpha1=t2; alpha2=t1; }

// Form the challenge
MessageDigest MD=MessageDigest.getInstance("SHA");
MD.update(b.toByteArray());
MD.update(alpha1.toByteArray());
MD.update(alpha2.toByteArray());
byte[] hash=MD.digest();
BigInteger challenge=new BigInteger(hash);
challenge=challenge.mod(q);

// Form the response
if (c.equals(BigInteger.ONE))
  { d1=d;
    d2=challenge.subtract(d1);
    r1=r;
    r2=a.multiply(d2);
    r2=r2.add(w);
  }
else
  { d2=d;
    d1=challenge.subtract(d2);
    r2=r;
    r1=a.multiply(d1);
    r1=r1.add(w);
  }
```

```
        d1=d1.mod(q); d2=d2.mod(q);
        r1=r1.mod(q); r2=r2.mod(q);
    }


    public boolean Check_Proof(Public_Commitment pub)
                    throws NoSuchAlgorithmException
    {
        Parameters P=pub.get_Params();
        BigInteger p=P.getP();
        BigInteger q=P.getQ();
        BigInteger g=P.getG();
        BigInteger h=P.getH();

        BigInteger b=pub.getB();

        BigInteger e1,e2;

        // Form the challenge
        MessageDigest MD=MessageDigest.getInstance("SHA");
        MD.update(b.toByteArray());
        MD.update(alpha1.toByteArray());
        MD.update(alpha2.toByteArray());
        byte[] hash=MD.digest();
        BigInteger challenge=new BigInteger(hash);
        challenge=challenge.mod(q);

        e1=d1.add(d2); e1=e1.mod(q);
        if (!e1.equals(challenge)) { return false; }

        e1=g.modPow(r1,p);
        e2=b.multiply(h);          e2=e2.mod(p);
        e2=e2.modPow(d1,p);
        e2=e2.multiply(alpha1); e2=e2.mod(p);
        if (!e1.equals(e2)) { return false; }

        e1=g.modPow(r2,p);
        e2=h.modInverse(p);
        e2=b.multiply(e2);         e2=e2.mod(p);
        e2=e2.modPow(d2,p);
        e2=e2.multiply(alpha2); e2=e2.mod(p);
        if (!e1.equals(e2)) { return false; }

        return true;
    }
}
```

B.5.6 prog.java

Finally we give the test program which puts all the above together.

```java
import java.security.*;
import java.math.BigInteger;

public class prog
{
  public static void check(int cc,Commitment_Factory CF,
                            SecureRandom random)
              throws NoSuchAlgorithmException
    {
      System.out.println("\n\nChecking with cc = "+cc+"\n");

      // Make the commitment
      CF.Commit(cc,random);

      Public_Commitment pub=CF.getPublic();
      Private_Commitment priv=CF.getPrivate();

      { BigInteger a,b,c;
        b=pub.getB();
        a=priv.getA(); c=priv.getC();

        System.out.println("Private Commitment");
        System.out.println("   a = " + a +"\n   c = " + c);
        System.out.println("\nPublic Commitment");
        System.out.println("   b = " + b);
      }

      /* Make the proof */
      Proof Sender=new Proof();
      Sender.Make_Proof(priv,random);

      BigInteger d1,d2,r1,r2,alpha1,alpha2;
      d1=Sender.get_d1(); d2=Sender.get_d2();
      r1=Sender.get_r1(); r2=Sender.get_r2();
      alpha1=Sender.get_alpha1(); alpha2=Sender.get_alpha2();

      System.out.println("\nProof");
      System.out.println("      d1 = "+d1);
      System.out.println("      d2 = "+d2);
      System.out.println("      r1 = "+r1);
      System.out.println("      r2 = "+r2);
      System.out.println("  alpha1 = "+alpha1);
      System.out.println("  alpha2 = "+alpha2);
```

```
    /* Check the Proof */
    System.out.println("\nChecking Proof");
    Proof Reciever=new Proof();
    Reciever.Assign_Proof(d1,d2,r1,r2,alpha1,alpha2);
    System.out.println(Reciever.Check_Proof(pub));
  }


public static void main(String[] args)
             throws NoSuchAlgorithmException,
                    NoSuchProviderException
  {
    SecureRandom random=new SecureRandom();

    Parameters domain=new Parameters(random);
    Commitment_Factory CF = new Commitment_Factory(domain);

    check(1,CF,random);
    check(-1,CF,random);

  }
}
```

Index